Chris,

Society's Anonymous

Thank you for speaking the truth ; for
being an advocate for positive change.
You make the world a better place.

D1595016

SA:
Society's Anonymous

The True 12 Steps To Recovery From What Brings Us Down

Written by: Jesse J. Jacoby

SoulSpire Publishing

Soulspire Publishing
Fort Bragg, CA, 95437

ISBN: 978-0-9885920-2-5
Library of Congress Control Number: 2014914449

Cover art is original art by Jalen Jacoby & Emily Kostelny.

Dedication

This book is dedicated to my brother, Darin. We only needed a few more years to accumulate the answers you were seeking to help you heal from depression and lift you up to the mountaintops of your desires.

To all of the beautiful people struggling with sadness, wishing you could overcome your feelings of despair, this book is also for you.

For every soul that suffers from the careless acts taking place in society today, I am writing on your behalf.

Finally, I want to dedicate this book to each person that has gone out of their way to make my life difficult, miserable, and sometimes seem as if it is not worth living. When I escaped your hatred, I grew wings. When I eluded your control, I blossomed. When I walked out on my own, I found my destiny. Without you, I never would have stepped outside of my comfort zone, and in society today, it is difficult to grow without discomfort.

James Darin Jacoby (1984-2007)

Disclaimer

Although supported by professional research and scientific studies, some of the recommendations and suggestions made in this book may not have been approved by the *American Medical Association* (AMA), *Food and Drug Administration* (FDA), or mental health board prior to publishing. Before making any decisions regarding prescription drug use, or procedures that could impact your health in any way, please consult with a naturopathic doctor or holistic health professional. The author is not liable for any health conditions or misfortunes that might arise from following the advice he provides.

Acknowledgments

I could go on forever thanking the important people in my life who helped make this book possible, but they already know who they are, so I will keep it simple.

To the woman who raised three children, endured years of stress getting a degree in the process, and dedicated thirty years of her life to parenthood, while also working full-time to pay for her home – and all of the other bills she is required to pay in order to be accepted into the current structure of living – thank you.

To the man who plays the guitar like BB King, and had the opportunity to do anything he wanted with his talent, but opted to be a father instead, laboring through hot summers and cold Chicago winters to provide food and shelter so his family could be happy. Thank you.

To the young man who has the potential to inspire a universal awakening with his brilliant mind, and who designed the cover for this book. Thank you.

To my beautiful baby girl who is still innocent to the mysteries of this world, I see a universe in your eyes. I manifest for you an imaginary mind, a spirit full of love, and a lifetime of true happiness. Your face, laugh, and smile could keep me satiated forever. Thank you for choosing us. To her gorgeous, intelligent, loving mother for putting up with me and showing me that love can be unconditional.

To all of my family members and extended family who have always been around to support me over the years. Thank you for being in my life.

To real friends who do not give up on those they love, no matter what the situation, and no matter what kind of mistakes are made. It is your acceptance, generosity, and loyalty that brings hope to society. You know who you are. Thank you all.

To the good forces working to balance out the evil in this world. You are appreciated.

For each person who has gone out of their way to help me, especially during the rough patches in my life, thank you.

To the many mentors who live in the world today and act on their duty to help others in need. You recognize those people who have talent and potential, and help them nurture these assets so they can learn to fly. You demonstrate what it means to truly leave a legacy. Thank you.

Table Of Contents

Foreword By Author

As happy as I am today, I admit that life has not always been easy for me. Still to this day, I am tested with obstacles and struggles that challenge me. These barricades have forced me to change my career-path numerous times. I have been obligated to move away from several places where I felt at home. I was compelled to leave healthy relationships, even when I did not want to. I have become versed in mourning the loss of loved ones. I have experience with knowing what it feels like to overdraft my bank account and be in debt. I have even been forced against my will to drink and eat chemicals, while being stripped of my freedom and denied access to clean water and fresh air.

I do not welcome these deterrents into my life. Somehow, they find me. Rather than fight them, or allow them to infiltrate my positivity, what works for me is choosing to remain upbeat. I refuse to see them as endpoints, and instead opt to search for their meaning. I think of them as new beginnings. If everything happens for a reason, as we have been conditioned to believe, then I am always going to unearth the hidden messages behind each of the obstacles that temporarily block my path in life.

While I cherish being unique, and take pride in the individual strengths I have garnered on my journey, I know that I never would have made it this far without hardships. As thankful as I am for finding ways to smile through my sorrows, I understand that not everyone thinks in alignment with me. Many of us are not happy with who we are, or with who we have become. A majority of our population frequently suffers from depression. People are so sad at times that their despair drives them to suicide. In 2010, on average, someone committed suicide every thirteen minutes in the United States, making it the tenth leading cause of death. Many of them were taking prescription, anti-depressant drugs at the time.

I lost my brother, a great mentor of mine, and several of my friends to suicide over the years. For someone to be suffering this much, that they would have the courage to take their own life, expresses a lot about their reality. Pain is real, and each of us handles our dolor and struggles differently.

Knowing that millions of people are searching for ways to find freedom from what is bringing them down, I find it in my nature to do whatever I can to be a helpful resource for them on their road to recovery. I want everyone to understand that life can change for the better in the course of a day, and struggles often build foundations for success. As Thomas Edison once observed, *"Many of life's failures are people who did not realize how close they were to success when they gave up."* I hope to motivate as many people as possible to fight through adversity so they can encounter true joy.

Because I cannot be there in person to successfully coach each of you through the steps to recovery, I decided to take the time to put it all together in these pages. This book is a source of encouragement and motivation that will lead you to take action; assist as you find ways to better yourself; and inspire you to improve your lifestyle so you will experience brighter days.

I hope to see you smiling soon.

Introduction

"Today you are you, this is truer than true. There is no one alive more youer than you." – Dr. Seuss

Congratulations, you are successfully unique. Even in today's society, where we are conditioned to follow the same path as everyone else, eat the same industrialized food, and learn the same antiquated beliefs and theories in classrooms – all while we live up to others expectations, abide by rules that govern our lives, and are dictated by a system that keeps our current economy thriving at the expense of our health and well-being – no matter what, no person can take away our individuality.

Although there are billions of people on Earth, your DNA singles you out and gives you the freedom to be different in a multitude of ways. This is worthy of embrace. Even if you were in uniform, standing among many men and women your age, you would stand out. Individuality is a precursor to happiness.

Knowing that each of us has an exclusive identity, and that we all have the capacity to emerge as leaders, have a profound impact on society, help others, and make a difference in our lives, the lives of those around us, and in the world as a whole, this hints that we all should be ecstatic. Assured that we have access to clean water, shelter, and a variety of fresh fruits, vegetables, nuts, and seeds, this should provide us with more incentive to be gratified.

As I navigate the sidewalks, take public transportation, and loathe in various cities, I spectate, and observe the energy, emotions, and expressions that the majority of people who I come in contact with, or pass-by, are transmitting. I am noticing a strange pattern wherever I go. I seem to be the only one smiling. Many walk around with grim faces and do not say *hello* as they walk past. They sip sodas and sugary coffee drinks, chew gum, smoke cigarettes, sneak swigs of whiskey from a flask, scarf down fast food before they appear to chew it, ingest prescription drugs, and constantly worry about where they have to be, whether or not they will be late, and how they are going to earn the income they need to support themselves and their families. These are the people that make up today's society.

At this moment, one in every ten Americans is experiencing what is known as depression; and every year, the amount of people diagnosed with depression increases by twenty percent. According to the *Centers for Disease Control and Prevention, "A study found the following groups to be more likely to meet criteria for major depression:*
- *Persons forty-five to sixty-four years of age*
- *Women*
- *Persons with less than a high-school education*
- *Those previously married*
- *Individuals unable to work or unemployed*
- *Persons without health insurance coverage"*

This spurs me to ask several questions. Why do women appear to be more depressed than men? Could it be hormonal? Are contraceptives and medications playing a role? What do people tend to do once they age past forty-five that could be amplifying their depression? Are they permitting themselves to become physically inactive? What can we do to insure our health without worrying so much about health insurance? Is eating healthy, exercising, and limiting our exposure to toxins the best way to attain good health? Are we confused over what it means to *eat healthy*? Is there a way to help those who are undereducated and unemployed to feel like they are worthy, so they are no longer sad? Are we all simply yearning to be loved?

As I scroll through the various definitions of depression in the Merriam-Webster, I cannot help but notice the word *inactivity*. The definition they provide is, *"A psychoneurotic or psychotic disorder marked especially by sadness, inactivity, difficulty in thinking and concentration, a significant increase or decrease in appetite and time spent sleeping, feelings of dejection and hopelessness, and sometimes suicidal tendencies."* An alternate definition is, *"A reduction in activity, amount, quality, or force; or a lowering of vitality or functional activity."* Finally, one last interpretation, *"A serious medical condition in which a person feels very sad, hopeless, and unimportant and often is unable to live in a normal way."* I read through these, and I think, *No wonder so many people are depressed.*

To begin, I do not feel it is safe, or necessary, to label depression as a *serious* medical condition. This does not help the patient seeking mental encouragement. They do not need to feel pitied, then get manipulated into taking chemical psychotropic drugs. This trend is not working. A 2011 report released by the *National Center for Health Statistics* informs us that, *"The rate of antidepressant use in this country among teens and adults (people ages 12 and older) increased by almost four-hundred percent between 1988–1994, and 2005–2008."* During these same years, the suicide rates also increased. This should not be acceptable in society. Too many people fail to decode how serious of a problem prescription drug use is, and in search of a quick fix, they trust their doctors and psychiatrists without doing research. Sadly, this often worsens their condition.

Let's look back at the first definition I provided. The disorder – being depression – is marked especially by sadness, inactivity, difficulty in thinking and concentration, problems with appetite, sleep disorders, and feelings of hopelessness. Okay, what if we redefine this term so it more accurately applies to the condition, and state, *Living a sedentary lifestyle characterized by inactivity; eating foods and drinking beverages that contain added chemicals which lead to difficulty in thinking and concentration, while also promoting sleep disorders; and ingesting prescription drugs that may lead to a decreased appetite, among many other health problems, is more than likely going to lead you to feeling hopeless, and diagnosed with a 'serious' condition known as depression?* Do you agree this would be a more appropriate explanation for why so many are afflicted with depression? I hope you are beginning to acknowledge where I am going with this.

We are not simply depressed. We are experiencing the symptoms of being inactive. We are feeling the side effects of taking too many prescription drugs, drinking excessive amounts of alcohol, smoking cigarettes, overexposure to chemicals, eating overloads of processed and genetically modified (GMOs) foods, severe dehydration, and playing the role of the victim who is afflicted with a *serious* medical condition which could be erased permanently from our lives by taking a few simple steps to address the minor issues that are blocking us from reaching a state of true happiness. We are being deceived by powerful industries that rely on our weaknesses, misfortunes, and *so-called* depression in order for them to accumulate staggering increases in profits annually. The mainstream media is failing to empower us by hiding relevant issues surrounding our health, and brainwashing us with mistruths and propaganda provided by corporations that are exploiting us for revenue.

In May 2013, CBS News published an article summarizing a report released by the *Centers for Disease Control and Prevention (CDC)*. The article was written by Ryan Jaslow, and titled, *"CDC: Eighty-Percent of American Adults Do Not Get Recommended Exercise."* CDC researchers analyzed survey data collected from more than 450,000 U.S. adults aged eighteen and older. They found that eighty percent do not get the recommended amounts of exercise each week. Not surprisingly, it was noted that the amount of education the adult received also impacted exercise rates. While close to twenty-seven percent of the adults who were college graduates engaged in exercise regularly, among those who had received less than a high school diploma, it was determined that only twelve percent exercise in accordance to recommended guidelines. Do you recall the CDC report I mentioned about the groups of people more likely to be depressed? Notice that one of the groups are those who received less than a high school diploma. Could it be that their failure to exercise regularly is leading them to depression, or do they simply not understand how important engaging in physical activity truly is for their well-being?

You do not have to do it right away, but I encourage each of you to research a man named Joe Cross. Access his website when you get a chance (*rebootwithjoe.com*). Joe is the man behind the documentary, *Fat, Sick, and Nearly Dead*. In 2005, Joe weighed 330 pounds, suffered from an autoimmune disease, and was taking several medications for years to *treat* this condition. At the age of forty, after his doctors informed him that he would die soon if he did not change his lifestyle, he decided to go on a sixty day juice fast, where he would ingest nothing other than fresh, organic juices, and documented his transformation. He dubbed his favorite juice as, *The Mean Green Juice*, and it consisted of kale, apples, cucumber, celery, lemon, and ginger, with about eighty percent of it being from vegetables, and twenty percent from fruits. The first few days were the most challenging for him. This is normal while experiencing symptoms of detoxification. However, he noted that after five days he already noticed improvements physically and mentally. After forty-nine days, Joe lost sixty-seven pounds. His total cholesterol had dropped from 204 to 135, and his LDL cholesterol was reduced from 132 to 86. Upon completing the sixty day juice fast, Cross lost a total of one-hundred pounds, and reported a complete reversal of his autoimmune disease. He did all of this without taking pills, or relying on a doctor to help him. Joe has now guided thousands of other people who were once sick, depressed, and overweight – as some of you may be – to find happiness, reverse their obesity, and heal from several ailments simply by coaching them, encouraging them to drink green juices and remove animal products (meat, dairy, cheese, etc.) from their diet, and leading by example.

I also want to suggest that you find time to research a man named Frank Ferrante. He is featured in the documentary, *May I Be Frank*. Frank was more than a hundred pounds overweight. He was taking several medications, positive for hepatitis C, depressed, and lacked a love life. His life changed one day while eating at a raw vegan restaurant in San Francisco, CA, called *Café Gratitude*. Frank was embraced by the health coaches in the establishment and embarked on a forty-two day journey that would forever change the way he approaches life. In the film you see the great impact that eating healthy food, exercising, and implementing internal cleansing services can have on your well-being. Frank loses over a hundred pounds, frees himself from all medications, cures his hepatitis C and depression, and revives his libido. The documentary is heart-warming and is a must-watch for anyone, especially those serious about restoring their health.

How many of you who are at battle with depression are overweight? Do you think you would feel better after losing up to one-hundred pounds? Are you afflicted with a disease or serious medical condition that is bringing you down? Feel like you would be happier if you did not have to take several medications? Are you tired of being sedentary, eating the same junk-foods, and living a life that you are no longer content with?

In the contents of this book, I am going to steer you in the direction you need to go in order to bring yourself to a level of happiness where you will be much closer to accomplishing these goals. Rather than dwelling on the topic of depression and enabling you to feel powerless over it, I will help you identify the driving force behind your despair. From there I will guide you as you shift your focus away from sadness, and divert the energy towards improving your life. I am going to introduce various methods that will assist you as you cleanse your body from years of built-up anger, anxiety, chemicals, fear, resentment, stress, and toxins. I aspire to equip you with basic, plant-based nutritional information that will help insure your health, even without coverage. I yearn to motivate you to incorporate physical activity into your life. I envision you bolstering your talents, learning a new language, picking up an instrument, pursuing your passions, and taking courses to expand your intellect.

I want each of you to recognize that there is no reason to live life any other way than being truly happy. I plan to inspire you to embrace nature, grow your own food, hug trees, listen to the sounds of the outdoor world, nurture plants, observe wildlife, and tend to your own gardens. I want you to be aware that you are not obligated to live up to others expectations that they have placed on you.

Jacoby

I am going to introduce synchronicity and explain how at this very moment you are exactly where the universe planned for you to be in this chapter of your journey through life. I will teach you how to effectively coach others to find their unique path as they venture into their versions of paradise – by using these twelve steps.

On my individual quest I came to the realization that no matter what was happening to me that I may, or may not, have been seeking; or whatever may continue to happen that is, or is not, a part of my vision; I can always find ways to keep myself upbeat and remain joyful. I simply do whatever it takes to refuse to allow gloom in my life. I accredit my success with this approach to my attitude, diet, and lifestyle. To accomplish my never-ending glee, I have devised a twelve step plan. This is something that has worked for me, and I am confident that if you follow closely and embrace this path, you can also climb out of despair and live a more fulfilling life no matter what difficulties you may encounter. I want you to feel beautiful, confident, and inspired to be the very best version of *you*.

"The most beautiful people we have known are those who have known defeat, known suffering, known struggle, known loss, and have found their way out of the depths. These persons have an appreciation, sensitivity, and an understanding of life that fills them with compassion, gentleness, and a deep loving concern. Beautiful people do not just happen." – Elizabeth Kübler-Ross

The original *Twelve Steps* to recovery was introduced in *Alcoholic's Anonymous* (AA), and devised to help *recovering* alcoholics overcome their drinking problems. Eventually this platform was used to form another alliance known as *Narcotic's Anonymous* (NA). The first step they abide by is, *"We admit we are powerless over alcohol, or our drug of choice, and that our lives have become unmanageable."* I know these programs have helped thousands of people all over the world. This is wonderful. My only concern is that I do not think it is safe to give up the power we have over our body and mind, or that we should ever allow another entity to gain control over our lives. When we admit we are powerless, we are granting these substances permission to rule us forever. With this logic, alcohol, or whatever drug we may be struggling with dependency over, interminably remains in our life. The same applies for depression. The way I removed this disorder from my life, and similarly, the steps I took to eliminate drugs and alcohol, comprised of keeping them out forever. They will never be back. I will never consider them again.

This series of steps, which I have titled, Society's Anonymous (SA), is somewhat similar, however, we take control over the culprit that is leading us to despair. We understand that we are not powerless over any emotion, situation, or substance, unless we choose to be. These guidelines are about mending society. We begin by bettering ourselves. After reclaiming our happiness, we start healing everyone around us.

"You are not a victim of the world you see, because you invented it. You can give it up as easily as you made it up." – A Course in Miracles

The Law of Attraction

"Everything you can imagine is real." — Pablo Picasso

For the last fourteen years of my life, I have had this poster hanging above my desk where I do the majority of my research and writing. The quotation, *"It is your mind that creates this world,"* is credited to the Buddha. The window looks out over Tibet. The significance is that I have created this world I live in from my actions and experiences. If I remain confined in one area all of my life, fill my mind with the same stagnant ideas, and I never take action, the world around me is always going to be the same. If I decline to use my imagination, or if I forbear opportunities that present change or adventure, chances are I will never allow myself to create a more exciting world. This all aligns with the *Law of Attraction*. This law states that we attract into our lives the things we think about most.

If we often think about how sad we are, according to this law, we will be sad often. If we regularly cling to the thought that we are trapped in a less than ideal living situation, or experiencing financial burdens, then chances are we will continue to live this way. By watching the news on television, we could easily submit ourselves to a world of crime, politics, and worry. This also goes for drug and alcohol use. Filling our mind with thoughts of drugs and alcohol makes it difficult for us to maintain sobriety. If our desire is to quit smoking, yet all we think about is how we are going to quit, then cigarettes are going to be on our mind. Abiding by this law, it is best for us to shift our thoughts entirely away from all of the things that bring us down. To do so successfully, we have to first understand why many of the things that we are clinging to – which are sources for unhappiness – do not belong in our lives. We also have to find alternate thoughts, and create new experiences to store in our memory, so that we can reshape our negative thinking patterns into positive elements of prosperity.

Rather than pondering how bad our living situation is, or stressing over how we are going to get out of debt, we can fill our head with thoughts of impeccable living arrangements. We may want to think of affluence and abundance. To avoid watching the news on television, we can opt to read about positive news (*positivenews.org.uk*). If we seek sobriety, it helps to talk about

18   Jacoby

anything other than drugs or alcohol. If we desire to quit smoking, an option is to pretend cigarettes do not exist (I know it is not this easy). These are simple examples explaining how the *Law of Attraction* works. It is important that we understand this concept before moving forward and learning the twelve steps.

"*Watching a bad TV program, we become the TV program. We are what we feel and perceive. If we are angry, we are the anger. If we are in love, we are love. If we look at a snow-covered mountain peak, we are the mountain. We can be anything we want, so why do we open our windows to bad TV programs made by sensationalist producers in search of easy money, programs that make our hearts pound, our fists tighten, and leave us exhausted? We are too undemanding, too ready to watch whatever is on the screen, too lonely, lazy, or bored to create our own lives. We too often turn on the TV and leave it on, allowing someone else to guide us, shape us, and destroy us. Losing ourselves in this way is leaving our fate in the hands of others who may not be acting responsibly.*" – Thich Nhat Hanh

The reason why I believe many drug rehabilitation centers, and programs such as *Alcoholic's Anonymous* (AA) and *Narcotic's Anonymous* (NA) sometimes fail, is because they immediately admit they are powerless over a drug that realistically does not contain power. I am sure you have read the book, *The Secret,* or watched the film, or at least have heard of it. The book is centered on the *Law of Attraction*. Again, this is the belief that we attract into our lives the things we think about most. Drawing from this philosophy, when we go into rehab with a drug or alcohol problem and immediately admit we have no authority over the substance we are using, we attract into our lives the notion that alcohol, or our drug of choice, dictates us. By giving up our power, we lose the ability to gain control.

Think about arriving at a rehabilitation center, and the program being comprised of groups where members talk about drugs, relapse, and relapse triggers. Participating in this group will likely attract drugs and relapse into our life. Consider that while we go through the program, we are being fed low-quality, nutrient-deficient meals in-between groups, and are not required to exercise. This could nurture depression. Also keep in mind that a percentage of the people in the program lack education, have minimal job skills, and know little about trades that could help them find employment once they complete the rehabilitation process. How is a program that only addresses alcohol and drug problems, while abstaining from teaching skills and trades, going to help anyone adapt to the real world? This is how many rehabs are structured. If we go through a program where all we talk about is alcohol, drugs, and relapse, while eating poorly and not exercising, what is it that we are inclined to attract into our lives? Most likely we will invite alcohol, drugs, health problems, relapse, and more of the things that bring us down. This would be the same for someone experiencing depression who goes in to see a therapist seeking help, and in the session all they do is speak about the problems they are dealing with. As they continue to refresh these dilemmas in their mind, they become more prone to the possibility of these complications escalating their sadness.

Contrary to this, envision going away to a rehab where group members did not talk about alcohol, drugs, relapse, or any of the things that bring them down. Naturally they would stop thinking about them. What if during the duration of the rehab program the *addicts* were eating the very best plant-based foods, learning skills or trades that could help them find employment, receiving an education, exercising regularly, picking up new hobbies doing things that interest them, setting goals, and choosing a life path they want to follow that aspires from their passions? Chances are, they would succeed.

Imagine if we went in to see a therapist, and rather than repeatedly telling him all of our problems, we shifted from the usual, and started talking about all of the good things in our life? What if we explored all of the possibilities and were encouraged to only think positively? Is it possible that this could change our outlook a slight bit?

To me, it seems as if traditional rehabs and recovery groups are not seeing an end result for those attending to get better. They simply expect them to come back. They condition them to fail. The model and structure of the programs calls for it. I have the same perception for some therapists and doctors who *treat* patients experiencing depression. It seems as if they are using a simple, model approach along the lines of: prescribe drugs, then schedule the next appointment. This way, the health *professionals* keep getting paid, the patient never fully recovers, and they continue coming back for more drugs. Mental health *experts* and organizations are running a business and their only source of revenue is from people like us who are distraught, in need of love, searching for acceptance, and vulnerable. If our health is failing, we are sedentary, and our diet is poor, we will likely be depressed. This makes us perfect candidates to be manipulated into their profit cycle. If we are not careful, they will use their sales pitch to persuade us into believing we need unnecessary pills. Once we fall victim, we will develop a dependency on these drugs. A better approach would be for us to change the way we eat, start exercising, and improve our health naturally.

The approach in Society's Anonymous (SA) is different. With this book, and these twelve steps, we can think of our own home and the natural world around us as the rehab center. These pages can be our therapy. We can eliminate the alcohol, depression, drugs, fear, financial troubles, insecurities, stress, worry, and whatever else may be bringing us down by simply being more positive, changing our lifestyle, connecting with nature, correcting ourselves, engaging in physical activity, fueling with the right food sources, and smiling regularly. This is our chance to escape sedation and find freedom from gloom. These steps will be our source of guidance.

"The whole world is my story, projected back to me on the screen of my own perception." – Byron Katie

I still remember the first time I attended an AA meeting. I was young. At sixteen I was far too young to legally drink alcohol. I had been cited by the police for underage drinking, and part of the court order was for me to attend one of these groups. Although most kids my age did not enjoy reading books, this was something I did often. I had just finished the book, *Think and Grow*

20   Jacoby

Rich, by Napoleon Hill. One lesson that I learned from this book is that thoughts are things. As I painfully sat through this AA group listening to everyone admit they are powerless over a substance that realistically does not contain power, I carried a different belief about alcohol. My belief was that the more we spoke of it, and the longer we sabotaged ourselves with constantly thinking of this dangerous substance, the longer we would face an alcohol dependency problem. Some of these men and women had been going to these groups for several years, and while I know today that they rely on the support to help them continue to abstain from alcohol, at the time I could not agree with the structure of the program. Keep in mind, I was still a child. Yet, even as a kid, the group *leaders* were trying to convince me that I was an alcoholic, I had a problem, and I was diseased. As I tried to convince them that I was definitely not an alcoholic, I did not have a problem with alcohol, and I was healthy, not diseased, they did not accept my testimony. They scoffed at me, attempting to assure me that I was wrong. This was when I realized that I could erase the majority of my problems by simply changing my attitude. I soon followed this by altering my lifestyle. I quit experimenting with alcohol and made the decision to eat healthy. I started writing down my goals. I began researching and discovered new passions. I let go of the weaknesses and negative emotions that were holding me back. I found ways to magnetize positivity. I constructed a new life.

"Successful people know what it is they want to do. They know where they want to land. They know what they want to get, and they continually work to get it. Successful people seek information that will help them. They research, prepare, and practice for getting the things they want. They work to transform themselves into their vision of how they see themselves living. They are actively engaged in manifesting their goals. In doing so, their brains are in the habit of functioning at the level of their success." – John McCabe, *Igniting Your Life*

As you read this book, I want you to focus on transforming yourself into the person you know you are capable of being. This could be the successful man that you aspire to be, or the beautiful woman that has been waiting to emerge as a leader. You already are this person, you simply have some obstacles that you need to find ways to step over and remove from your life before you can activate the strengths needed to awaken this version of you. Your true potentiality has been suppressed by boundaries, inactivity, limitations, poor eating habits, and restrictions that you have created. This is your chance to discover how great you are.

"If you want to outdo where you are, you must outbe who you are, and outbelieve your limitations." – Karen Salmansohn (*notsalmon.com*)

By overcoming these hindrances, you will gain control and reclaim your health. Once you are healthy, happiness will soon find its way back into your life. Living healthfully and happily, you will have no choice but to find success. Start thinking positive, and you will attract the life you desire.

"If you have good thoughts they will shine out of your face like sunbeams and you will always look lovely." – Roald Dahl

A Guide to Happiness, Health, and Success

"When I was five years old, my mother always told me that happiness was the key to life. When I went to school, they asked me what I wanted to be when I grew up. I wrote down 'happy.' They told me I did not understand the assignment. I told them they did not understand life." – John Lennon, *Legendary Musician*

When you get a chance, search online for Logan LaPlante and watch his speech at the 2014 *TEDx* conference. Logan is thirteen years old, and he speaks eloquently, with passion, and has a powerful message. Being home schooled away from the standard schooling system that the majority of children his age are experiencing, he believes that he has more freedom to focus on the things that make him happy. He insists that when adults ask him what he would like to be when he grows up, that he answers, h*appy*. This makes perfect sense. Too many of us expend energy worrying about how we are going to answer such a simple question. We stir up frustration and other negative emotions in the process. We negate our happiness by trying to force ourselves to settle on a career path, even when none of the careers capture our interest. This is undermining our self worth. Do you agree that life would be much more simple if we could answer this question the same way Logan does? Is it wrong to assume that we are all seeking happiness? Why do we feel it is more appropriate to answer differently?

"Be happy for no reason like a child. If you are happy for a reason you are in trouble, because that reason can be taken from you." – Deepak Chopra

To obtain true happiness, we have to determine what is stealing our good vibes. We have to eliminate these malefactors, stop thinking about them, and introduce new experiences, ideas, and opportunities. One major component of happiness is good health. When we are healthy, we are more likely to be radiant. This does not mean every person who looks healthy on the exterior is happy, nor does it imply that someone who is not physically healthy cannot be happy. I am insisting that the healthier we are emotionally, mentally, physically, and spiritually, the greater are our chances of being truly happy.

Too often we believe we are at our happiest, yet we neglect the many opportunities waiting that could elevate our joy further. I had a relative who always insisted that she was happy, so she had no reason to change her diet or lifestyle. I do not doubt that she was happy – to a limited degree. She created happiness by choosing to remain in high spirits, and not permitting her health conditions to take that emotion away. As her health failed, and continued to get worse, she still maintained the belief that she was *as happy as can be*. She was suffering from several degenerative conditions, had trouble breathing, and clearly was not as joyful as she had the potential to be. Being a holistic health coach and plant-based nutrition consultant, I knew that she could reverse her conditions and be much healthier if she would change her diet and lifestyle. *If only she could experience what optimal health feels like,* I thought, t*hen she will elevate her happiness to a level she has never been at before.*

The reason I mention this is because I want you to understand there is a clear link between health and happiness. When you are truly healthy, you are capable of experiencing true contentment. Of course, one can still be happy and unhealthy, however, they will lack an important component of happiness. This is similar to how another could appear healthy, and still live without glee. In each situation, they will never be as healthy, or happy, as possible. When I define true happiness, optimal health is a requirement.

"There are two types of people in the world: those who choose to be happy, and those who choose to be unhappy. Contrary to popular belief, happiness does not come from fame, fortune, other people, or material possessions. Rather, it comes from within. The richest person in the world could be miserable while a homeless person could be right outside, smiling and content with their life. Happy people are happy because they make themselves happy. They maintain a positive outlook on life and remain at peace with themselves." – Chiara Fucarino

Another component of happiness is success. When we think of success, most often what comes to mind is materialism. We tend to judge success based on the type of vehicle we drive, the job title we may have landed, or the size of our homes. We use our material gains to fuel arrogance. When I think of success, I like to envision never-ending smiles. Are we doing what we desire with our lives, or do we simply have the material items that we want, yet have to pay for them by working endless amounts of hours day in and day out? If we can find a way to get what we want, while doing what we enjoy and maintaining good health, I would consider this success. If we add to this list having extra time to help others, then we are on a winning path.

I would much rather spend my days hiking through national parks, eating nourishing foods, loving my family, and being as active as I possibly can; opposed to sitting in an office, stressing over arriving to meetings on time, and waiting to punch in and out of the time clock at work. Sure, I may have to trade my chances of acquiring luxurious material items for the opportunity to live this way, but I know what makes me happy. Working to enrich the bank accounts of others is not my idea of doing what I enjoy. Putting my life on hold so I can work an outrageous amount of hours and store my earnings in a retirement fund that I cannot access for thirty or forty years, if I see it at all, does not appeal to me either. I want to enjoy every moment I am alive. This is what I strive for each day. We should not have to wait until our mortgage is paid, or until we save enough money to start living. The right moment is now.

"Success is getting what you want. Happiness is doing what you want." – W.P. Kinsella

My mission with these twelve step guidelines is to help us identify what brings our spirits down, address the issues, and accurately alter our attitude and lifestyle to bring about the positive change we need. Accomplishing this goal should help us elevate to a happier place.

"When one door of happiness closes, another opens; but often we look so long at the closed door that we do not see the one which has been opened for us." – Helen Keller

What Brings Us Down?

"Simply put, we believe that things or people make us unhappy, but this is not accurate. We make ourselves unhappy." – Wayne Dyer

Whether we choose to notice, or look the other way, a large percentage of people are relying on prescription drugs as they attempt to break free from their depression. It is estimated that one of four women in their forties and fifties is taking an antidepressant medication. One of every ten Americans is on a pill to *treat* their sadness. While the widespread belief is that depression is a *serious* disease that cannot be cured, and that ingesting pills is somehow of benefit to those who are unhappy, what we are discovering is that these drugs simply numb and sedate them, often deepening their depression and leading to a drug dependency. Because we cling to these false beliefs, we are evading the opportunity to truly heal from our pain. At some point, we have to accept that we are permitting someone, or something – or possibly multiple people and things – to bring us down.

"There is only one cause of unhappiness: The false beliefs we have in our head. Beliefs so widespread, so commonly held, that it never occurs to us to question them." – Anthony de Mello, *Indian Jesuit Priest*

Maybe we are clinging to pain from our childhood, or from a tragic event. It could be that we are grieving from losing a loved one. Often our dietary and lifestyle choices have the most profound impact on how we feel. We may be struggling with a dependency on alcohol, drugs, or medications. Stuck in a relationship that we are simply not happy with. Many are battling terminal illness, or suffering from sickness and disease. Maybe we are lacking confidence and feel as if we are not good enough, or that we are inferior to others. We may be burdened with too many insecurities that could be related to employment, finances, our level of education, or personal relationships. We are often ruled by a fear of failure, or the unknown, so we refuse to take risks or embrace change. We may work in a lousy environment, getting paid less than what we are worth, and feel like we are never going to get ahead. This could devalue our self-worth. Another potential barrier could be an overexposure to chemicals. Whatever our reasoning may be, we can improve our circumstances.

I did research and discovered some of the most common excuses for why we tend to sink into a depressed state. I will elaborate further on each in step one when we identify the culprits that are bringing us down. These are the ten most recognized reasons for why we experience depression, according to various mental health organizations. I refer to this as the *antagonist list*. They are the problems we too frequently blame for melancholy, and the scapegoats for our troubles. We allow them to enable our sadness each day as we continue to defeat ourselves by refusing to change our current patterns of living.

Following this list, I have provided alternate reasons for why I believe we are woeful. These reasons go beyond what various mental health organizations want us to believe. They are problems that we have power over, and there are simple solutions for correcting them. We will dub this the *protagonist list*.

Antagonist List
- Age (Elderly at higher risk)
- Biology (Monoamine theory of depression)
- Family & Social Environment (Abuse, poverty, violence)
- Gender (Women are twice as likely to be depressed)
- Genetics (Depression runs in the family)
- Health Conditions (Cancer, Heart Disease, Obesity)
- Life Changes & Stressful Events (Divorce, financial, job loss)
- Medications & Substance Abuse (Drugs, Alcohol, Prescription)
- Negative Self Image (Appearance, fear of rejection)
- Trauma and Grief (Loss of loved one, Injury)

This list of the most commonly recognized reasons for why so many of us are depressed does not resonate well with me. Many of the factors targeted involve circumstances which we have no control over. Surely there must be other components affecting our state of joy that we can adjust and dictate. If we want to truly recover from what brings us down, we have to understand that we can only blame ourselves for why we are morose. By constantly shifting the responsibility of maintaining our happiness towards blaming other people or circumstances for our unhappiness, we never move forward. As we remain sedentary, and our potential stagnates, we regress deeper into our funk.

It has become a trend now to blame genetics for all of our problems. If we have a health issue, it runs in the family. If we are unhappy, well, other family members are not happy either. When we struggle financially, of course that runs in the family too. We are trigger-happy to release bullets of blame at genetics. All of these problems seem to run in the family, but does anyone in the family who is experiencing these *genetic* misfortunes ever physically run? There is a concept known as *epigenetics* that I will discuss in the first step. Epigenetics declares that we can turn gene cells on and off by altering our lifestyle. Simply put, if we change the way we eat, engage in physical activity, and alter our perception so that we are not eating the same deleterious foods as those in our family; and we are avoiding being sedentary the same way our relatives are, while viewing life uniquely – in a special way that is distinct from the perceptions that *run in the family* – we will not end up with the same diseases, financial struggles, or low spirits that have been plaguing our family members generation after generation. Once we are aware that we cannot justly blame our genes, we have to acknowledge that we are in control of our happiness. It is up to us to determine whether or not we will elevate our mood.

"The best years of life are the ones in which we decide our problems are our own. We do not blame them on our mother, the economy, or the President. We realize that we control our own destiny." – Albert Ellis

Rather than being accusatory, and blaming other people, places, or things that we have little or no control over for our lack of joy, why do we not choose to instead pinpoint some of the real reasons for why we are downcast? Here is a list of many common deficiencies, or problems, most people can relate to. I will identify this as the *protagonist list*. These problems are all linked to our actions and decisions. We can reverse, and heal from, each of these dilemmas.

Protagonist List

- Physical inactivity, or lack of exercise
- Eating low-quality foods that are not nourishing
- A synthetic environment that lacks nature
- The belief that medications will heal us
- Trapped negative emotions that need cleansing
- A pessimistic attitude
- Living up to other people's expectations
- Wanting to *fit-in*
- Not doing what we love
- The inability to expand our intellect
- A poor sphere of influence
- Living without compassion
- Lack of motivation, or inaction
- Failing to help others
- Harmful microbes in the bowel

If you can relate to some of the elements on the antagonist list that are recognized by mental health organizations as the most common reasons for depression, you have identified the scapegoats for why you are feeling disconsolate. Now that you are aware of what you have consistently blamed your depression on, take a look at the protagonist list and determine which personal problems you need to address. You should notice for each of the reasons targeted on the antagonist list, that they are interrelated with some of the identified issues on the protagonist side. As you continue reading this book, I will discuss these quandaries, and help you make corrections.

Because I have never had the opportunity to live your life, I cannot tell you exactly what is bringing you down. I can only offer advice. Whatever the reasons may be for why you are depressed, I want you to pinpoint why you are attracting these impediments into your life, learn to let them go, and shift your energy to creating positive change. The time has come for you to broaden your mental horizon. If you keep seeing the world through a narrow lens, repeat yesterday's schedule every new day, and do not break the habits that restrict you from reaching the height of your potential; then you will always live in the same environment, retaining the usual negative thoughts. If you want change, and if it is truly happiness that you are seeking, then you must take action.

"Action may not always bring happiness; but there is no happiness without action." – B. Disraeli

To understand what is bringing us down, we can focus on two components: *Sedentary depression* and *active happiness*. Remember that depression is characterized by inactivity. The more sedentary we are, the longer we find ourselves a companion to depression. Contrary to this, as we convert to

26

being more active, we often befriend happiness. This does not only pertain to physical exercise and movement. This applies to our feelings, financial situation, food choices, intellect, living arrangements, thoughts, and every other facet of our lives.

When we stimulate our minds by expanding our knowledge, reading, and finding other ways to be mentally active, we often generate new thoughts and ideas, and this can lead us to happiness. When we abstain from bolstering our intellect, this sedentary approach keeps our mind stagnant, and we tend to repeat the same thoughts and feelings.

If we are eating processed foods from a box, cafeteria, container, diner, or fast-food restaurant, we are eating food that is sedentary. It was never alive. The food is made up of various chemicals and is a synthetic product. When we eat this kind of food, we are fueled with synthetic (dead) energy. This inhibits us from reaching the height of our potential. Contrary to this, when we eat living foods that are organic, raw, and unprocessed, we fuel ourselves with living nutrients that provide rejuvenative energy. This helps generate the positivity we need to stimulate feelings of love and happiness.

If we are not pleased with our current financial situation, will it get us anywhere by continuing to work at the same job that is limiting our income potential? Are we going to get ahead by remaining unemployed if we do not have work? There are always opportunities everywhere. If you are unemployed, rather than being unproductive, you can always volunteer. By volunteering somewhere, or donating your time to help others, someone may notice your potential and hire you for work. If you are undereducated, and lack the skills needed to find work, you can simply read books that will equip you with the necessary knowledge. There are several series' of books, such as *how-to* books, *Idiot's Guides*, and books *for dummies*, that could help nurture the intellect required, and develop the skills necessary to find employment. These books go in-depth about various subjects, and by the time you finish reading them, you could practically consider yourself an expert on whatever topic you have chosen. If you cannot afford to purchase these books, you can likely check them out at the closest public library. No matter what your situation, if you want to increase your income, this is going to force you to take action. You cannot be sedentary about your financial situation and expect it to change.

What if you are living in an environment where you do not feel comfortable? Are you going to benefit from being active about getting out of there, or from sulking in depression as you ask over and over why you are stuck in this terrible place? Maybe it is simply that you are too comfortable where you live and this is impeding on you being physically active. Perhaps you have grown so accustomed to your normal routine that you have forgotten about the beauty attached to the world around you. Do you lack the drive that is required from you to actively pursue change? Are you waiting for your new living arrangements to find you? Whatever the problem, I cannot stress enough the importance of being active. To change the outcome of our actions, sometimes we have to remodel our approach. If something feels wrong, chances are our intuition is urging us to make improvements. Do not ignore these feelings.

The dictionary.com definitions for sedentary are:

1.) Characterized by or requiring a sitting posture: a sedentary occupation.
2.) Accustomed to sit or rest a great deal or to take little exercise.
3.) Abiding in one place; not migratory.
4.) Pertaining to animals that move about little or are permanently attached to something, as a barnacle.

The dictionary.com definitions for active are:

1.) Engaged in action; characterized by energetic work, participation, etc.; busy: an active life.
2.) Being in a state of existence, progress, or motion: active hostilities.
3.) Involving physical effort and action: active sports.
4.) Having the power of quick motion; nimble: active as a gazelle.
5.) Characterized by action, motion, volume, use, participation, etc.: an active market in wheat; an active list of subscribers.

If we want to start a career, what preliminary steps must we take to accomplish this goal? The process often involves doing extensive research. It may even require years of schooling, followed by some experience as an intern, or volunteer. We more than likely will need to build a resume. We have to seek employment somewhere. It definitely obligates us to take action. We cannot find a job by sitting comfortably at home, in the same stagnant environment, hoping and wishing for a job to find us. Life does not work this way. Social involvement and interaction are also components of happiness. We cannot interact or be socially engaged if we are living sedentary. This lack of action is inhibiting our chances of finding the many opportunities that are searching for us in places we still do not know exist – simply because we fail to be adventurous and do not discover them in the process. We are blocking happiness, health, and success by choosing to avoid activity.

"Most of the shadows of this life are caused by our standing in our own sunshine." – Ralph Waldo Emerson

So why is it that we stand in our own sunshine, all too often from the comfort of our homes? What are we afraid of? Why do we feel incapable, or unworthy, of excelling beyond being average or simply feeling good, to being above-average and feeling great? Are we clinging to a fear of failure? Could it be that we are afraid of rejection? Rejection can and will bring us down – if we permit it to. I am confident that not one person can honestly claim to enjoy or embrace rejection. While the discomfort from being rejected can help us grow, the majority of us would rather avoid it entirely before we seek it on our journey. I have exciting news for you. I know one thing that loves to be rejected. This is something that many of us attract into our lives. It is known as depression.

Depression loves to be rejected. Depression does not like us, we simply force it to be in our lives. It is liberating, not only for depression to be set free, but also for us to detach from it. We cannot run away from rejection forever if we want acceptance. It is not wise to spend the duration of our lives worrying that we might fail if we try something different when we want to change the way we are presently living. It is best to confront all obstacles, accept that they are only temporary, conquer them, and continue moving forward.

"We spend more time developing means of escaping our troubles than we do solving the troubles we are trying to escape from." – David Lloyd

Most frequently, diet and lifestyle trigger depression. Do you consider yourself an active person? Are you exercising regularly? How many ingredients are in the food packages that you keep in your refrigerator, or on your cabinet shelves, that you cannot pronounce or are unsure of why they have been added to the food? Are you aware of what you are eating? Did you ever consider that these chemicals being added to the foods you choose to eat could very well be creating imbalances in your brain? Do you take medications? Have you studied the side effects from ingesting these drugs? How often do you spend time in nature connecting with Earth's energy? Would you say that you are more likely to sit in front of the television than you are inclined to take a hike through your local forest preserve? Are you living in reality, or trapped in a video game version of the world? Is your home cluttered with synthetic items, or do you have house plants mixed in to provide balance? Are you breathing fresh air, or do you damage your lungs with the gases from air conditioning and chemicals being emitted from air *fresheners*? These are some questions to think about as you begin the twelve steps to recovery from what brings you down.

Whatever it is that may bring you down, it could be helpful to recognize the culprit, accept that it exists, and use the guidelines in this book to help pull you through. No matter what your situation is at the moment, restoring your mental faith, and knowing that you have the option to engage in activities and events that boost your positivity – with people who bring you up rather than spiral you down – will only be helpful to you on your road to recovery. If you are living a sedentary lifestyle, and you never leave your house, this alone could be the root of your unhappiness. Ralph Smart – the artist and visionary behind *infinitewaters.net* – released a *YouTube* video in March 2014 where he speaks about the many reasons why we are depressed. The first reason he suggests is that we are stuck in the same surroundings. He encourages viewers to, *"Let go of what no longer serves us and to leave the same environment."* If you never leave your house, consider going for a walk. If your job is taking over your life, plan a vacation. If you live in a place where you feel like you cannot get ahead, or are surrounded with people who demotivate you, contemplate relocating. Equip yourself with the components needed to keep you smiling.

There are countless reasons why so many of us sulk in our sorrows. What I find most important is how we confront these challenges, and what we do to overcome depression. Are we looking for a temporary escape or a permanent solution? Are the decisions we make fueling the problems or solving them? When was the last time we analyzed our situation, identified what has been bringing us down, and made a commitment to ourselves that we would find a way to move forward, leaving all of our past issues behind?

"I had the blues, because I had no shoes. Until upon the street, I met a man who had no feet." – Denis Waitley

Your situation is likely not as bad as it seems. If it is, your circumstances could get better before you give them the leeway to worsen. Remember that some people are living in regions of the world where their food is being sanctioned by foreign governments that are stationed there to steal raw materials and natural resources, and they are forced to watch helplessly as grains are fed to livestock that never miss meals, while they starve daily. There is a photo circulating around the web of four healthy, happy African children standing out in nature having a conversation about America. One of the boys asks the other three, *"Did you know that kids in North America are forced to sit in classrooms all day, and if they move around, get excited, or make too much noise, they are given drugs to keep them quiet? Their only form of exercise is playing video games, and most of their food is fake and full of dangerous chemicals."* Then, another boy responds by saying, *"That is terrible. We should take up donations for them."* I saved the photo to my computer because there is so much truth behind it. We have more material items here in America than we know what to do with, and we are still seeking more. It seems as if the more we accumulate, the less satisfied we are. We are wandering through palaces full of gold and silver, searching for diamonds and platinum. We demand more of the luxuries we simply do not need, failing to recognize that we are destroying Earth's natural resources in the process. As corporations and industries happily supply our demands, our levels of depression continue to rise. Meanwhile, in poor regions of Africa, children who have only nature, friends, and family, with the materials necessary for survival are much happier. Whatever you are struggling with, do not forget that someone else has endured much worse pain and still found a way to remain happy. For every hardship you are confronted by, if you have faith and you persevere, happiness and success will follow.

"It is not what happens to you that matters. It is how you respond to what happens to you that makes a difference." – Zig Ziglar

Let this book be your guide to good health, many successes, and true happiness. As you follow these twelve steps, familiarize yourself with the *Law of Attraction*. The things you think about most are generally what you attract into your life. Do not expend energy scrutinizing the assortment of constituents that bring you down. Acknowledge what is enabling your depression, let it go, and move forward. Always remain hopeful no matter how discouraging your surroundings might be. Remember that when the world says *give up*, hope whispers *try it one more time*. With this in mind, I wish you the best on your road to recovery. You are now ready for the first step in Society's Anonymous.

"There are three simple rules in life:

1.) If you do not go after what you want, you will never have it.

2.) If you do not ask, the answer will always be no.

3.) If you do not step forward, you will always be in the same place."

   – Dennisse Lisseth

Jacoby

The 1ˢᵗ Step: Identifying the Culprit

"I wore goofy hats to school and did musical theater. Most people thought I was a dork. But if you have a sense of humor about it, no one can bring you down." – Zac Efron

Why is it that someone like Zac Efron could go to school wearing goofy hats, acknowledge that people might think he is *dorky*, not let it get him down, and then go on to establish himself as a famous actor; while others may feel bullied, victimize themselves, and let it bring them down forever? Is it simply because they do not have a sense of humor? I think it goes beyond that. This could have a lot to do with how they are raised, or as mental health practitioners would suggest, it might be genetics, or their biological make-up being comprised differently. A crucial determinant that we are not recognizing is their attitude and perception.

If we let someone call us names and belittle us, and they upset us in the process, we are not helping ourselves at all. Say you are in Zac's shoes, and you wear a dorky hat to school. What if everyone around you calls you a *dork*, and makes fun of you for it? Would you let this bring you down? If you answer *yes* to this question, now analyze the situation. Some of your peers poked fun at you, and you allowed them to upset you. What is your reasoning for being upset? Are you sad because these other kids called you a dork, or could this emotion be triggered by something more complex? Why is it that someone like Zac would go unaffected by it, and you are allowing it to upset you? Seeking the answer to this question takes us on our journey through Society's Anonymous.

The first step of our expedition into Society's Anonymous is, *"We acknowledge the notion that someone or something is bringing us down. To lift ourselves back up, we learn to identify what this culprit is. Once enlightened, we recognize the actions required from us to combat our sorrows."* In this step we diagnose what is triggering our discontent, and acquire knowledge that will equip and prepare us to change our beliefs, empower ourselves, and effectively magnetize happiness.

To explain why you might get upset about your peers bullying you in class, let us review the antagonist list of reasons for depression:

Antagonist List
- Age (Elderly at higher risk)
- Biology (Monoamine theory of depression)
- Family & Social Environment (Abuse, poverty, violence)
- Gender (Women are twice as likely to be depressed)
- Genetics (Depression runs in the family)
- Health Conditions (Cancer, Heart Disease, Obesity)
- Life Changes & Stressful Events (Divorce, financial, job loss)
- Medications & Substance Abuse (Drugs, Alcohol, Prescription)
- Negative Self Image (Appearance, fear of rejection)
- Trauma and Grief (Loss of loved one, Injury)

Drawing from this list, you may accurately support that the reason why you are upset over the bullying situation is because of negative self-image, social environment, and stressful events. You might have a low self-esteem from a lack of encouragement, and this could be generating a fear of rejection. When trying to explain why you are permitting this circumstance to trigger depression, a mental health practitioner may suggest that your biological make-up is driving you to be more prone to depression, or that depression runs in your family. Where they fail, is in discussing how you can turn gene cells on and off, and how you can change your biological make-up through diet, lifestyle, and correcting your attitude and the way you perceive things.

Rather than pointing the blame on conditions we are powerless over, such as the other kids bullying us, or on concepts that we think cannot be changed – in this case being biological make-up and genetics – let us review the protagonist list of suggestions for why we are often afflicted with depression:

Protagonist List
- Physical inactivity, or lack of exercise
- Eating low-quality foods that are not nourishing
- A synthetic environment that lacks nature
- The belief that medications will heal us
- Trapped negative emotions that need cleansing
- A pessimistic attitude
- Living up to other people's expectations
- Wanting to *fit-in*
- Not doing what you love
- The inability to expand your intellect
- A poor sphere of influence
- Living without compassion
- Lack of motivation, or inaction
- Failing to help others
- Harmful microbes in the bowel

After reviewing this list, which of these factors can you apply to the bullying situation? It is possible that you are depressed because you want to *fit-in*, and being called a dork is not helping. Judging by your reaction, you definitely have some trapped negative emotions inside. Most importantly, if your biological make-up reveals that you do not produce enough neurotransmitters, or that you are overproducing the monoamine oxidase enzyme, this means you are simply not eating nourishing foods. You may need to consume more raw fruits and vegetables, and restrict your intake of deleterious foods that contain chemicals which are partially responsible for your biological imbalances. If depression runs in your family, be aware that by eating the same way these other depressed family members are eating, and living an equivalent lifestyle, chances are you will also be depressed. You do not have to be a victim in this situation. You can overcome the bullying by simply altering your perception, changing your diet, and improving the quality of your lifestyle. If the bully does not like you, why should this prevent you from liking yourself? Focus on making improvements daily.

In the following pages, I am going to elaborate on why each of the common reasons for depression listed by various mental health organizations on the antagonist list are not the ruling factors that are promoting our despair. As I go through each reason, I will present evidence, examples, and studies supporting my explanations. This should help us change our perception and come to the realization that we can indeed overcome these obstacles that block our pathways to happiness. As we move on to step two, after learning that we are not powerless, and that we have control over what is bringing us down, we can then begin the process of transformation which will carry us through the remainder of the twelve step guidelines. The first reason on the antagonist list that we blame for our low spirits is age.

"Whatever happens to you, do not fall in despair. Even if all the doors are closed, a secret path will be there for you that no one knows. You cannot see it yet but so many paradises are at the end of this path. Be grateful. It is easy to thank after obtaining what you want, thank before having what you want." – Rumi

Age

"Count your age by friends, not years. Count your life by smiles, not tears." – John Lennon

The *National Alliance on Mental Illness (NAMI)* reports that 6.5 million of the thirty-five million people aged sixty-five or older in the United States live with depression. They go on to provide a few reasons for why these men and women tend to be depressed. They suggest biological make-up, genetics, trauma and grief, and of course, reliance on medications for ailments including high cholesterol and blood pressure, as well as dependency on alcohol or some other substance.

"In truth, no one will hold your age against you if you do not. Remember, you are never too old to love, to smile, to give a compliment, or to think positively. Be ageless today. Let your inner light shine." – Eckhart Tolle

I do not think anyone knows truly why elderly folks are at a higher risk for depression, or why people in general are more prone to depression as they age. We can certainly search for reasons. They may simply see their final days closing in on them, and as they reflect on their lives, feel there is a void. Maybe they did not accomplish some goals that they always hoped they would, and now assume it is too late. Perhaps they are debilitated, and cannot get around the way they could in earlier years. Often, after retirement, they simply do not know what to do with their time, so they let their minds become stagnant. Whatever the reasons may be, statistics show us that depression rates rise as we age.

What I notice is that people are generally less active as they get older. They do not exercise or participate in events that require brisk movement. This inactivity could be a trigger for their sadness. In addition to being sedentary, they frequently eat out at restaurants and fast-food establishments for convenience – failing to avoid food chemicals and not adequately nourishing their bodies. This poor diet could also be a factor in their depression. Some people smoke cigarettes and drink alcohol, and they increase their consumption of both as they age. It is common today for them to be taking a variety of medications. The combination of poor diet, lack of activity, and unhealthy lifestyle choices, is very likely what is causing the symptoms for which they are prescribed these medications. Among the many prescription drug side-effects, depression happens to be in the array. Of course, the *NAMI* explanation for why depression rates increase with age revolves around issues that cannot be controlled – such as biological make-up, genetics, and traumatic experiences. This is not mentally encouraging, and does not help alleviate depression. The belief that we are powerless only paves the path for deeper depression to occur and welcomes a reliance on prescription drugs. Perhaps if *NAMI* and other mental health organizations recognized the role that diet, exercise, and lifestyle plays in attitude, biological make-up, and overall well-being, we would see depression rates decrease with age. We might even witness levels of health improving with age.

"Youth is happy because it has the capacity to see beauty. Anyone who keeps the ability to see beauty never grows old." – Franz Kafka

There is a man named Jim Morris who is seventy-eight years old. He is a bodybuilder. He smiles often, looks phenomenal, and is a happy man. Karyn Calabrese is an author, motivational speaker, restaurant owner, and youthful woman. She is sixty-seven years old. Cherie Soria is also sixty-seven, exceptionally healthy, owns a culinary school, and has written several books. Mimi Kirk is seventy-five years old, smiles regularly, and has a fresh young energy she carries with her. Annette Larkins is seventy-two. She could pass for being in her forties. Dr. Brian Clement, director of *Hippocrates Health Institute*, is in his seventies. Dr. Richard Oppenlander, author of *Comfortably Unaware*, is in his sixties. All of these people who I just mentioned have at least two things in common: they age well, and they eat plant-based, vegan diets.

If you do an image search online for each of them, you will notice that they preserve their youth well. They do not debilitate with age. They do not take advantage of *senior discounts*. They simply do not let depression enter their domain because they are engaged in lifestyles that elevate their moods. By eating organic, plant-based diets, they are avoiding the free radicals in processed foods and animal-based food products that shorten telomeres and cause premature aging. By replacing meat, dairy, eggs, cheese, refined sugars, processed foods, and gluten flours with fresh, organic fruits and vegetables, they are eliminating the free radicals, mucoid plaque, GMO contaminants, food chemicals, preservatives, saturated fats, trans-fats, dietary cholesterol, foreign hormones, bacterial endotoxins, advanced glycation end-products, arachadonic acid, and cooked meat carcinogens that often nurture depression, disease, and premature aging. By choosing to eat organic and vegan, they are providing

34   Jacoby

their bodies with nourishing antioxidants and phytonutrients, which are known to regenerate the body, lengthen telomeres, and preserve youth. As they eat plant-based, and adhere to vegan diets, they preserve their youth and assure good health by protecting the epithelial cells lining the organs, and endothelial cells lining the arteries. They generate happiness by staying active, eating well, and maintaining positive attitudes. In doing so, they also decrease their risk of developing diseases or chronic conditions.

Telomeres are combinations of DNA and protein that protect the ends of chromosomes and affect how rapidly cells age. As they become shorter, and as their structural integrity weakens, the cells age and die quicker. Shorter telomeres are closely linked with a vast array of aging-related diseases, including many forms of cancer, cardiovascular disease, dementia, diabetes, obesity, osteoporosis and stroke. Advanced glycation end-products (AGEs) are compounds that speed up oxidative damage to cells and alter their normal behavior patterns. They develop when glucose binds to cooked animal proteins in a process called glycation. They also form from smoking cigarettes. Once in the body, these harmful end-products shorten telomeres, make cells more prone to damage, and cause premature aging. This explains why those who eat meat and smoke cigarettes tend to age so much faster than those who choose to be smoke-free and eat plant-based. What researchers and scientists have discovered is that we can lengthen telomeres, and preserve our youth, by abstaining from smoking, adapting a plant-based diet free of harmful animal proteins, eating more organic fruits and vegetables that contain antioxidants and phytonutrients, and exercising regularly. In step four I provide a study led by Dr. Dean Ornish that explains telomeres, AGEs, and aging more thoroughly. We will also discuss diet further, and discover ways to revamp our eating patterns. We will learn that it is never too late to revise our lifestyle and embrace the necessary changes required for achieving optimal health.

"It is never too late to be what you might have been." – George Eliot

As I examine age, I notice that getting older is not always what brings us down. Sometimes we feel we are too young to succeed and wish we could be older, wiser, and in a better position to achieve our goals. I want you to know that no matter how young or old you are, it is never too sudden, or too late, to accomplish what you were born to attain. Do you know that Mozart was already composing, and competent on the keyboard and violin at the age of five? Shirley Temple was only six when she became a movie star on *Bright Eyes*. At thirteen years old, the young Magnus Carlsen became a chess grandmaster. At fourteen, a Romanian gymnast named Nadia Comăneci accumulated seven perfect 10.0 scores at the Olympics, winning three gold medals. In 1958, a talented young soccer star led Brazil to win the world cup. Pele was seventeen at the time. At nineteen, Elvis Presley already had women all over the world swooning at him as they watched him in concert, or on television. The Beatles' first concert in 1961 marked the beginning of a frenzy known as *Beatlemania*. John Lennon was twenty years old, and Paul McCartney was eighteen. By the age of twenty-three, Beethoven was a piano virtuoso. Albert Einstein was twenty-six when he wrote the *Theory of*

Relativity. When Michelangelo was twenty-eight, he had already created the sculptures of *David* and *Pieta*. J.K. Rowling finished the first manuscript for Harry Potter when she was thirty. At thirty-four, Oprah Winfrey started her talk show that would eventually help her emerge as a leader of her generation. A young Martin Luther King Jr. was also thirty-four when he delivered what may be the most powerful speech of all time, *I Have A Dream*. Mark Twain was forty when he wrote, *The Adventures of Tom Sawyer,* and forty-nine when he published, *The Adventures of Huckleberry Finn*. At forty-three, John F. Kennedy became the President of the United States. Leonardo Da Vinci was fifty-one when he painted the *Mona Lisa*. Dr. Seuss was fifty-four when he wrote, *The Cat in the Hat*. J R R Tolkien was sixty-two when *The Lord of the Rings* book came out. At seventy years old, the healthy Jack LaLanne defied skeptics and towed seventy rowboats while handcuffed and shackled. Finally, an idol of mine, who spent twenty-seven years in prison for non-violent protests, became President of South Africa at the age of seventy-six. His name is Nelson Mandela. He kept his hopes alive through the worst oppression, and did not allow depression to defeat him.

Reading through these accomplishments, and noting the age of each person when they achieved their grandeur, I feel inspired. I am reassured that I can find success at any age. I recognize that even if I fail with a project that I am working on today, I can always find success tomorrow, next year, or even ten, twenty, or thirty years in the future. What is most important then, is not how old I am, but how I use my time, and the experience I gain through my trials and errors as I continue to be productive.

"I do not think, sir, you have any right to command me, merely because you are older than I, or because you have seen more of the world than I have; your claim to superiority depends on the use you have made of your time and experience." — Charlotte Brontë, *Jane Eyre*

If age is bringing you down, I want you to know that you can still be happy. No matter how young or old you are, numbers should not be a factor in your well-being. While age is something you cannot control, there are other elements that you can dictate, which may help you feel better as you progress through the years. By correcting your attitude and the way you perceive things; engaging in physical activity; avoiding alcohol, cigarettes, food chemicals, and prescription drugs; and eating more organic fruits, vegetables, and plant-based foods, you will no longer feel like you are *getting old*. You will simply mature with age. Do not let anyone epitomize you, or persuade you that there is nothing you can do to improve your mood, or that you need to rely on prescription drugs to elevate your joy. Avoid falling victim to flu shots, senior discounts, and unnecessary chemical drugs. You have control over your happiness. There are always natural improvements that can be adapted. By incorporating these twelve steps into your life, not only will you find happiness, you may even discover the fountain of youth.

I now want to touch on biology, and the belief that we are depressed because of chemical imbalances in our brain.

Biology

"The moment you change your perception is the moment you rewrite the chemistry of your body." – Dr. Bruce Lipton, The Biology of Belief

It is quite common for doctors and psychiatrists to blame depression on biology. Yes, biological make-up does play a role, but they use chemical imbalances as scapegoats, and then prescribe medications to *boost* levels of dopamine, norepinephrine, and serotonin. Often, the side effects from these drugs are creating more imbalances. Too frequently, they fail to consider the role that diet plays in the biology or make-up of the body. Most of these *experts* have no idea how important of a role that maintaining a clean internal environment plays in our overall mental well-being. They never mention our relationship with the bacteria living in our gut.

An August 2011 study published in *Gastroenterology* journal, *The Intestinal Microbiota Affect Central Levels of Brain-Derived Neurotrophic Factor and Behavior*, found that, "*The gut bacteria and intestinal microbiota influences brain chemistry and behavior independently of the autonomic nervous system, gastrointestinal-specific neurotransmitters, or inflammation.*" Researchers believe that gut microbes may communicate with the brain by modulating the immune system or by producing their own versions of neurotransmitters. John Cryan, from *University College Cork* in Ireland, explains that the big nerve – known as the vagus nerve – which runs from the brain to the abdomen acts as the, "*Highway of communication between what is going on in the gut, and what happens in the brain.*" What this reveals is that the health of our bowel, and the food and drinks that constitute our diet, have a significant impact on our attitude, behavior, feelings, and mood. To assure that we will not negatively alter our biological make-up, we want to be sure that we keep our bowels clean, and that we are eating healthy, plant-based diets. I will address this relationship between the gut and the brain further in steps three and four.

While mental health practitioners frequently blame genetics or neurological degeneration for dysfunctions associated with biological make-up, various new studies are providing evidence that diet and nutrition may play more of an important role. Researchers are discovering that compounds in raw fruits and vegetables can improve mood by altering biological make-up.

A 2012 article from the journal, *Histories of the Neurosciences*, titled, *Monoamine Theories of Depression: Historical Impact on Biomedical Research*, introduces the *monoamine theory of depression*. The article states that, "*Billions of nerves in our brain communicate with one another through chemical signals called neurotransmitters. For the nerve cells to effectively communicate, they release chemicals known as monoamines.*" Three of the most recognizable monoamines are dopamine, norepinephrine, and serotonin. These are the three neurotransmitters that mental health practitioners prescribe medications to *boost*. The article continues, "*As more monoamines are produced, an enzyme – known as monoamine oxidase – is produced to moderate, and assure that we maintain the right amount of these neurotransmitters.*" In November 2006, a study titled, *Elevated Monoamine Oxidase A Levels In The Brain,* was published in the *Archives of General Psychiatry.* This study found that, *"People who are depressed appear to have elevated levels of monoamine oxidase in their brain."* Monoamine oxidase is the enzyme that breaks down and balances our neurotransmitters. When levels are elevated, our number of neurotransmitters – such as serotonin, dopamine, and norepinephrine – decreases. The study goes on to inform us that there are phytonutrients found in spices and herbs such as cinnamon, cloves, nutmeg, and oregano, that inhibit the production of this monoamine oxidase enzyme. An additional study, published in the July 2011 *Journal of Neural Transmission*, titled, *Dietary Inhibitors of Monoamine Oxidase A,* explains how a group of phytonutrients – known as flavonoids – found in apples, berries, grapes, kale, onions, green tea, and several other plant-based foods, may effect our brain biology enough to significantly improve our mood.

A May 2012 review in *Nutritional Neuroscience*, titled, *Natural Mood Foods: The Actions of Polyphenols Against Psychiatric and Cognitive Disorders,* suggests that eating plenty of organic fruits and vegetables may, *"Present a non-invasive, natural, and inexpensive therapeutic means to supporting a healthy brain."* Researchers found that certain compounds known as polyphenols – which are found in abundance in plant-derived foods such as fruits and vegetables – provide a broad spectrum of molecular and cellular actions against neurological degeneration. Two specific polyphenols are EGCG – found in green tea and broccoli – and curcumin – extracted from turmeric. According to the review, *"These two compounds are highly associated with higher cognitive function, better mood, and protective effects against various brain diseases."*

In addition, a 2008 study published in the *Neurochemical Research* journal, *Benefits From Dietary Polyphenols For Brain Aging and Alzheimer's Disease,* states that, *"Dietary Factors have emerged as effectors of the brain by influencing cellular energy metabolism and modulating the signaling pathways of molecules involved with brain plasticity."* The study goes on to conclude, *"Food consumption and physical activity stimulate metabolic processes present in mitochondria – the main vessels of energy metabolism in the body that breakdown organic matter into usable energy."* Similar to the previous study, this research also points out polyphenols, and encourages increased consumption of organic fruits and vegetables. Polyphenols were shown to have antioxidant and anti-inflammatory activity, and also to assist in reversal of neuronal atrophy and behavior deficits.

In the *Oxidative Medicine & Cellular Longevity* journal, a 2009 study, *Plant Polyphenols as Dietary Antioxidants in Human Health and Disease,* describes polyphenols as, *"Natural organic compounds produced by plants as defense mechanisms against pathogen attacks, UV radiation, and physical damage. Over eight-thousand polyphenic compounds of plant origin have been identified – many of which are widely studied and recognized for their brain-protective properties."*

To learn more about the monoamine theory of depression, and how eating more fruits and vegetables can improve our mood, I suggest watching Dr. Michael Greger's video, *"Fighting The Blues With Greens."* You can access this on his website (*nutritionfacts.org*).

Not only is it important to eat more fruits and vegetables if we want to alter our brain chemistry and regulate neurotransmitter activity, but it is also wise to avoid eating meat. Researchers are discovering that chemical imbalances in the brain are associated with neuroinflammation that is caused by ingesting arachadonic acid. This acid is found primarily in chicken, eggs, beef, processed meats (hot dogs, sausages, bacon and ribs), fish, burgers, pork, and pizza. According to a cross-sectional study published in *Nutrition journal* in 2010, *Vegetarian Diets Are Associated With Healthy Mood States,* it is noted that, *"Arachidonic acid is a key substrate for the synthesis of proinflammatory eicosanoids and downstream cytokines. This can adversely impact mental health via a cascade of neuroinflammation."* I will elaborate further on the dangers of arachadonic acid in step four when we advance to discussing energy sources. In addition to arachadonic acid being present in animal-based foods, new studies are showing that meat and dairy-based diets cause intestinal microbiota changes that carry the potential for human enteric disease. *Harvard University* scientists have even discovered that, *"A diet high in meat and cheese – yet low in fruits and vegetables – alters the trillions of microbes living in the gut that influence weight, immunity, behavior, and mood."* In steps three and four, you will learn more about these studies.

"Thoughts are an important part of your inner-wisdom, and they are very powerful. A thought held long enough and repeated often enough becomes a belief. A belief then becomes your biology." – Dr. Christiane Northrup

Why is it that we have believed for so long that our biological make-up cannot be improved by any means other than chemical pills prescribed by psychiatrists or doctors? Because we have been conditioned to believe this, we never thought to seek other expert opinions. We all want a quick-fix, so we rely on pills while continuing to eat poorly, and rather than get better, we let our health regress deeper. As Dr. Northrup exclaims, these thoughts do become powerful. As we hang on to the belief that our depression is a genetic disorder that we have to live with forever, this becomes our biology. This credence also enables us to develop dependencies on prescription drugs. My goal is to convince the masses that by letting go of this belief, changing their diet and lifestyle, correcting their attitude and perception, restoring their bowel health, and following these guidelines, they can successfully correct most chemical imbalances in their brain. We need to recognize that we are not powerless over depression.

If age and biological make-up are not real reasons to be depressed, then what about living with a dysfunctional family, or residing in a negative social environment? Is there a way to elevate our level of happiness when we are living around others who are sulking in sorrows? Perhaps we will discover that there are many ways.

Family & Social Environment

"There are two things in life you cannot choose. The first is your enemies; the second your family. Sometimes the difference between them is hard to see, but in the end time will show you that the cards you have been dealt could always have been worse." — Carlos Ruiz Zafón, *The Midnight Palace*

Life is not always fair, but how we react to the difficulties, and the attitude we maintain, always has an impact on what we make out of our experiences. When things do not go my way, my mother reminds me, *"When life gives you lemons, you have to make organic lemonade."* Some things happen that we simply do not have control over. Our upbringing, the families we are born into, and the social environment where we are raised are examples of components that we cannot control. If we blame any of them for our despair, we will never find happiness.

Unfortunately for some, this means being born into abuse, neglect, poverty, and violence. If you have been raised in an abusive family, and subjected to neglect and pain, you may have wished over and over that you could escape. You may have dreamt of finding happiness and love – somewhere, somehow. This constant sorrow is an invitation for misery. If you live in poverty, this creates hopelessness and worry, often resulting in anxiety and depression. If you spend your childhood around violence, you may see life as being cruel, difficult, and simply ugly. This exposure will likely lead you away from appreciating the joys of life or marveling at the beauties of nature.

"I am not what happened to me. I am what I choose to become." – Carl Jung

No matter what your situation is, you can always find ways to love yourself, and there are numerous approaches to attracting happiness in your life. Sometimes you have to search outside of the world you are a victim in. To accomplish this, you may have to broaden your horizons. You might need to refrain from searching for pity. There is no reason for any of us to seek out reasons for why other people should feel sorry for us. This is simply giving up our power. Why dwell over the things we have never had authority over when we can discover new entities that enliven us and make us happy? We need to gain control of our lives by means of self-empowerment.

In 2011, the *Gallup-Healthways Well-Being Index* conducted a study on U.S. adults and looked at the prevalence of chronic illnesses among those living in poverty, and those considered *above* poverty. While cancer and heart disease rates were higher among those not in poverty (likely a result of meat and dairy-heavy diets), the strongest disparity was with incidence of depression. Thirty-one percent of Americans under the *U.S. Census Bureau's* poverty threshold in 2011 were diagnosed with depression, while only fifteen percent of Americans not in poverty struggled with this disorder. This affirms that the continuous worry attached to living with little income can indeed trigger sad emotions.

Jacoby

Often, in impoverished conditions there are few birds, flowers, trees, or wild animals. The food that is available is less than ideal, processed, and saturated with chemicals. The public schools fail to provide substantial education. There are little opportunities for employment. Crime rates are higher. With this lack of nature, nourishment, and real education, there is not much room for optimism. What can be done to rise above these conditions?

The way society is structured today, there will always be physical poverty. In the May 2011 edition of *Vanity Fair*, Nobel Laureate Joseph Stiglitz points out that the top one percent of Americans owns forty percent of the nation's wealth, and takes home twenty-four percent of the nation's income. Additionally, sociologist William Domhoff declares in his 2011 article, *Wealth, Income, and Power,* – published by the sociology department at *University of California* Santa Cruz – that the same one percent are responsible for only five percent of the nation's debt. This is another component we are powerless over. For as long as the current system is in place, we will always experience the extremes of poverty.

Living in poverty does not mean we are obligated to restrict ourselves from dreaming big or accomplishing goals. There are ways to climb out of mental poverty, just as there are ways to escape internal poverty. Poor health is the epitome of internal poverty. Negative thoughts imprison us in mental poverty. Eating optimal foods, exercising, and thinking positively helps to establish a balance. If we are happy, our living situation should not matter much. We can promote happiness by nourishing our bodies with organic plant-based foods; fueling our minds with exercise; and expanding our intellect with unbiased knowledge. Unfortunately we cannot learn from our television set.

If we are fortunate enough to live comfortably, and we have been blessed with prosperity, finding ways to nourish those who are impoverished can be rewarding for us, and will simultaneously build our character. This can be accomplished by providing them with fresh fruits and vegetables. To do so, it is important to teach those living in these conditions how to grow their own food. We can also help by donating boxes of fresh organic produce to food pantries. It does not help to simply drop off cans and packages of chemically saturated food look-a-like substances. These processed foods are partially responsible for why they remain in poverty. Are you familiar with the story about Adam Purple and his *Garden of Eden*? Please search for him on *YouTube*. There is a short documentary that is available for viewing. Adam started building a community garden in the project-housing where he resided in the 1970's, and the garden eventually became a source of nourishment for many families.

Today, several people, and various organizations have gathered together to grow their own community gardens. Imagine if we started a growing revolution and we equipped those who have little income with the ability to provide food for themselves? This could potentially drive out the liquor stores, corporate fast-food chains, and manufacturers of processed foods that contribute to the downfall of those buying their products. Not only would avoiding these products and eating optimal foods improve their mood, it would also reconnect them with nature. Spending time in nature has been shown to elevate happiness. Additionally, it would relieve them of the stress attached to worrying about how they will be able to afford food.

"If people can grow safe, healthy, affordable food, if they have access to land and clean water, this is transformative on every level in a community. I believe we cannot have healthy communities without a healthy food system." – Will Allen, CEO of *Growing Power* (*growingpower.org*)

Will Allen is a former professional basketball player, and co-author of the book, *The Good Food Revolution: Growing Healthy Food, People, and Communities.* He is the proud founder of *Growing Power* (*growingpower.org*) and has been hailed as, *"One of the most influential leaders of the food security and urban farming movement."* According to their website, *"Growing Power transforms communities by supporting people from diverse backgrounds, and the environments in which they live, through the development of Community Food Systems. These systems provide high-quality, safe, healthy, affordable food for all residents in the community. Growing Power develops Community Food Centers – as a key component of Community Food Systems – through training, active demonstration, outreach, and technical assistance."* Will and his employees are dedicated to growing food for those living in urban areas. Their goal is to, *"Grow Foods, grow minds, and grow community."* Mr. Allen knows how much of an impact having access to affordable, organic food has on our health and well-being.

"If kids grow kale, kids eat kale. If they grow tomatoes, they eat tomatoes. But when none of this is presented to them, if they are not shown how food affects the mind and the body, they blindly eat whatever you put in front of them." — *Ron Finley*

In South Central L.A., where there are countless liquor stores, fast food restaurants, and vacant lots, a man named Ron Finley (*ronfinley.com*) began to grow his own food. His method is known as *Guerilla Gardening*. He plants vegetable gardens in abandoned lots, on traffic medians, and along curbs. Ron does this to provide alternatives for fast-food. He states that, *"The drive-thrus are killing people faster than the drive-bys."* He describes South Central as a *food desert*, and the truth is, most impoverished places are food deserts. Over twenty-six million people in the U.S. reside in these *food deserts*. This lack of real food is closely associated with why many of these people are also experiencing depression. Ron is doing his part to reverse this trend and change the pattern. If you are seeking inspiration, check out his speech at the February 2013 *TEDx Conference*. You can access it on *YouTube*.

Are you aware of the organization known as *EarthSave* (*earthsave.org*)? *EarthSave* is a 501(c)(3) non-profit organization that was formed in 1988. Their mission is to educate and teach people how to make healthy food choices. They offer a thirty day *Meals for Health* intervention program that helps low-income participants reduce their health care costs, and guides them on a path to wellness and recovery using a low-fat plant-based diet. *EarthSave* is guided by founder John Robbins' philosophy: *May all be fed, may all be healed, may all be loved*. John is also the author of several books, including, *Diet For A New America*, and *The Food Revolution*.

In Boulder, CO, a non-profit organization known as *Growing Gardens* (*growinggardens.org*) was established in 1998. Their mission is, *"To enrich the lives of the community through sustainable urban agriculture. Growing Gardens envisions people experiencing a direct and deep connection with plants, the land, and each other. Through its many gardening-based programs, Growing Gardens strives to reach gardeners and would-be gardeners of all ages to work alongside the organization and build community through urban agriculture."* They currently maintain five urban agriculture projects. These include: *The Cultiva Youth Project* (ages twelve-nineteen); *The Children's Peace Garden* (ages four-ten); *Horticultural Therapy* (seniors and people with disabilities); *Fresh Food, Families, & Fitness*; and *The Community Gardens* (general public). With the combination of these five projects, they find ways to get the entire community involved in gardening. By getting acquainted with the *Cultiva Youth Project*, children aged twelve to nineteen have been able to successfully turn their lives around and find their role in society. The goal of this project is to find kids from low-income families and teach them youth leadership skills; give them opportunities to give back to the community by helping those in need; connect them with the environment, promote sustainable agriculture, and teach them to grow food for themselves; and to provide them with valuable life skills, business skills, interpersonal skills, and entrepreneurial opportunities.

Imagine if we had similar organizations in every community. By working together we can make this possible. If we can follow the lead of Adam Purple, Will Allen, and Ron Finley, and start growing community gardens everywhere, then we can help those who are living in poverty find happiness by nourishing them with healthy food. If we can launch organizations similar to *Growing Gardens* and *EarthSave*, or simply help them expand by donating money or volunteering our time and energy, we will see progress. By accepting the current system where the only options for food and leisure are fast-food, drugs, and liquor, we can expect people living in these conditions to continue eating poorly, drinking alcohol, and being involved with drugs in some way. We need to provide them with better options. I believe it is our duty to start growing organic fruits and vegetables in abandoned lots, and in places where crops will flourish.

While growing and having access to our own food can help alleviate depression, this is a single component of happiness. It is not the only solution. To remain positive while living in an impoverished community also requires a good attitude, and an optimistic outlook. There is no reason to victimize yourself if you live in these conditions. You can always find ways to grow above and beyond your current situation. You do not have control over how you were raised, or where you resided, but you do have the power to create your future differently. You have the capacity to manifest your dreams into reality. If you have pure intentions, are ambitious, and you seek something grand, you will manifest the changes you envision into your life when you are ready.

43

"It is important for people to know that no matter what lies in their past, they can overcome the dark side and press on to a brighter world." — Dave Pelzer, *A Child Called "It"*

Dave Pelzer is the author of seven inspirational books. His most recognized book is, *A Child Called 'It.'* As a child, Dave was abused severely by his alcoholic mother. The abuse was so bad that his case was identified as the most gruesome and extreme case of child-abuse in California history. He lived each day afraid that he would be tortured to death or killed. Today, as an adult, *Dave's inspirational work has encouraged countless organizations and millions of individuals to recommit their efforts and remain steadfast to their personal convictions (Davepelzer.com).* Even after spending the entirety of his childhood being tortured and abused, he moved forward, turned his struggles into successes, and now helps others around him overcome similar challenges. He refused to let uncontrollable circumstances limit him.

In her book, *Succeed Because of What You've Been Through*, Rhonda Sciortino explains how she, "W*ent from poverty to affluence, loneliness to a network of wonderful friends and family, and the feeling of being unwanted and unloved to a genuine sense of worth and value."* For eighteen years, Jaycee Lee Dugard kept her kidnapper's secrets – *that he had kidnapped her when she was eleven years old, abused her, fathered two daughters through that abuse, and kept them all captive in his backyard.* After being rescued, she tells her story in, *A Stolen Life.* She eluded his hatred, and managed to find happiness through it all.

It does not matter who you are, where you come from, or who raised you, if you are human, you are going to face adversity at times. Things are not always going to be perfect. You will not wake up every day to blue skies, warm winds, and beautiful forests. Clouds do exist. Extreme winds can get bone-chilling cold. Tall trees come crashing down. However, sunny days soon follow the cloudy ones. Warm winds come blowing in shortly after the cold front passes. New saplings sprout and eventually take the place of fallen trees. We have to learn to accept the things we cannot change, and if we cannot, then we simply must change our perception.

"Do not ever take things personal. Nothing anyone does is because of you, it is because of something that is going on in their lives. If someone is attacking me, they are attacking the part of me that they do not want to look at in themselves. If they did not have it in them they would not be able to see it in me." – Dan McDonald *(regenerateyourlife.org)*

We each have a gift, and the Universe is fighting to help us locate this treasure so we can share it with the world. Abuse cannot change this. Poverty cannot restrain us from our pursuit of finding it. Violence cannot scare it away. We need to align with the universe so that we can reach our true potential. The twelve steps in this book will help prepare us for our calling.

For those of you who have experienced violent upbringings, or were involved in gangs at a young age, it is possible to find escape routes. It does not matter how heavily involved you might be, one thing that people always respect is the determination to succeed. If you start to adapt good health, fuel your

Jacoby

mind with exercise, expand your intellect, and unearth your passions, you will earn the respect to be able to walk away without a problem. Chasen Crossley joined his first gang when he was twelve. He was raised without a father in Compton – a dangerous neighborhood in Southern California. Crossley found self-expression while performing in drama class. He discovered his gift for public speaking in 2007 when he was asked to do a Martin Luther King speech. People constantly assured him, *"You have a gift for public speaking."* He utilized his potential, was able to walk away from the *gang-life*, and today he is President of the *Los Angeles Trade Technical Speech Club*, President of a Toastmaster's Club, and has spoken at many churches. He also coordinates several youth events. Richard Santana, a.k.a. Mr. Chocolate, is a former gang member who earned his degree from *Harvard University*. He is now a motivational speaker. There are many former gang members who have turned their lives around, found happiness, and are now promoting positivity. They do not dwell on the past, they move forward to brighter days. They use their past as fuel to help them push ahead. Check out Simeon Moore's *TedX* speech.

"Everybody wants happiness, and nobody wants pain, but you cannot have a rainbow without a little rain." – Zion Lee

If you have experienced abuse, neglect, poverty, and violence in your lifetime, I want you to know that none of it is your fault. There is nothing you can do about it now other than move forward and let it all go. It is best to use the struggles you faced then to build foundations for success today. Something will always try to dim our shine, but we do not have to permit it to. It is easier to acknowledge whatever this hurdle is, step over it, and leap ahead. Too often those who deal with adversity allow it to defeat them, but not you.

If thoughts of your family and social environment generates feelings of sadness and despair, shift your cerebration to anything that makes you happy. Why search for pity when good fortunes are waiting to be pursued? There is always an alternative to dwelling over situations that took place in the past. You will feel much better if you discover where these alternatives are hiding.

"Rather than dwelling on the fact that certain people in your life were not exactly perfect examples of loving nurturers, consider making yourself into the person you hoped they would be. You can endlessly twirl around thoughts in your mind about why certain people were various levels of badness to you, but this likely will bring about no good, and will also likely keep you lost in the past. You cannot improve your life by focusing on the wasted energies and damaging memories of your past. But you can work beauty into your life by using the lessons of your past, and the energy and resources of the present to continually build a better life." – John McCabe, *Igniting Your Life*

Gender

"A recent study found that women who carry a little extra weight live longer than the men who mention it."

Humor is essential for happiness. I do not think this study is factual, but it made me laugh. Men and women alike enjoy laughter. With all jokes aside, studies suggest that women are twice as likely as men to suffer from depression. Concurrently, statistics show that men are more likely to commit suicide. Maybe we are not laughing enough. Perhaps we take life too seriously at times. Whatever the reasoning may be, there is strong evidence supporting that women tend to get depressed more easily, and men seem to battle depression much more difficultly. Mental health practitioners are quick to blame gender for depression, prescribe pills, and play it off like it is no big deal. There is no reason why any of us should be depressed, or taking pills. I assure you that we can alleviate our gloom by altering our lifestyle and changing our perception.

The common widespread belief for why women are thought to be more depressed than men is due to hormonal imbalances. In some instances, this has been associated with birth control pills, prescription drugs, and other forms of contraception. Occasionally, women experience what is called postpartum depression, where they encounter ennui after giving birth. For men, according to a June 2013 study out of *Lund University* in Sweden, it was determined that being young, single, and having a low level of education were among the greatest risk factors for suicide.

For the men considering suicide, if you are young, single, or have a low level of education, please analyze your situation before you go any further. I admit that growing pains are not always enjoyable and can be difficult to cope with at times, but I assure you that you will grow out of them. You should be celebrating your youth now, because when you get a little older, you are going to be so happy and successful that you may not get a chance to look back. If you are single, consider that there are millions of single men and women in the world who are alone, and could be your perfect match. Try joining your local gym. Get outside more. Make changes in your life that could attract a mate. Be passionate. Find meetup groups online (*meetup.com*). Luckily, today there are online dating sites – such as *match.com* or *eharmony* – where you can search for potential partners. If you feel like you will not find someone on those sites, you can go a step further and pay for your date on sites such as *seekingarrangement.com* or *whatsyourprice.com*. Sitting alone inside of your apartment or house and wishing you had a significant other in your life is not going to change things. Unfortunately, this is not how the *Law of Attraction* works. Even with this law, action is required. If you are undereducated, you can begin your education by seeking your GED (*gedtestingservice.com*). Beyond a high school diploma or GED, you can enroll in classes at your closest community college or university. If you simply cannot afford to enroll, check to see if you are eligible for Pell grants, financial aid, or scholarships. You can even take some college courses online for free. Access *coursera.org* to see what classes they offer.

While researching reasons for why women are depressed, I found evidence that contraceptives and birth control can indeed be a trigger. Dr. Wendie Trubow, a board certified gynecologist and quality director at *Visions HealthCare*, said in an email that birth control pills can have the ability to affect mental health. She wrote, *"Any contraceptive that contains hormones*

Jacoby

has the potential to impact a woman's mental health due to the effect that synthetic hormones can have on a woman's body. For any woman who is prone to depression, anxiety, sadness, or mood swings, the hormone-containing contraceptives can magnify these responses. She should consider how well she manages her mental health prior to beginning a hormone-containing contraceptive, because for a subset of women, taking this type of contraceptive can worsen an underlying mental health issue. The mechanism is complicated, and involves the woman's innate state of health, her overall toxic burden, and the way her liver processes and her gut excretes the hormones she has taken. It is very important to optimize the function of her liver and intestines by avoiding processed foods, detoxifying the diet, and taking supplements that improve the liver's function."

Professor Jayashri Kulkarni, of Australia's *Monash University*, conducted a study in March 2005 that compared depression symptom scores between users and non-users of combined oral contraceptives. Results showed that, *"Women using the pill had an average depression rating scale score of 17.6, compared to a score of 9.8 among the non-user group. The women involved in the study were aged over eighteen, not pregnant or lactating, had no clinical history of depression, and had not been on anti-depressant medication in the previous twelve months."*

In an October 2005 article published on the *Aphrodite Women's Health* page, *Is The Pill Playing Havoc With Your Mental Health?*, the author – Katherine Burnett-Watson – provides results from an informal survey conducted by an Aphrodite member. She noticed her happiness beginning to fade after taking birth control and wanted to know if other women experienced equivalent downheartedness after taking oral contraceptives. The results of her survey found that, *"Fifty-seven percent of respondents reported mood swings, sixty-three percent were irritable, sixty-five percent experienced irrational crying, and sixty-nine percent felt anxious and depressed after taking hormonal contraceptives. Furthermore, of the sixty-six percent of respondents who stopped taking hormonal contraceptives because of side-effects, nearly two-thirds noticed partial or complete recovery from their symptoms. Other statistics from the survey revealed that seventy-three percent of respondents stated hormonal contraceptives had a negative impact on their lives, and over fifty percent of respondents who were taking anti-depressant medication were doing so to treat depression that occurred after beginning hormonal contraceptives."*

These studies are alarming. What is also startling is the February 2013 *Centers for Disease Control and Prevention* (CDC) report revealing that roughly four out of every five women have used birth control pills. Could the correlation between taking these contraceptives and experiencing downheartedness be enough to accurately label birth control as a trigger for depression? I cannot provide staggering amounts of evidence that these pills are causing depression, but I do know that they create hormonal imbalances. These imbalances are commonly linked to melancholy.

I am not going to encourage anyone to get off of birth control, but I do want you to be aware that if you are experiencing depression as a woman taking these pills, this may be the only solution. Eating a plant-based diet rich in fruits and vegetables can also be helpful – as meat, milk, cheese, and eggs all contain foreign animal hormones that are known to disrupt hormonal balance. These animal-based foods are also acidic, and can prompt an inflammatory response, often stimulating depression.

An October 2013 study in *Brain, Behavior, and Immunity, found that women* whose diets include more foods that trigger inflammation – such as sugar-sweetened or diet soft drinks, refined grains, dairy, meat, and trans-fats – have up to a forty-one percent greater risk of being diagnosed with depression than those who eat a less inflammatory diet consisting of yellow and green vegetables. This study was conducted by researchers at *Harvard School of Public Health (HSPH)*. For more than twelve years, the researchers conducted a prospective study of 43,685 women – aged fifty to seventy-seven – participating in the *Nurses' Health Study*. At the start of the study, none of the participants had been diagnosed with depression or were taking antidepressant drugs. The researchers tracked the women's dietary patterns and depression, and they tracked several biomarkers for inflammation through blood tests. They documented 2,594 cases of depression using a strict definition (a diagnosis of depression *and* antidepressant use) and 6,446 using a broader definition (a diagnosis of depression *and/or* antidepressant use). The conclusion was that, *"Women who regularly drank sodas, and ate red meat or refined grains, and infrequently consumed vegetables were twenty-nine to forty-one percent more likely to be depressed than those who ate the less inflammatory diet."*

Whether you are a man or woman, blaming your depression on gender does not provide relief from this disharmony. It is not normal for anyone to be depressed. If you are, you simply need to address other issues that you can control, such as your diet, lifestyle, and mental approach.

Genetics

"Genetics loads the gun, lifestyle pulls the trigger." – Dr. Caldwell Esselstyn

When I speak to people who are depressed, and I ask them why they assume they feel this way, the most common reply I get is, *"It runs in the family."* I want you to know that simply because other people in your family may be afflicted with a condition, this does not mean you have to join them. Blaming depression on genetics is a cop-out, and is only enabling you to continue to avoid nature, eat poorly, live sedentary, and maintain a pessimistic attitude. In *The China Study*, Dr. T. Colin Campbell lists eight principles of food and health. Principle number four states, *"Genes do not determine disease on their own. Genes function only by being activated, or expressed, and nutrition plays a critical role in determining which genes, good and bad, are expressed."* When genes are not activated or expressed, they remain

48   Jacoby

biochemically dormant. These genes then have no effect on our health. Nutrition and lifestyle are often the factors that determine the activity of genes. Dr. Dean Ornish, founder and president of the *Preventive Medicine Research Institute*, elaborates further by explaining, *"Our genes, and our telomeres, are not necessarily our fate. So often people think 'Oh, I have bad genes, there is nothing I can do about it.' My findings indicate that telomeres may lengthen to the degree that people change how they live. Research indicates that longer telomeres are associated with fewer illnesses and longer life."*

Epigenetics is a term applied to the belief that gene cells can be turned on and off, and states that the environment of the cell determines which genes will be activated or deactivated. Diet and environmental conditions play the most important role in epigenetics. If you eat poorly and live an unhealthy lifestyle, chances are you will activate bad gene cells, which will also be passed down from generation to generation.

"This exciting new field of epigenetics – meaning literally 'around' the gene – allows us to see how environmental factors alter our gene expression in a specific place within each cell. As a result, we now know that when we take active control of these factors, we can literally help control our health and genetic destiny." – Woodson Merrell, M.D., *The Detox Prescription*

While genes do determine much, the only way genetics can lead to depression or a degenerative condition is through diet and lifestyle choices. You eat what your parents eat and they eat what their parents ate and so on. If your parents were smokers or drinkers and you are also a smoker or drinker, then chances are you will develop a disease or health condition. If you eat processed foods, you are more likely to develop diabetes and cancer. If you eat meat and dairy, chances are increased that you will have high cholesterol and develop heart disease or cancer. If you feed your child fast food and processed foods, chances are increased that your child will have a lower IQ, weaker bones, and be prone to serious disease.

By mistreating our internal organs and damaging our intestinal flora, we pave the way for depression to embed its thorns into our terrain. Microbes in the gut communicate with our brain, and when we have an abundance of harmful bacteria invading our internal environment from eating processed foods and animal products, ingesting pharmaceutical drugs, drinking alcohol, and smoking, the messages being relayed are not going to stimulate positive emotions. This is not genetic or hereditary, this is simply the fact that we are lacking an array of nutrients needed for vibrant health, and are consuming a variety of unhealthful substances. We have to be more appreciative of how privileged we are to be alive. Simply because our parents were responsible for our conception, and we share certain genetic traits, this does not take away from our individuality or demote our differences. We are gifted, talented, and unique in our own special ways. This alone should motivate us to break a link in the genetic chain that has been plaguing family members with misfortunes each generation. The last thing we want to be doing is following the footsteps of others. We choose to set our own trends. Our health should be a reflection of the conscious lifestyle choices we make.

"At bottom every man knows well enough that he is a unique being, only once on this earth; and by no extraordinary chance will such a marvelously picturesque piece of diversity in unity as he is, ever be put together a second time." — Friedrich Nietzsche

Health Conditions

"My blood type is 'Be Positive.'"

While statistics reveal that one out of every ten Americans suffers from depression, let us not forget that seven out of ten deaths in America are a result of diseases and chronic conditions. The *Centers for Disease Control and Prevention* (CDC) reported in 2005, that one in every two Americans — or 133 million Americans — were living with at least one chronic condition or degenerative disease. In 2007, the *National Center for Health Statistics* (NCHS) determined that one in every three adults is obese. A 2003 study published in the *Journal of the American Medical Association* (JAMA) concluded that one in three Americans who were born after the year 2000, will develop diabetes in their lifetime. Cancer rates continue to rise, and the *World Health Organization* (WHO) expects the number of new cases to increase seventy percent over the next two decades — from fourteen million a year in 2012, to twenty-five million new cases a year in 2025. Heart disease still remains the number one cause of death, and according to the *World Health Organization (who.int)*, an estimated 17.3 million people died from cardiovascular disease in 2008, representing thirty percent of all global deaths. Of these deaths, approximately 7.3 million were due to coronary heart disease and 6.2 million were from stroke. They expect the annual death rate from cardiovascular disease to reach 23.3 million by 2030.

As a society, our health is failing. We can only blame our diet and lifestyle. Genetics are not as much of a factor as the medical system wants us to believe. It may be difficult to accept this notion, but we do have control over our health. We are not powerless. In fact, we orchestrate our well-being.

Knowing that one in every two Americans lives with at least one chronic condition, how is it that only one of ten reports being depressed? Could it be that they have been manipulated into believing they do not have control, and are powerless over their circumstances? Perhaps this belief that they cannot improve has bribed them into accepting they will always live stricken with these conditions? Whether you express it or not, living with a chronic condition is always going to inhibit your ability to reach your full happiness potential.

By reading books such as *Whole,* or *The China Study,* both by Dr. T. Colin Campbell; *The Raw Cure: Healing Beyond Medicine; Sunfood Diet Infusion,* by John McCabe; *Preventing & Reversing Heart Disease,* by Dr. Caldwell Esselstyn; and *Disease-Proof Your Child,* by Dr. Joel Fuhrman, you will gain access to information that could help you avoid being debilitated by these conditions, and keep you off of chemical drugs. The documentary, *Forks Over Knives,* also shares vital information. Simply following the steps in this

50   Jacoby

book will improve your overall quality of life and could help prevent sickness and disease. Do you agree that you would be much happier if you were off of medications, healthier, and found ways to reverse your health conditions?

Health conditions arise from any of the following:

1. A lack of something, whether it is activity, happiness, healthful digestive processes, mental faith, nutrients, or water.

2. An excess of something, whether it be animal products in the diet, chemicals, cooked food, inflammation, mucus, or toxins.

3. The accumulation of poisons or harmful microbes from chemicals, inorganic nutrients, and other foreign substances.

4. The enervation of the natural elimination process by means of prescription drugs and unnecessary medical procedures.

5. A weakened immune system, likely from poor bowel health.

If you are lacking healthy digestion, mental faith, nutrients, physical activity, or water, this can be an invitation for disease to develop, and will likely lead to depression. To combat this, you can create an abundance of good health by hydrating with pure water, partaking in physical activity, nurturing optimism, and satiating your bodies demands for nutrients by ingesting truly healthy, plant-based foods. If you have accumulated an excess of acids, mucus, or toxins from eating less than ideal foods, you can undergo internal cleansing services. If you are being exposed to chemicals, and this is triggering your ailments, you can embrace ways to reduce your chemical intake. If you are constantly sick, and relying on prescription drugs – not recognizing that they are likely worsening your condition – it may be time to accept that drugs do not provide cures, or improve health. You may want to find vegan probiotics to replace antibiotics. You could benefit from adapting a new diet and lifestyle that emphasizes eating organic plant-based foods, exercising, interacting with nature, mental stimulation, and promoting positivity and self-empowerment. This new diet, lifestyle, and mental approach could very well be your path to activating the natural defense mechanisms in your body that will strengthen your immune system. Knowing that you no longer have to accept sickness as something that is inevitable, and that you can free yourself from the pain and suffering attached to the symptoms of inactivity, negativity, and poor dietary choices, this should be enough to enhance your mood.

"The best six doctors anywhere,
And no one can deny it,
Are sunshine, water, rest, and air,
Exercise and diet.
These six will gladly you attend,
If only you are willing.
Your mind they'll ease,
Your will they'll mend,
And charge you not a shilling."

– Wayne Fields, *What the River Knows*

Since the approval for genetically-modified (GMO) ingredients to be added into our food supply was granted in 1996 (*nongmoproject.org*), we have witnessed the emergence of staggering numbers of new diseases. This growing epidemic of disease is not a natural part of evolution, it is an expression of systematic reactions. What this tells us is that we are doing something unnatural which is leading to disease. Eating factory-farmed animals and their by-products; drinking milk from another species; stocking our cabinets, counter-tops, and refrigerators with processed food-like substances; smoking cigarettes; drinking excessive amounts of alcohol; and eating crops that have been genetically manipulated to withstand a global annual application of millions of pounds of the chemical known as Glyphosate is not natural. To exclude yourself from falling victim to one of these new diseases, I encourage you to raise awareness encompassing around the foods you eat and lifestyle choices you make. Now is a good time to start caring about your health and well-being – especially if you want to break free from depression. In step four, I provide more information on the dangers of GMOs.

When we eat animal proteins, the body produces uric acid as a toxic by-product from protein metabolism. All foods derived from animals contain arachadonic acid – which is known to trigger depression. When we drink sodas, our bodies become overwhelmed with phosphoric acid. When we eat sugary food, the acids that are produced in the body can spiral out of control. Consuming dairy creates excess mucus and is acid forming. Cigarettes contain nicotinic acid, among thousands of other acidic chemicals. Alcohol's primary metabolite is acetaldehyde, and secondary metabolite is acetic acid. Acetaldehyde breaks down further into carboxylic acid. All of this compounds into what is known as acidosis.

Disease starts to develop in the body when acidosis is present. In a sense, acidosis is equivalent to inflammation. We always want to avoid this condition. To reverse acidosis, we have to drink clean water and fresh organic juices, eat more alkaline forming foods such as leafy green vegetables and algae, and eliminate the acid forming substances. We have to break away from acid forming habits like eating bleached foods, clarified sugars, dairy, eggs, fried oils, gluten grains, meat, and synthetic chemicals; drinking alcohol; and smoking cigarettes. In addition to changing what we eat, drink, and consume, to successfully rid the body of unwanted acids we also have to let go of the negative emotions we are storing. When I transitioned to eating plant-based several years ago, I reached a level of happiness I had never before imagined was possible. You are capable of doing the same. In addition to acidosis cultivating disease, another culprit that kindles poor health is candida overgrowth.

"Many people are unknowingly infected with Candida albicans. This fungus deoxygenates our cells and the yeast grows until it eventually invades organ tissues, such as the lungs and liver." – Dr. Brian Clement, *LifeForce*

Candida is yeast that naturally occurs in the body. When we eat excessive amounts of refined sugars with fatty foods, the sugars cannot be metabolized efficiently and may linger in the system. When this happens, our

Jacoby

blood sugar levels rise and the candida yeast feeds on the sugars, eventually growing out of control. If we eliminate the animal-based and cooked fats, and allow our blood sugar levels to drop, we will metabolize the sugars, and the candida will no longer have a source of nourishment, eventually atrophying.

Candida thrives on the sugars from dairy. Because we cannot digest dairy efficiently, candida yeast multiplies while feeding on its sugars. The best way to solve this problem is to eliminate dairy from our diet. There are much better sources for calcium. Try drinking almond, chia, or hemp milk. Eat more broccoli, brussels sprouts, butternut squash, carrots, collard greens, figs, kale, legumes, oranges, raisins, sesame seeds, spinach, and sweet potatoes. If you have excess mucus and dairy in your system and you are overweight, chances are you have candida overgrowth. To help alleviate this condition, you will need a stronger bacterium that will eat the sugars before the candida. This is where acidophilus and lactobacilli come into play. These two bacterial cultures thrive on the sugars in dairy products, and are not harmful to your body. To overcome candida overgrowth, after eliminating *all* dairy sources, it is helpful to take a vegan probiotic supplement to erase the food source for the candida. I recommend the supplement known as *Vitamineral Green,* or *The Ultimate Probiotic,* both made by *Healthforce Nutritionals.* To speed up the elimination process, you may also consider a supplement known as *Scram.* This is known to kill off candida and other parasites that may be invading your body.

"If you do not think your anxiety, depression, sadness and stress impact your physical health, think again. All of these emotions trigger chemical reactions in your body, which can lead to inflammation and a weakened immune system. Learn how to cope, sweet friend. There will always be dark days." – Kris Carr, *Crazy, Sexy, Raw*

Kris Carr and Chris Wark have more in common than simply sharing the same first name. They both beat cancer using a combination of mental faith, nutrition, natural healing, and physical activity. They refused conventional treatment, restored their mental faith, and transitioned to a plant-based lifestyle to aid their recovery. Access their websites (*kriscarr.com* and *chrisbeatcancer.com*) to learn more. At the *Gerson Institute (Gerson.org)* and *Hippocrates Health Institute (Hippocratesinst.org)*, thousands of people are reversing the conditions in their body that trigger cancer cell formation by incorporating changes in diet and lifestyle. Dr. Caldwell Esselstyn and Dr. Dean Ornish have helped masses of people successfully reverse heart disease. Dr. John McDougall is rescuing his patients from serious digestive issues by encouraging them to eliminate animal products from their diet. Look for his book, *The Starch Solution.* Dr. Gabriel Cousens offers a diabetes reversal program at his *Tree of Life Rejuvenation Center (treeoflifecenterus.com)* in Patagonia, AZ. Dr. Neal Barnard is tackling diabetes, obesity, and other health conditions using a similar approach. Dr. Joel Fuhrman has written several good books. If you are experiencing health conditions, do not lose hope. Rather, adjust who you are trusting to *treat* your conditions. If a doctor or psychiatrist has you believing that you will need to take pills for the rest of your life, and that you will never recover, I hope you will seek advice elsewhere. You have the power to heal yourself. If you have a condition that truly cannot be cured, you can still greatly improve your quality of living and reduce the symptoms you are encountering. Igniting happiness should be your priority.

If you are experiencing arthritis, cancer, depression, diabetes, heart disease, high cholesterol, obesity, osteoporosis, stroke, or any other similar conditions, and your doctor or psychiatrist tries to use the scare tactic of telling you that you are genetically predisposed and cannot avoid the condition, do not believe them. Take control of your health. Most medical doctors and mental health practitioners simply lack the education needed to solve nutritional deficiencies and teach their clients how to clean up their diet to be free of toxins – which is the main way of overcoming many of the common degenerative and chronic conditions. If you are sick – even with a cold, fever, or flu – the last thing you need is chemical drugs. You need nutrients, you need internal cleansing, and you need to take measures to maintain vibrant health. It is obligatory that you learn more about the foods you are ingesting and how they impact your well-being. You must empower yourself.

"When you consider that an addiction is a craving for something that is void of the true needs of the person, and that satisfying the craving takes time and energy, and that the craving is often related to substances that are liable to have damaging effects on the person, then low-quality food is addictive in every sense of the word. Low-quality food causes a chemical change within the body. The consumption of low-quality food leads to a physio-chemical pattern that alters the body and limits the ability of the body and mind to function at their best level, leading to diseased organs and to traumatic health events like heart attacks, strokes, organ failure, immune disorders, and cancers." – John McCabe, *Sunfood Diet Infusion*

Life Changes & Stressful Events

"People usually consider walking on water or in thin air a miracle. But I think the real miracle is not to walk either on water or in thin air, but to walk on earth. Every day we are engaged in a miracle which we do not even recognize: a blue sky, white clouds, green leaves, the curious eyes of a child, our own two eyes. All is a miracle." – Thich Nhat Hanh

You are not alone if you have felt like you are the happiest you have ever been, and that life could not get any better, and then suddenly it all came crashing down. This has happened to me several times, and on each occasion, not only did I learn a great deal about oppression and overcoming adversity, but I also questioned why it occurred. I felt immediate uncertainty, and at times thoughts of giving up crossed my mind. Today I know that these episodes are normal. When we get too comfortable, feel like we are not accomplishing the feats that we are capable of, or are living a meaningless life, the Universe has ways of throwing obstacles at us so that we begin to follow a new path. It may be true that our life had purpose, and that we knew which direction we would proceed with. We may not have been lost. We could have been ecstatic. Whatever the case may be, it is history now. Everything happens for a reason, even when the logic does not seem fair. The greatest resolution is to accept that these endpoints are new beginnings disguised as rough patches.

Life changes and stressful events could include: losing our job, getting divorced or ending a relationship, failing to pay our bills, losing our home to foreclosure, or being charged with a crime that could land us in prison. This could also pertain to situations such as: deciding where we will go to college, moving to a new location, or taking on extra responsibilities at work by means of a promotion, or new job title. While we do not have control over the certitude of whether we will experience similar circumstances, we do have authority over how we react to, and overcome these obstacles.

"We are all faced with a series of great opportunities, brilliantly disguised as impossible situations." – Charles Swindoll

If you lost your job, do not worry, there are plenty more opportunities for employment. Do you know that according to the *Current Employment Statistics (CES)* survey conducted by the *Department of Numbers*, in March 2014 there were a total of 137,928,000 jobs in the U.S.? Surely there is an opening for you somewhere. Do not be discouraged. If you are having trouble finding a position, consider volunteer work, or an internship. If you have to let go of something to maintain this type of work, let it go. You will likely be rewarded for your commitment and dedication.

Do you recall ever hearing the story of a man named Chris Gardner? As a single father, he and his son lived homeless for close to one year while he completed an internship at a brokerage firm. He was rewarded with a job for his hard work, and eventually opened his own multi-million dollar firm. His story was published as a memoir, and soon after was transformed into a major motion-picture, titled, *The Pursuit of 'Happy'ness*. If an ordinary man with a vision, determination, and passion can accomplish what he did, there is nothing stopping a normal woman like yourself, or an average man like you, from pursuing happiness and redefining your life.

Do you know that there is a network of national organizations that facilitates placement of volunteers on organic farms? This network is known as *Worldwide Opportunities on Organic Farms (WWOOF)*. There are hosts in ninety-nine countries around the globe. In exchange for working on these organic farms, you receive food and shelter. You are also provided with the opportunity to travel to a farm anywhere in the world, so long as you are accepted. You can access a database (*wwoof.net*) online to determine what is available, and to fill out applications.

Work opportunities arise every day, the secret is that you must actively seek employment. Too frequently, when one loses their job, they search for pity, and choose not to look for new possible avenues of earning income. If you need work, have a computer background, and are a social person, send me an email and I will try my best to help you find an opportunity for earning a steady monthly income from home (*Jesse@societysanonymous.com*).

"When two people decide to get a divorce, it is not a sign that they 'do not understand' one another, but a sign that they have, at last, begun to." – Helen Rowland

According to *Microsoft Network (MSN) Living*, the eight most common reasons for divorce are: t*oo much arguing, lack of commitment, infidelity, marrying too young, unrealistic expectations, lack of equality, abuse, and lack of preparation*. These are all legitimate reasons for divorce. The 2011 *National Marriage and Divorce Rate Trends* show that 3.6 per 1,000 people get divorced annually. According to *U.S. Census Bureau Data*, 2.4 million people divorced in the year 2012 alone. These statistics present evidence that marriages are not lasting in today's society. If you are one of the millions of people who are encountering this life change, keep your vibrations positive.

I know divorce can be terrible, especially when there are children involved. I have never been married, but my parents separated during my teenage years. It was difficult for our entire family. As challenging as this was for us, we got through it. I am still smiling today. If you are experiencing divorce, try your best not to think of this as the end. Adjust your perception and see it as a new beginning. Focus on improving yourself. Be active. Eat healthy. Add nature into your life. Pick up a new hobby. Engage in physical activity. Do everything you can to focus on improving yourself. Most importantly, be civil and keep the peace. Divorce can get ugly. If children are involved, it is adamant that you refrain from yelling or being abusive in their presence. Do not make the situation worse for them. Do not use them as leverage to get what you want. Remember that you brought them into this, so it is your responsibility to protect them from allowing the quandary to bring them down. To permit your kids to be victims in this circumstance is irresponsible and selfish.

If you are heartbroken because a relationship you truly wanted to last has ended, I encourage you to work on yourself. Be social. Try to avoid the same environment. Meditate. Practice yoga. Exercise as often as you can. Generate happy thoughts in your brain. Most importantly, eat healthy. It is common for people who are experiencing heartbreak to lose their appetite. In this case, drink fresh organic green juices, and try snacking on organic fruits and vegetables. You will feel much better. You can always resort to the *Law of Attraction* and start magnetizing good things into your life. Rather than dwelling on the darkness of the past, manifest a brighter future.

Remember, there is no such thing as heartbreak. It is only a disguise that quickly passes you by. It is another opportunity coming your way, that brings another face, another mind, at a better time. It is simply a messenger that will strengthen you, help you grow, and push you to create a more fulfilling life. By thinking positively, you can mend your pains, erase what makes you sad, let it go, and watch it fade away.

"If the American people ever allow private banks to control the issue of their currency, first by inflation, then by deflation, the banks and corporations that grow up around them will deprive the people of all property until their children wake up homeless on the continent their Fathers conquered." – Thomas Jefferson

Sadly, we have allowed the banks to control the issue of our currency, and as a result, we are witnessing foreclosures, homelessness, and poverty

Jacoby

rates dramatically increasing each year. According to *RealtyTrac*, there are close to 150,000 foreclosure filings per month in the U.S. In the April 2013 report, *The State of Homelessness In America,* the *National Alliance to End Homelessness (endhomelessness.org)* determined that, *"At a point in time in January 2012, 633,782 people were experiencing homelessness."* A *Washington Times* report in January 2014 points out that fifty million Americans are living below the poverty line, and that forty-seven million of them receive food stamps. The worst part of this is the fact that there are enough abandoned houses and buildings in the world to shelter every person in need. The problem is that banks own these properties. Unfortunately, nothing will change by sitting, waiting, and wishing. If we want change, this requires us to demand change. The best way to create this difference we are seeking, and to alter these statistics, is to work on improving ourselves. We need to empower our minds, redefine our attitudes, and take pride in being leaders.

I want to share a few success stories of people who started with close to nothing and accumulated great wealth. I will start with a woman named Oprah Winfrey. Oprah was born into abject poverty in rural Mississippi. She went from being a young girl clothed in potato sacks to the richest and most powerful female media mogul in the world. According to Forbes, as of 2009, she is worth $2.9 billion. J.K. Rowling wrote the Harry Potter book series and started a $15 billion industry. As of 2008, she was worth $843.92 million. She began writing the series while she was on welfare. She even incorporated her battle with depression, and loss of her mother, into the novels. At sixty-seven, renowned art collector and philanthropist David Geffen is worth an estimated $4.6 billion. Geffen grew up poor in Brooklyn, and lived in a one-bedroom apartment with his family. After dropping out of college, he discovered his natural gift was for spotting talented musicians and developing musical talent. He eventually signed Crosby, Stills and Nash, Bob Dylan, and Nirvana, and started *Geffen Records*. He is also a founding member of *Dreamworks* studio. David became a millionaire by the time he was twenty-six. As of September 2013, Ralph Lauren has an estimated net worth of $7.7 billion. He graduated high school in the Bronx, N.Y., but later dropped out of college to join the Army. While working as a clerk at *Brooks Brothers* making very little money, Lauren questioned whether men were ready for wider and brighter designs in ties. In 1967, he branched off on his own and sold $500,000 worth of ties. Ralph started *Polo* the next year. Demi Moore, one of Hollywood's most recognizable faces, grew up in trailer parks in Roswell, New Mexico, and moved over thirty times during childhood. She dropped out of high school at age sixteen. Today, her net worth is estimated at around $150 million.

"I have always thought that each person invented himself, and that we are each a figment of our own imagination. Some people simply have a greater ability to imagine than others." – David Geffen

I shared these stories because I want us to understand it is normal to face oppression. It is only when we give up that the problems escalate further into a deeper depression. If you are forced to move out of your home, do your best to stay positive. Find a place where you have shelter, start writing down your goals, devise a plan for your future, and make it your priority to accomplish these desires. You may want to look for a commune where you can reside during tough times, or a work-trade situation where you can live on the premises in exchange for work. Access *workaway.info* or *helpx.net* to find the perfect suitors for your needs. Opportunities always arise when we stay positive. Struggles are a part of life. Struggling is what molds us into strong characters. We should never run from these experiences because we grow from them.

"The things people say of a man do not alter a man. He is what he is. Public opinion is of no value whatsoever. Even if people employ actual violence, they are not to be violent in turn. That would be to fall to the same low level. After all, even in prison, a man can be quite free. His soul can be free. His personality can be untroubled. He can be at peace. And, above all things, they are not to interfere with other people or judge them in any way. Personality is a very mysterious thing. A man cannot always be estimated by what he does. He may keep the law, and yet be worthless. He may break the law, and yet be fine. He may be bad, without ever doing anything bad. He may commit a sin against society, and yet realize through that sin his true perfection." – Oscar Wilde, *The Soul of Man under Socialism*

If you are facing prison time, or have been charged with a crime that has landed you in prison, you are not alone. According to data from the *U.S. Justice Department*, in 2012 there were 1,570,000 inmates in state and federal prisons. This number exceeds the amount of school teachers and social workers in the country combined. 756 per 100,000 of the national population is behind bars. Among the incarcerated, eighty-six percent are serving time for victimless crimes. Over fifty percent are locked up for drug offenses. While locked behind bars, the inmates are fed genetically-modified foods. They are not offered filtered water – meaning they drink sodium fluoride and chlorine. They get little fresh air. Life is hell for them. They are truly suffering.

All conditions aside, the law is the law, and when you break it, or are accused of a crime, there are always consequences. For someone who is charged with a non-violent, victimless crime – that has maintained a clean history and has never been convicted of a prior felony – the best policy is honesty. If you are in this situation, acknowledge that you made a mistake, show the court that you are not a menace and that you are truly a model citizen, and make them feel good about giving you another chance to redeem yourself. People always pick up on good intention, and all of us make mistakes. Chances are, the lawyers, prosecutors, and judges have also made mistakes in their lives. They are human too, and they have tough jobs. When they see you are a good person, they could make considerations.

If you are in jail or confinement, consider that many successful people today were in your shoes at some point in their lives. In his book, *The Prisoner Turned Millionaire,* Samuel Muthui writes about how he overcame a troubled past to become a millionaire at the age of twenty-six. He did this only three months after being released from prison. The comedian, Tim Allen, once served prison time for cocaine trafficking. He overcame this adversity, cleaned up his life, and eventually became a Hollywood millionaire. At sixteen, the famous actor, Mark Wahlberg, was charged with attempted murder, and sentenced to two years in prison. He found success through it all and today has a net worth of around $200 million.

"While awaiting sentencing, I decided to give stand-up comedy a shot. The judge had suggested I get my act together, and I took him seriously." – Tim Allen, *Comedian*

Whatever life change or stressful event you are encountering, do your best to remain positive. Remember the *Law of Attraction*. Think of affluence and abundance. Fill your head with thoughts of a new job, new home, new lover, or freedom. Work hard to climb out of the hole you unexpectedly fell into. Your hard work and positivity will reward you.

Medications & Substance Abuse

Often, when experiencing depression, individuals will resort to relying on medications, and in some instances, illicit drugs, or alcohol for relief. The common widespread belief is that drugs can help us, or that we can simply *drink away our sorrows*. What we are looking past is factual evidence indicating that these are not realistic beliefs. Getting *high* on certain illicit drugs, drinking alcohol, and taking anti-depressant pills or other pharmaceutical drugs, have all been identified as actions that deepen depression. The statistics revealing the number of people who are abusing these substances are startling. The annual *National Survey on Drug Use and Health (NSDUH),* conducted by the *Substance Abuse and Mental Health Services Administration,* reports, *"In 2012, an estimated 23.9 million Americans aged twelve or older – or 9.2 percent of the population – had used an illicit drug or abused a psychotherapeutic medication (such as a pain reliever, stimulant, or tranquilizer) in the past month."* This survey also reveals, *"In 2012, 30.4 percent of men twelve and older and sixteen percent of women reported binge drinking (five or more drinks on the same occasion) in the past month; and 9.9 percent of men and 3.4 percent of women reported heavy alcohol use (binge drinking on at least five separate days in the past month)."* Additionally, it was indicated from the survey, *"In 2012, an estimated 57.5 million Americans aged twelve or older, or twenty-two percent of the population, were current cigarette smokers."* To summarize, millions of people are abusing substances that are linked to depression. A dependence on alcohol, cigarettes, drugs, and medications plays a major role in determining our level of happiness.

Knowing that our behavior and mood can be influenced by the health of our gut – ingesting antibiotics, illicit drugs, and painkillers is without a doubt affecting us. In May 2011, *Gastroenterology journal* published a study, *The Intestinal Microbiota Determines Mouse Behavior and Brain BDNF Levels.* Researchers discovered, "By *disrupting the normal bacterial content of the gut with antibiotics, mice displayed changes in behavior and had decreased levels of brain-derived neurotrophic factor (BDNF) – which is linked to depression* and anxiety. When the antibiotics were discontinued, the bacteria in the gut returned to normal, and this was accompanied by restoration of normal behavior and brain chemistry." What we have been blinded to for decades now as a society is the fact that eating pills – especially antibiotics and painkillers – and abusing substances is damaging our intestinal microbiome and paving the way for a slew of mental health disorders and diseases. We are refusing to acknowledge that a clean bowel and healthy internal environment will provide us with a greater high than we have experienced in all of the years we previously spent chasing after drugs and indulging in alcoholic beverages.

"The problem is that most people think that because prescription drugs are legal, they are not dangerous. It does not matter whether you buy your drugs in a liquor store, a pharmacy, or on the street. You are going to be just as dead at the end. You know, addiction does not care where you get your drugs." – Dr. Hal Vorse, *Addiction Specialist*

The routine belief about substance abuse is that it pertains only to alcohol, or illicit drugs. However, by doing simple research, you will discover that the majority of substance abuse problems are related to legal, prescription drugs. A 2013 *Mayo Clinic* study found that *nearly seventy percent of Americans are on at least one prescription drug, and more than half take two. According to the findings – published online in the journal Mayo Clinic Proceedings – one of five patients are on five or more prescription medications.* Could the overwhelming amount of harmful, yet legal drugs being distributed to oblivious patients be partially responsible for why we are experiencing so much depression, and why we are witnessing so many people developing addictions to these substances which they are abusing? What has been established today is the knowledge that most illicit drug use begins with prescription drugs. According to the *National Center on Addiction and Substance Abuse* at *Columbia University*, *"Teens who abuse prescription drugs are twice as likely to use alcohol, five times more likely to use marijuana, and twelve to twenty times more likely to use illegal street drugs such as heroin, ecstasy, and cocaine than teens who do not abuse prescription drugs."* The *Foundation for a Drug-Free World (drugfreeworld.org)* states, *"Of all deaths linked to drug abuse; depressants, opioids and antidepressants are responsible for more overdose deaths (forty-five percent) than cocaine, heroin, methamphetamine, and amphetamines (thirty-nine percent) combined. Of the 1.4 million drug-related emergency room admissions in 2005, 598,542 were associated with abuse of pharmaceuticals."*

We cannot deny that we are facing a pandemic of prescription drug abuse. Many of these drugs are prescribed to ordinary people like me and you. We have been so conditioned to believe that illicit drugs are the most dangerous – and that anything a doctor prescribes is okay – that we are bypassing the warning labels and statistics that are telling us otherwise. Today we know that prescription drugs create more problems than illicit drugs, and are responsible for more than 100,000 deaths per year. What too many of us may be failing to recognize is that our medications are bringing us down.

In the August 2012 issue of *Addictive Behaviors: An International Journal*, a study, *The association between non-medical prescription drug use, depressive symptoms, and suicidality among college students*, revealed, "The use of prescription drugs – particularly painkillers like Vicodin and Oxycontin – is related to depressive symptoms and suicidal thoughts and behaviors in college students." According to *medicinenet.com*, we learn that, "Certain medications prescribed for various medical conditions do cause such feelings as sadness, despair, and discouragement. These are feelings that are often associated with depression. Other medicines prescribed for medical problems can trigger mania (excessive elation and joy) that is usually associated with bipolar disorder. Medications that cause mania or depression appear to alter brain chemicals in some way. Although the drugs may be necessary to treat the condition, the side effect is hardly acceptable. As an example, Accutane, which is prescribed for the treatment of acne, has been found to also cause depression. So have oral contraceptives, high blood pressure drugs, and even statins that treat high cholesterol."

Rather than pointing the blame at drugs, why do we not choose to empower ourselves? Connecting with nature, eating optimal foods, exercising, and enhancing our beliefs is essential for overcoming problems related to substance abuse. Because many prescription drugs come equipped with serious side effects, and suppression from them can result in dangerous withdrawal symptoms, it is important that you wean yourself from them under professional supervision. Do not let the doctor or psychiatrist convince you that you need to stay on these drugs, simply inform them that you want off of them as soon as possible and that you expect their help. If they refuse, seek holistic consultation elsewhere. As you saw with Joe Cross in *Fat, Sick, and Nearly Dead*, and Frank Ferrante in *May I Be Frank*, changing your diet, lifestyle, and mental perception can be enough to free you from unnecessary prescription drugs. Eliminating these chemicals from your life is liberating.

"*Medical practice has neither philosophy nor common sense to recommend it. In sickness the body is already loaded with impurities. By taking drug medicines, more impurities are added, thereby the case is further embarrassed and harder to cure.*" – Elmer Lee, M.D., Former Vice President Academy of Medicine

Aside from pharmaceutical drugs bringing us down, alcohol, cigarettes, and illicit drugs also pose a threat. Alcohol is a dangerous drug, yet is accepted in society as a norm. In February 2014, U.S. President Barack Obama announced that marijuana is far less dangerous than alcohol. The U.S. Drug Czar agreed with him. Most depressed people that I initiate conversation with drink this poison regularly. They allege that drinking a *little*, or *in moderation*, is healthy. This is false. Alcohol is never in any way good for the body. It is acid-forming, and feeds acidosis, while also greatly damaging the liver and other organs. Many misleading articles, reports, and studies have been released by the alcohol and wine industries, helping to improve their sales, but believing these lies is not in any way improving our health or level of happiness. A 2008 article published in *Psych Central*, titled, *Why Alcohol and Depression Don't*

Mix, documents that, *"Thirty to fifty percent of people with alcoholism, at any given time, are also suffering from major depression."* Similarly, the *National Longitudinal Alcohol Epidemiology Study* signifies, *"Amongst those with major depression, 32.5 percent met criteria for a lifetime diagnosis of alcohol dependence, compared with only 11.2 percent of those who did not meet criteria for major depression."* There is a strong correlation between those who drink regularly and major depression. If something is bringing you down, consider that alcohol could be partially to blame, and because you are drinking it, you can really only blame yourself. Try eliminating alcohol from your life. Replace alcoholic drinks with fresh organic green juices. Nourish your organs with real beverages. You will likely notice improvements in your quality of life.

"The wreath of cigarette smoke which curls about the head of the growing lad holds his brain in an iron grip which prevents it from growing and his mind from developing." – Hudson Maxim

It is outrageous that close to sixty million Americans still smoke cigarettes despite the warnings and dangers attached. In addition to causing cancers, immune suppression, premature death, and respiratory issues – among numerous other diseases and chronic conditions – these *death sticks* have also been associated with depression. Researchers from the *University of Otago* in New Zealand investigated the relation between depression and cigarette smoking. The team took figures from over one-thousand men and women aged eighteen, twenty-one, and twenty-five years. Smokers had more than twice the rate of depression. The study was published in the June 2010 *British Journal of Psychiatry.* The researchers concluded that, *"There is a cause and effect relationship between smoking and depression in which cigarette smoking increases the risk of symptoms of depression."* If you are a smoker, and are also experiencing depression, you may have found your culprit. I hope that the steps in this book will help you overcome your addiction. Please do everything you can to quit.

Using illicit drugs such as cocaine, heroin, methamphetamines, or ecstasy is also dangerous. A study by researchers from the *University of Michigan* and the *Ann Arbor Veterans Affairs Medical Center* – published in the January 2003 issue of the *American Journal of Psychiatry* – suggests, *"Chronic cocaine use may cause damage to brain cells that help produce feelings of pleasure, which may contribute, in part, to the high rates of depression reported among cocaine abusers. It is well-known that cocaine increases levels of the brain chemical dopamine, resulting in the 'high' that abusers feel. Prolonged use of the drug, however, may reduce dopamine levels, making it harder for abusers to experience positive feelings."* According to the website, *heroin.net,* *"When an individual is going through heroin withdrawal, they often become depressed, as their own body lacks the ability to create any pleasurable sensations without the aid of heroin."* By using this drug, you begin *chasing* a sensation that is reflective of an illusion. You keep using the drug, expecting different results, and dig yourself deeper and further down into a tunnel of depression. The *Drug Policy Alliance (drugpolicy.org)* states, *"The discontinued use of methamphetamine by heavy users will create withdrawal symptoms, including severe depression, lethargy, anxiety and fearfulness."* Meth is a scary drug, and has the capacity to destroy lives.

Some people describe ecstasy as the *happy drug*, because they feel good while they are on it. Sadly, as the *happy* effect wears off, intense feelings of sadness often infiltrate their emotions. The website, *dancesafe.org*, explains how this process works when describing the active ingredient in ecstasy – MDMA. They disclose how, *"MDMA works by releasing from certain brain cells large amounts of the brain chemical, serotonin. This release of serotonin is what triggers the mood elevation effect, as well as the feelings of empathy, self-acceptance, and emotional closeness with others that so many people find valuable and rewarding about the drug. By releasing large amounts of serotonin, MDMA also depletes the brain's supply. It then takes some time for the brain to replenish what was released. How long does it take for serotonin levels to be fully restored after someone takes MDMA? This depends on the individual's diet, general heath, genetic make-up, how much MDMA the person took, and other random factors. There is no way to tell for sure, but based on animal studies, scientists say that it could take anywhere from forty-eight hours to an entire week. The mild depression some people feel after taking MDMA could be related to this temporary depletion of serotonin."*

The greatest *happy drugs* available are not considered drugs. Try watching the sunrise. Love your children. Spend the day out in the woods. Eat wholesome organic meals from local farmers. Spend time with people you love. Work in your garden. Complete a project. Exercise your body, mind, and spirit. Free yourself from stress and worry by means of meditation. Help other people to succeed. These are natural methods for inviting happiness to stay permanently in your life. You do not need alcohol, cocaine, ecstasy, heroin, methamphetamines, or prescription drugs to assure happiness. These substances will only make your condition worse.

"My mind may be sober, but my confidence is high." — Habeeb Akande

Interestingly enough, I discovered evidence that two illicit drugs have been actualized to contain compounds that can heal depression. These drugs are marijuana and *magic* mushrooms. Please do not mistake me as advocating for these substances. I do not believe smoking anything can be beneficial for health, I am only relaying information that I find to be compelling. In the January 2012 study, *High on Life? Medical Marijuana Laws and Suicide,* – published by the *The Institute for the Study of Labor (IZA)* – researchers established evidence that marijuana use decreases suicide rates among those who use the plant. The study concludes that, *"Consistent with the hypothesis that marijuana can be an effective treatment for depression and other mood disorders, there appears to be a sharp decrease in the suicide rate of fifteen to nineteen year-old males in the treatment states as compared to the control states approximately two years after legalization. Our results suggest that the legalization of medical marijuana is associated with a five percent decrease in the total suicide rate, an eleven percent decrease in the suicide rate of twenty through twenty-nine year-old males, and a nine percent* decrease in the suicide rate of thirty through thirty-nine year-old males." In an April 2006 study published in *Addictive Behaviors, and* titled, *Decreased Depression in Marijuana Users,* it was determined, *"Those who consume marijuana occasionally or even daily have lower levels of depressive symptoms than those who have never tried marijuana. Specifically, weekly users had less depressed mood, more positive affect, and fewer somatic complaints than non-users. Daily users reported less depressed mood and more positive affect than non-users."* In the 1997 book, *Marijuana Medical Handbook,* a quotation from Dr. Tod Mikuriya, a former psychiatrist and medical coordinator, was provided. He stated, *"The power of cannabis to fight depression is perhaps its most important property."*

"In strict medical terms marijuana is far safer than many foods we commonly consume. For example, eating ten raw potatoes can result in a toxic response. By comparison, it is physically impossible to eat enough marijuana to induce death. Marijuana in its natural form is one of the safest therapeutically active substances known to man. By any measure of rational analysis marijuana can be safely used within the supervised routine of medical care." – Francis Young, DEA Administrative Law Judge 1988

Jay Cavanaugh, PhD, and *National Director for the American Alliance for Medical Cannabis,* wrote in his 2003 article, *Cannabis and Depression,* which was published on the *American Alliance for Medical Cannabis* website: *"Numerous patients report significant improvement and stabilization with their bipolar disorder when they utilize adjunctive therapy with medical cannabis. While some mental health professionals worry about the impact of cannabis on aggravating manic states, most bipolar patients trying cannabis find they 'cycle' less often and find significant improvement in overall mood. Bipolar disorders vary tremendously in the time spent in the depressive versus manic states. Those who experience extended depressive episodes are more likely to be helped with cannabis. Patients who use cannabis to 'relax' may be treating the anxiousness sometimes associated with depression. Cannabis aids the insomnia sometimes present in depression and can improve appetite. Better pain control with cannabis can reduce chronic pain related depression."* Finally, the last bit of evidence I found supports medical marijuana as a solution for eliminating use of pain pills and other harmful drugs. Dr. Frank Lucido, a private practice physician, stated in his article, *Implementation of the Compassionate Use Act in a Family Medical Practice: Seven Years Clinical Experience,* "With appropriate use of medical cannabis, many of these cannabis-using patients have been able to reduce or eliminate the use of opiates and other pain pills, Ritalin, tranquilizers, sleeping pills, anti-depressants, and other psychiatric medicines, as well as to substitute the use of medical cannabis as a harm reduction measure for specific problematic or abused substances with a much more serious risk profile."

The active compounds in raw cannabis are powerful antioxidants with many health benefits. By choosing to juice organic raw cannabis and drink the juice, there is no psychoactive effect, and one only receives the nutrients that are known to reverse disease. The problem attached to marijuana in this

64   Jacoby

society is not so much that the vast majority of people support and use this herb, but they do not know how to use it effectively. Rather than smoking it to get high, they should be juicing the plant for the many health benefits.

As of May 2014, three of America's most respected doctors – Sanjay Gupta, Mehmet Oz, and Richard Besser – declared their support for legalizing marijuana after assessing the many benefits this plant provides for humans. While some argue that marijuana may be a *gateway* drug that leads to hard-drug use, what truth tells us is that prescription drugs are the real *gateway* drugs that lead to serious drug abuse. A May 2014 study published in the *National Bureau of Public Research*, titled, *The Effect of Medical Marijuana Laws on Marijuana, Alcohol, and Hard Drug Use*, concluded that *marijuana use had no discernible impact on hard drug use in either age group studied*. This information provokes me to suspect that we may have our priorities as a society mixed up. Alcohol, cocaine, ecstasy, heroin, methamphetamines, prescription drugs, and tobacco should all be considered equally dangerous. There is no reason why drinking alcohol excessively and smoking cigarettes should continue to be culturally accepted. This is destructing our health and diminishing our values.

"Herb is the healing of a nation, alcohol is the destruction." – Bob Marley

While psilocybin – the active ingredient in *magic* mushrooms – is known to trigger wild sensory experiences and changes in consciousness, a December 2011 study titled, *Neural correlates of the psychedelic state as determined by fMRI studies with psilocybin*, and published in *Proceedings of the National Academy of Sciences*, suggests otherwise. *"Scientists gave psilocybin to thirty people and monitored their brain activity with an MRI scanner. The scans showed that psilocybin was linked to reduced activity in regions of the brain associated with high-level reasoning. One brain region affected by psilocybin, the medial prefrontal cortex, is typically overactive in depressed individuals. Researchers suspect the drug may help alleviate depression by curbing activity in that region. This would explain previous research that found that when patients with anxiety were given psilocybin, their depression scores fell."* In a separate study, published in the *British Journal of Psychiatry*, researchers asked ten people to think about memories associated with strong positive emotions. *"Participants who had taken psilocybin reported their memories as more vivid compared with participants given a placebo. Two weeks later, the same people were asked to rate changes in their emotional well-being. Researchers discovered a strong link between participants' ratings of how vivid their memories were, and their well-being two weeks later. They conjecture that psilocybin facilitates access to personal memories and emotions, which may boost mental health."* David Nutt, professor of neuropsychopharmacology at Imperial College London, concluded by exclaiming, *"We are not saying go out there and eat magic mushrooms, but this drug has such a fundamental impact on the brain that it has to be meaningful – it must be telling us something about how the brain works. My belief is that we should be studying it for therapeutic benefits."*

Before simply stating that drugs or alcohol are the culprits that are responsible for bringing you down, ask yourself a few questions. Take some time to analyze why you are empowering these substances to depress your mood. Why are you allowing a drug to take control of your life? Are there alternatives to using drugs or drinking alcohol that are safer and healthier? What steps can you take today that will clear the trail for a brighter way of living? I often spend time observing why drug and alcohol abuse has escalated into the serious problem it is among today's society. Here is a list I devised of some common reasons why people use drugs or drink alcohol:

- They think of it as an escape.
- They enjoy the experience.
- They are associating with the wrong people.
- Their sphere of influence enables them.
- They know no other way.
- They have been programmed with misinformation leading them to believe they have a disease and are powerless.
- It is socially accepted to drink alcohol.
- Advertisements.
- Alcohol and drugs fill a void for them.
- Poor nutrition and food chemicals are creating imbalances.
- There are no other alternatives appealing to them.
- When they go in for help, they are too often misguided and led to weakness and fear by so-called *professionals*.
- They are drowning away pain and sorrows, which is creating more pain and more sorrows.
- They are deviant and do it because it is *illegal*.
- Society has warped their mind.

Whatever your reason may be for using drugs or alcohol, I challenge you to follow these twelve steps. You are not physically addicted to these substances, you are mentally controlled. You can break free. Admitting that you are powerless is like giving up your freedom. As for addiction in general, an addiction is a desire for a substance that has no connection with the needs of the mind and body. To overcome addiction then, it is important to eat wild foods such as plants, roots, and various seaweeds. Your main goal should be creating alkalinity in your body. When you are in an acidic state, the effects of the alkaloids from alcohol and drugs gives you a false alkaline high and fools your body into believing you have reached an alkaline state. By eliminating excess acids, you can alkalize and clear up the acidosis in your body. In doing so, you will no longer crave stimulants. Internal cleansing is imperative when recovering from addiction.

"Addiction is not getting enough of what you never should have had."
– Deepak Chopra

Now we can discuss self-image, and how important it is for us to maintain a positive perception of ourselves.

66   Jacoby

Negative Self-Image

"For Attractive lips, speak words of kindness.
For lovely eyes, seek out the good in people.
For a slim figure, share your food with the hungry.
For beautiful hair, let a child run their fingers through it
once a day.
For poise, walk with the knowledge that you never walk alone.
People, more than things, have to be restored, renewed, revived,
reclaimed, and redeemed.
Remember, if you ever need a helping hand, you will find one at
the end of each of your arms.
As you grow older, you will discover that you have two hands,
one for helping yourself and the other for helping others."

– Sam Levenson

Rejection has the capacity to make any one of its targets believe they are simply not good enough. It can result in the most confident person feeling discouraged. Being rejected is hurtful, yet unavoidable. Similar to rejection, when we are bullied, this generates insecurities. Not only are these insecurities present within the bullying victim, but they are most heavily rooted in the bully himself. If a person has the capacity to bully, or belittle someone, it is a clear reflection of their lack of confidence. The best way to boost our own ego, and to emit positivity, is by uplifting the morale in others around us.

We all want to be accepted, and unfortunately, there will be moments when we are hit by rejection. There will be situations where we may be bullied. Sometimes we simply will not fit in with other groups of people. There might be someone else who takes our place. Perhaps we carry the assumption that we are not beautiful enough. Maybe we are overweight, and uncomfortable with the way our body looks. It could be that we are battling health conditions, or have been afflicted with a disability at birth. People who are depressed tend to perceive themselves negatively, and they focus excessively on their imperfections. They are often insecure. Likewise, those who view their appearance with disapproval, and seek perfection, are often depressed. Being bullied or rejected frequently stirs up these negative emotions and creates a sense of inferiority. We are each fighting our own battles on unique personal journeys, and being bullied or rejected; bullying; or rejecting others can make our adventures difficult – either for us, or for those around us.

"I am thankful to all of those who said 'no' to me. It is because of them that I did it myself." – Albert Einstein

I know how it feels to be rejected. It can be heart-wrenching. In fact, I did not have a girlfriend for the entire duration of high school simply because the only girl I was interested in wanted nothing to do with me. This always made me feel like I was not good enough. I did not quite understand what was wrong with me. I ate healthy, took care of myself, exercised, maintained a nice physique, and had a lot of other girls expressing interest in me. For some

67

reason, there was nothing I could say or do that would attract her into my life. It took years for me to realize that some things are simply not attainable. This experience helped me grow in a number of ways. It also motivated me to improve myself, and correct the character flaws that may have been pushing her away.

If we put our heart and soul into something – whether it be a significant other, an idea, a project, a sport, or any task – and we are rejected, this can easily delude us into believing we are not good enough. Often, it results in a loss of interest, quitting, or losing hope. Let me refresh your hope and enthusiasm with a few stories of rejection being transformed into success. Are you aware that J.K. Rowling's book about a boy wizard was rejected by twelve publishers before a small London house decided to take a chance on, "*Harry Potter and the Philosopher's Stone.*" *Decca Records* turned down a contract with the Beatles, saying, *"Guitar groups are on the way out, and the Beatles have no future in show business."* They believed otherwise, and signed the following month with *EMI's Parlophone* label. A young Walt Disney worked as a graphic artist for an advertising agency. When he expressed interest in animation, he was told that he, *"Lacked ideas and the imagination needed to be successful."* He went on to create a multi-billion dollar animation enterprise. Michael Jordan, who is arguably the greatest basketball player to ever play the game, was cut from his high-school varsity basketball team during his sophomore year. He used this as fuel to improve his game, and went on to win six championships. When Steve Jobs and Steve Wozniak proposed early versions of *Apple* computers to *Atari Inc.* and *Hewlett-Packard Co.*, they were rejected. This led them to their success with *Apple*.

What would have happened if Dr. Seuss would have given up after his twenty-seventh time being rejected for his first book, *"To Think I Saw It On Mulberry St.?"* Would he have gone on to sell over two million books, and win two Academy Awards, two Emmy Awards, the Pulitzer Prize, and a Peabody Award? Can you imagine if Thomas Edison would have simply lost interest after his contributions to the light bulb invention failed for the 5,999[th] time? It is said that it took Thomas Edison up to six-thousand tries before he was successful. It is possible that we would still be reading by candlelight.

If you get rejected for any reason, this is a message that you must decipher for its benefits. You are likely being directed towards something greater, yet you are seeing it as a form of defeat or failure. Do not ever let judgments or opinions decimate your ambition. Rejection can be our greatest teacher, and could even be thought of as a sterol to enhance our emotional, mental, and spiritual growth. Use it wisely.

Contrary to rejection stirring up feelings of hopelessness and defeat, being bullied can make us feel awkward, fat, ugly, and unwanted. The impact that bullying can have on someone has been recognized to affect people for their entire lifespan. If you are a victim of bullying, join the millions of other people who have also experienced this abuse at some point in their lives. It does not matter what you look like, how much you weigh, or what others think of you. If you maintain a beautiful mind, smile often, and weigh yourself on a

Jacoby

scale of happiness and kindness, you are always going to surpass that bully and his insecurities. This happens frequently. Some of the world's most famous artists, athletes, entertainers, and musicians were bullied growing up. They used it as a fuel source to find success and happiness.

The famous entertainer, Justin Timberlake – who can do pretty much anything – confronted his past in an interview with Ellen DeGeneres. Surprisingly, he was bullied growing up. He explains, *"I grew up in Tennessee, and if you did not play football, you were a sissy. I got slurs all the time because I was in music and art. I was an outcast in a lot of ways, but everything that you get picked on for, or that you feel makes you weird, is essentially what is going to make you sexy as an adult."* I guarantee not one of the bullies who picked on him growing up is anywhere near as successful or happy as he is today – although I do have confidence that those same bullies possess the capacity within to create this success and happiness for themselves.

In an interview with *Yahoo Sports*, the Olympic gold medalist, Michael Phelps, spoke of his many incidences where he was bullied about his lisp and big ears. Many of his perpetrators now attempt to speak to him and gain his respect. He explained it by saying, *"It is a little crazy. When I go up to the neighborhood in Baltimore where I once lived, I still see the same people who were picking on me. They are still around, busing tables or whatever, probably still acting the same way. They see me and try to talk to me and the whole time I am thinking, 'Yeah, why are talking to me now? You were picking on me then.'"* He rose above and beyond the bullying and made himself a champion in doing so. The famous actress, Sandra Bullock, once addressed her past experiences she had with bullying by stating, *"When I would come back to school from Europe, I looked like a clown compared to the cool way the other students looked and dressed. So I got my ass whooped a little bit. Kids are mean, and the sad thing is that I can still remember the first and last names of every one of those kids who were mean to me!"* The well-known actress from Transformers, Megan Fox, told *E! News* in an interview, *"I was bullied and it is hard. You feel like high school is never going to be over. It is four years of your life and you just have to remember the person picking on you has their own problems and their own issues."* Today she is considered one of the *sexiest women alive*.

The *Twilight* star, Robert Pattinson, informed *Parade Magazine*, *"I got beaten up by a lot of people when I was younger. I was a bit of an idiot, but I always thought the assaults were unprovoked. It was after I first started acting and I liked to behave like an actor, or how I thought an actor was supposed to be, and that apparently provoked a lot of people into hitting me."* Look at where Robert is now. I do not think he allowed bullying to bring him down. The actress, Jessica Alba, told the *Daily Mirror*, *"I was bullied so badly my dad used to have to walk me into school so I didn't get attacked. I would eat my lunch in the nurses' office so I did not have to sit with the other girls. Apart from my being mixed race, my parents did not have money so I never had the cute clothes or the cool back pack."* Even Christian Bale, who played Batman in Dark Knight, was bullied growing up. He told *People Magazine*, *"I* took a beating from several boys for years. They put me through hell, punching and kicking me all the time. If you can face the bullying at school and come through it stronger, that is a lesson for life." If you want to be a bully, take it out on depression. Bully it out of your life.

"Sometimes people are beautiful. Not in looks. Not in what they say. Just in what they are." — Markus Zusak, *I Am the Messenger*

I want you to take a few minutes of your time to watch Lizzie Velasquez's *TEDx* speech, *"How do YOU define yourself?"* A few years ago, Lizzie was labeled *the ugliest woman in the world* in a *YouTube* video. The video received more than four million hits. Imagine how she must have felt when this was brought to her attention. She suffers from a rare condition that she refers to as, *skinny bones,* which is so uncommon, that it afflicts only two other people in the world. The main symptom is that she is not able to gain weight. At birth, she weighed only two pounds, eleven ounces, and has never weighed more than sixty pounds. Today, at the age of twenty-five, she is a motivational speaker, and author of two books. She is a reflection of true beauty. She describes her beauty as, *"The beauty that is not always perceived by the eye."* If you feel like you are not beautiful enough, I urge you to learn more about her. She may inspire you to think otherwise. Access her website at *aboutlizzie.com.*

"As you get older, you will understand more and more that it is not about what you look like, or what you own, it is all about the person you have become." – Anonymous Source

In an interview with *Psychologies* magazine (*psychologies.co.uk*), Sharon Osbourne claims that being, *"Short, fat, and hairy,"* encouraged her to, *"Develop a brain and personality, and to be fun and smart."* This helped her succeed in the entertainment industry as Ozzy's wife. She announced, *"In the music business in the Seventies, girls were beautiful. You were a performer, or you could be a girlfriend or groupie, but you still had to look good. I did not have the face or the body that opens doors. Not being beautiful was an education."* In society today, women are conditioned to believe they need make-up, surgeries, and other alterations to be beautiful and succeed. This is all a delusion. The best make-up you can apply starts internally with a clean, plant-based diet. It includes exercise. It involves nature. If you think you need to alter something in your life to enhance your physical features, you likely need to change your attitude. Be honest. Be loving. Be unforgettable.

"No matter how plain a woman may be, if truth and honesty are written across her face, she will be beautiful." — Eleanor Roosevelt

If you are overweight, it is not the end of the world. You are simply experiencing *meat paunch,* or what I refer to as the *dairy padding.* If you engage in exercise, eat healthy, and remove all animal products (meat, dairy, and eggs) from your diet, you will lose weight fast. According to the *World Health Organization,* there are an estimated 1.6 billion overweight adults and almost five-hundred million who are obese. I guarantee a large percentage of them eat a high intake of dairy products, or still abide by the antiquated belief that we need meat for protein. If not now, then they most likely did during childhood or adolescence. According to several health experts, dairy and meat are among the worst foods for our health (*nutritionfacts.org*).

The *American Journal of Clinical Nutrition* published an article in March 2010, *Vegetarian Diets and Childhood Obesity Prevention*, in which epidemiologic studies indicated, "*Vegetarian diets are associated with a lower body mass index (BMI) and a lower prevalence of obesity in adults and children. A meta-analysis of adult vegetarian diet studies estimated a reduced weight difference of 7.6 kg for men and 3.3 kg for women, which resulted in a two-point lower BMI. Similarly, compared with non-vegetarians, vegetarian children are leaner, and their BMI difference becomes greater during adolescence. Studies exploring the risk of overweight and food groups and dietary patterns indicate that a plant-based diet seems to be a sensible approach for the prevention of obesity in children. Plant-based diets are low in energy density and high in complex carbohydrate, fiber, and water, which may increase satiety and resting energy expenditure. Plant-based dietary patterns should be encouraged for optimal health and environmental benefits.*"

In the 2012 article, *Meat Consumption and Prospective Weight Change in Participants of the EPIC-PANACEA Study* – published in the *American Journal of Clinical Nutrition* – a total of 103,455 men and 270,348 women between the ages of twenty-five to seventy were analyzed. Researchers assessed the association between consumption of total meat, red meat, poultry, processed meat, and weight gain after a five year follow up. The results determined that t*otal meat consumption was positively associated with weight gain in men and women, in normal weight and overweight subjects.* This was established even after controlling for calories, meaning that the intake of 250g of meat daily resulted in annual weight gain higher than the weight gain experienced from an isocaloric diet with lower meat content (same amount of calories, less meat). The conclusion of the study was, "A *decrease in meat consumption can improve weight management.*"

"*If we are creating ourselves all the time, then it is never too late to begin creating the bodies we want instead of the ones we mistakenly assume we are stuck with.*" – Deepak Chopra

The very best way to tackle your weight problem is to begin by changing your belief system. Remember how I mentioned when we believe something for a long enough period of time, that it becomes a part of our biology? Well, the propaganda surrounding animal products that promotes them as being healthy has conditioned us to believe that eating these foods is somehow beneficial. As the bearer of good news, I want to inform you that we have been fooled by the meat, dairy, and egg industries, and that we no longer have to abide by these outdated beliefs. We can follow a healthy, plant-based, organic vegan diet, and as long as we know what we are doing, we will thrive eating fruits, vegetables, and other nourishing foods derived from plant sources. This means we can lose weight, and reach optimal health with no meat, eggs, or dairy of any kind. This is exciting news. If this information had gone mainstream decades ago, our planet would be much cleaner, and the rainforests would not be threatened.

One reason why we lose weight when transitioning to a plant-based diet is because the fatty tissue in obese people is deficient in lipase, which is the enzyme that breaks down fats into simpler substances. This is often a side effect attached to overloading on harmful fats, or failing to ingest enough healthy fats. When we do not provide our bodies with any fats whatsoever, or fuel with trans-fats or saturated fats, our fat-storing lipogenic enzymes are activated. As a result, we store the fat we already have, and continue adding to the fatty tissues. By eating foods with plant-based fats, while cutting out animal fats and cooked fats, we activate our lipolytic enzymes – which are more like fat-burning enzymes. They help us to rid our bodies of unwanted fat deposits. Many people struggle with losing weight because they get lost in *fad* diets that have them limit caloric intake. In doing so, these diets also limit their nutrient intake. So while some may lose weight, they are far from becoming healthy. All of the chemicals they are given permission to eat on these diets continue to accumulate in their bodies and increase the risk of common degenerative and chronic diseases. Dr. Robert Atkins was the man who created the low carbohydrate, high protein, Atkins diet. Atkins himself died while battling heart disease – which was likely a result of following this dangerous diet. Additionally, the thirteen billion dollar a year weight loss supplement industry caters to the struggles by continuing to promote diet pills that are of no benefit.

"Did you know that our bodies protect us from toxins by storing them in our fat cells, and in order to allow our body to lose weight, we must reduce the intake of toxins (such as pesticides, chemicals, drugs, artificial sweeteners, high fructose corn syrup, partially hydrogenated oil and substances found in processed food). These toxic chemicals are also affecting our hormones and liver functions in charge of metabolism. So instead of reducing calories, reduce toxins to lose weight, regain health and youth, and enjoy life." – The Detox Advisor

In November 2010, Helena Gibson-Moore published an article in the *Nutrition Bulletin* titled, *Do Slimming Supplements Work?* In the article, she includes research from two studies that were presented at the *Eleventh International Congress on Obesity* in Stockholm, Sweden, in July 2010. The two studies tested the results of common slimming supplements versus placebo pills consisting of clarified sugars. After completion of the studies, the conclusion was made that there is no difference between the supplements and placebo pills, and their impact on test subjects. In a separate study, the *Weight Management Center* at *Johns Hopkins University* made a similar conclusion about diet pills. Researchers concluded that, *"It is fitting to highlight that perhaps the most general and safest 'alternative' approach to weight control is to substitute low-energy density foods in place of high-energy density, and processed foods, thereby reducing total energy intake. By taking advantage of the low-energy density and health-promoting effects of plant-based foods, one may be able to achieve weight loss, or at least assist weight maintenance without cutting down on the volume of food consumed or compromising its nutrient value."*

"Calories are far less important than the quality of the food you are ingesting. Your body absorbs the vitamins and minerals from raw, natural foods far more effectively than the Standard American Diet foods. The helpful fats in nature actually help your body burn fat. Stop counting calories and feed your body nutrient rich foods that sustain and regenerate it." – Karyn Calabrese, *Soak Your Nuts*

If you want to lose weight, stop worrying so much about calories. Rather, start counting the chemicals in your food. Be sure the added chemical count is zero. Shift your attention to eating organic living foods that are full of amino acids, antioxidants, biophotons, enzymes, essential fatty acids, fiber, minerals, and vitamins. Calories are not everything. Eat raw organic fruits, sprouts, vegetables, and some raw nuts and seeds. Drink plenty of water and be sure to cleanse regularly. Avoid the nine worst food groups, which are, meat, dairy, eggs, clarified sugars, flours, cooked oils, gluten, foods containing synthetic chemicals, and processed salts. By following this advice, you can expect to experience a reduction in weight.

"Disregard appearances and conditions. Disregard all evidence of your senses that deny the fulfillment of your desires. Rest in the assumption that you are already what you want to be, for in that determined assumption you and your Infinite Being are merged in creative unity, and with your Infinite Being all things are possible." – Neville

The *U.S. Department of Health & Human Services* reports that 19.3 percent of the U.S. population lives with a disability. This equals to one in every five people. The *U.S Census Bureau* marks the total number with disabilities at fifty-four million. Of those affected, around fifteen percent were born disabled. There is no reason for any of these people to let this bring them down. Being born is enough to be grateful for. Hardships will only make life more interesting. If everyone born with a disability were to give up, we would have never witnessed such amazing people as Nick Vujicic, Rick Hoyt, Stevie Wonder, Helen Keller, or Christy Brown.

Nick Vujicic is a motivational speaker who was born with tetra-amelia syndrome – a rare disorder characterized by the absence of all four limbs. As a child, he not only struggled physically, but was also challenged mentally and emotionally. By the age of seventeen, he overcame the mental and emotional barriers and started his own non-profit organization – *Life Without Limbs*. Nick now delivers motivational speeches worldwide. He has addressed more than three million people in over forty-four countries on five continents. He speaks to corporate audiences, congregations, and schools. Vujicic also promotes his work through television shows and writing. His first book, *Life Without Limits: Inspiration for a Ridiculously Good Life*, was published in 2010. He also sells two motivational DVDs, *Life's Greater Purpose*, and, *No Arms, No Legs, No Worries*. Nick is a prime example of someone who refuses to let his disability bring him down.

Rick Hoyt was diagnosed with cerebral palsy at birth. His umbilical cord became twisted around his neck in the womb, and this resulted in the blockage of oxygen flow to his brain. Due to this rare occurrence, his brain no longer communicates with his muscles. Despite being informed by several medical doctors that he would never be *more than a vegetable*, his parents remained hopeful because they acknowledged that his eyes would follow them around the room. At the *Children's Hospital* in Boston, they met a doctor who encouraged them to treat Rick like any other child. His mother, Judy, would spend hours each day teaching Rick the alphabet with sandpaper letters and posting signs on every object in the house. It did not take long for Rick to learn the alphabet. At the age of eleven, it was established that Rick was indeed intelligent. He was fitted with a computer that enabled him to communicate by typing words. This allowed Rick to attend public schools. He eventually graduated in 1993 from *Boston University* with a degree in special education. What makes Rick's story so special, involves his father, Dick Hoyt. In 1977, Rick asked his father if they could run in a race together to benefit a lacrosse player at his school who had become paralyzed. Dick Hoyt was not a runner, and was thirty-six years old, but agreed to stroll him as he ran. After their first race, Rick said, *"Dad, when I'm running, it feels like I am not handicapped."* This motivated his father to start training so they could compete in more races – marking the beginning of a legacy, known as *Team Hoyt*. As of April 2014, Rick and his father have competed in 1,079 endurance events, including seventy-two marathons, and six *Ironman* triathlons. They have run the *Boston Marathon* thirty-two times. Additionally, Dick and Rick biked and ran across the U.S. in 1992, completing a full 3,735 miles in forty-five days.

Stevie Wonder is a musician, singer, and songwriter who was born blind. Being born six weeks early, there were some complications with his birth. The blood vessels at the back of his eyes had not yet reached the front and aborted their growth. This was responsible for his disability. Despite his conditions, he was labeled as a child prodigy. Stevie signed with his first record label at the age of eleven. Over the course of his successful music career, he has recorded over thirty U.S. top ten hits, including his singles, *Superstition, Sir Duke,* and *I Just Called to Say I Love You.* He is an example of someone who does not allow obstacles to block his path. You can also be this type of person.

Helen Keller was the first deaf and blind person to earn a college degree. Her story was famously portrayed in the play and film, *The Miracle Worker*, which documented how her teacher, Anne Sullivan, was finally able to develop a language that Helen could understand. Helen wrote a total of twelve published books in her lifetime, including her spiritual autobiography, *My Religion*. She accomplished more in her life than most people do with perfect vision, as well as the ability to hear.

Ralph Braun was born with muscular dystrophy. However, he was determined to bring the freedom of mobility to others like him who live with disabilities. Ralph started his career in 1966, by creating the first wheelchair accessible van, equipped with hand controls. In 1991, Ralph's company, *BraunAbility*, created the first accessible minivan. Because of his vision, millions of people around the world now have mobility on four wheels. In honor of his life, the American President, Barack Obama, hailed him as, *"A champion of change."* He used his disability as fuel to make a difference.

Christy Brown was an Irish author, painter, and poet who had severe cerebral palsy. Due to his disablement, he was incapable of controlled movement or speech. Most doctors also considered him to be intellectually disabled. His mother did not believe it. She spoke with him, worked with him, and taught him lessons. Her love and strong beliefs worked wonders. One day, Christy famously snatched a piece of chalk from his sister with his left foot to make a mark on a slate. He was able to communicate using his foot. He went on to write an autobiography, *My Left Foot*.

If you are disabled, I hope these success stories will motivate you to use your hardships to create a better situation for yourself – as these people have done. Opportunities always present themselves when you are thinking in alignment with the universe. Do not let a disability restrict you from pursuing what you are most passionate about.

"You will never rise above the image you have of yourself."

If you are experiencing negative self-image symptoms, please keep in mind that there are other people who have clung to the same attitude, beliefs, perceptions, and thoughts that are bringing you down, yet they found ways to let go, rise above, and paint brighter futures. If you do not feel beautiful externally, always keep in mind that the best way to enhance true beauty is from the inside out. Changing your attitude; cleansing internally; eating an organic plant-based diet with an emphasis on raw fruits and vegetables; and exercising your body, mind, and soul will help magnify your beauty. Again, do not search for pity. Instead, refuse to let physical limitations bring your down.

"I believe the word 'health' is synonymous with the word 'beauty.' My definition of beauty is that it is deep, lasting, and magnetic, and it grows from the inside out." – Kimberly Snyder, *The Beauty Detox Solution*

Trauma & Grief

"Perhaps they are not stars, but rather, openings in heaven where the love of our lost ones pours through and shines down upon us to let us know they are happy." – Eskimo Proverb

When I was twenty-one years old, my brother – who was seventeen months older than me – took his own life by walking face first with his arms out into an oncoming train. This was a major traumatic experience for me and my family. I learned all about the grieving process, and would not wish this on anyone. I have never felt so much pain in my life. I wrote a speech for him, and presented it at his service. I remember getting in front of everyone, trying to remain strong, and after the first two words, starting to cry. I continued to speak, gave it my all, and felt so much better after doing so. I felt like I honored his life. A spiritual guide who was at the service commented that he saw a golden aura hovering above me for the entire duration of the speech.

Since that time, I have lost three other close friends to suicide. Each instance hit close to home for me, stirring up emotions and difficult memories. I had to make a choice after every death: let it defeat me, or let it become a part of me, strengthen me, and build my character. I chose the latter of the two. My belief is that when we lose someone, they always remain with us in dreams, memories, and in spirit. My view is that we gain pieces of their energy and this nurtures our soul. They become spiritual guardians and protect us as we adventure through life.

"Do not grieve. Anything you lose comes round in another form." — Rumi

Trauma and grief can arise as a result of losing a loved one, tragic injuries, or complications from the confusions called war. When we are afflicted, it is common to feel pain, and a mixture of several negative emotions. It is simple to blame traumatic events, or grief for depression. Sure, this may help us get prescriptions to dangerous pharmaceutical drugs. It will not however, help us feel better about ourselves – or our situation. To elevate our happiness through traumatic experiences, we need to eat well, exercise, spend time in nature, socialize, shift our thoughts, and build our character. It is important for us to remain forgiving, loving, and nurturing.

"Only people who are capable of loving strongly can also suffer great sorrow, but this same necessity of loving serves to counteract their grief and heals them." — Leo Tolstoy

When I dealt with the loss of my brother, mentor, and other good friends, I chose to help myself by staying active. I exercised daily. I removed all animal products from my diet. I fueled with organic, fresh vegetable juices. I also got involved, and engaged in social interaction. This helped me to wean from the grieving process. I used my talent for writing as a channel to express my emotion through various poems and journal entries. I did everything I could to avoid sadness. Eventually, I emerged as a truly happy person. I feel like I found ways to bulletproof myself from depression after experiencing these painful occurrences from my past.

"Grief is a most peculiar thing; we are so helpless in the face of it. It is like a window that will simply open of its own accord. The room grows cold, and we can do nothing but shiver. But it opens a little less each time, and a little less; and one day we wonder what has become of it." — Arthur Golden, *Memoirs of a Geisha*

I have always appreciated the quotation, *"Please, teach us to laugh again, but do not ever let us forget that we have cried."* It is okay to grieve. It is normal to cry. However, it is not healthy to let traumatic events spiral downward into being far worse than they have to be. When we truly heal from these horrendous experiences, they may leave permanent scars or stains, but we no longer allow them to control us. We do not search for pity over these episodes. We gain strength from them, and we carry on to reaching the pinnacle of our dreams. We refuse to grant them the power to make less out of us.

"If I let a blue mood run rampant, before I know it I'm obsessing about the color of the satin lining in my coffin – will it match my dress? That is when I feel like Alice in Cancerland falling down the rabbit hole and just have to stop." – Kris Carr

Do you recall the story of the South African swimmer, Natalie du Toit? She was only seventeen when she lost her leg in a road accident. On her way to a training session on her motorbike, she was hit by a car and her leg had to be amputated at the knee. While most people did not believe she would be able to swim competitively again, they were soon proven wrong. Natalie was back in the pool only three months after the accident. One year after the accident, at the Commonwealth Games in Manchester, she swam the 800 meter in nine minutes, 11.38 seconds and qualified for the final. She was not competing with others who were disabled. This was the qualifying for able-bodied athletes as well. She explained the traumatic event by saying, *"I remember how thrilled I was the first time that I swam after recovering from the operation. It felt like my leg was there. It still does. The water is the gift that gives me back my leg. I am still the same person I was before the accident. I believe everything happens in life for a reason. You cannot go back and change anything. Swimming was my life and still is. My dream is to swim faster than I did before the accident."* Natalie had the choice to give up and allow the situation to belittle her, or to confront the obstacle and carry on. Her decision strengthened her, and elevated her happiness.

At thirteen years old, Bethany Hamilton was surfing in Hawaii when a tiger shark attacked her and tore off her left arm. This did not keep her from pursuing her dream. Shortly after leaving the hospital, she began practicing at the beach again. Later that year, she finished in fifth place at the National Surfing Championships. Bethany eventually signed a contract with Rip Curl, wrote a book about her experiences, *Soul Surfer*, and eventually turned the book into a movie. She describes surfing as, *"When you surf a wave, it is like walking on water, and when you are in the air, it is like flying."* Natalie and Bethany are prime examples of people who were changed by traumatic events, yet never allowed these changes to reduce them.

"I can be changed by what happens to me. But I refuse to be reduced by it." – Maya Angelou, *legendary poet & author*

Lenin Moreno was the Vice President of Ecuador from 2007 to 2013. Before getting involved in politics, he was shot, and this forced him to live with a disability. Despite his hardships, he brought attention to the needs of disabled people in his country. For his efforts, Lenin was nominated for a Nobel Peace Prize in 2012. Sudha Chandran is one of the most well-known dancers and TV actresses in India. After a car accident in 1981, she lost one of her legs to infection. Even on one leg, she became a Bharatanatyam dancer, after teaching herself how to dance using a prosthetic *Japir foot*. She also emerged as one of the most highly acclaimed dancers in the world. A film, titled, *Mayuri*, was also made about her life. The adored Mexican artist, Frida Kahlo, is one of the most well-known artists with disabilities of the twentieth century. She contracted polio when she was six years old and had a misshapen leg from it. She also broke her back in a trolley accident as a teenager. Because of these traumatic events, Frida moved around in a wheelchair. Frida is most known for her self-portraits, many which portrayed her in her wheelchair. Stephen Hawking was diagnosed with ALS at the age of twenty-one, yet still went on to become a famous physicist. His disability was never an excuse to give up on his desire to study the universe. His book, *A Brief History of Time*, stayed on the Sunday Times bestsellers list for an astonishing 237 weeks. Beethoven is recognized as one of the greatest composers in history. He gave his first public performance as a pianist when he was only eight years old. In the year 1796 Beethoven began to lose his ability to hear. In spite of his deafness, he was still able to create some of the greatest works of music and he wrote these pieces being completely deaf for the last twenty-five years of his life.

It does not matter how severe your situation might be, if you truly do not want to permit it to bring you down, then you have to adjust a few things in your life to inspire happiness. Often this includes attitude, diet, lifestyle decisions, perception, and how confidently you believe in yourself.

What Is Your Culprit?

"The only way that we can live, is if we grow. The only way that we can grow is if we change. The only way that we can change is if we learn. The only way we can learn is if we are exposed. And the only way that we can become exposed is if we throw ourselves out into the open. Do it. Throw yourself. We cannot be afraid of change. You may feel very secure in the pond that you are in, but if you never venture out of it, you will never know that there is such a thing as an ocean, a sea. Holding onto something that is good for you now, may be the very reason why you do not have something better."
— C. JoyBell C.

In preparation for step two, remember that you are never depressed solely because of entities that are out of your control. A high percentage of sadness is generated from meager things that you may not realize are bringing you down. Take some time to go over the protagonist list. As you review the list, think of all the improvements you can make. Determine what is really causing your melancholy, and then continue on, knowing that you are only experiencing depression because you are choosing to allow these constituents to infiltrate your positivity. Know in your mind that you can overcome any obstacle.

Maybe you are stuck in the same environment. Perhaps you need more nature in your life. It could be you are not exercising enough. There is a possibility your diet needs to be altered. It is up to you to make the necessary corrections.

As the Law of Attraction states, w*hat we think about most is what we attract into our lives.* It is imperative once we establish what is bringing us down, that we shift our thoughts away from these triggers, and adapt new patterns of thinking. We have to correct ourselves by improving our attitude and gaining mental faith. Rather than accepting the things we cannot change, we should attempt to change the things we cannot accept. We are all strong, and we each have a purpose. Knowing this, there is no room for denial, pity, ridiculous excuses, or weaknesses. The time to change is now.

The 2ⁿᵈ Step: Correcting Ourselves

"Correcting oneself is correcting the whole world. The sun is simply bright. It does not correct anyone. Because it shines, the whole world is full of light. Transforming yourself is a means of giving light to the whole world." – Ramana Maharshi

Now that we have targeted the causes for our depression, it is time to work on correcting ourselves. We know that the *Law of Attraction* always magnetizes what we think about most into our lives. Abiding by this law, it is best for us to shift our thoughts away from the things that bring us down. After pinpointing our triggers for sadness, rather than dwell over them, we are going to draw our focus elsewhere and divert the energy towards all of the things that inspire happiness. We have to spawn alternate thoughts, and create new experiences to store in our memory so that we can reshape our negative thinking patterns into positive arrangements of cognition.

"Detachment is not that you should own nothing, but that nothing should own you." – Ali Ibn Abi Talib

As we continue on our adventure, the second step of Society's Anonymous is, *"We analyze our current situation and recognize all of the people, places, and things that elevate our happiness. We begin to appreciate and summon them back into our lives. We correct ourselves by understanding it is our attitude and perception that determines the way we see the world around us. We restore our mental faith and improve our thinking patterns. We learn by changing our beliefs that we can also erase the problems that are leading us to despair."*

In this step, we focus on being respectful of others. We adjust our attitude so that we see everyone as a probable friend, and everything as a potential opportunity. We laugh often, smile frequently, and recognize that the time has come to start improving our attitude. During this stage, we prepare the body and mind for a personal revolution.

"If you want to awaken all of humanity, then awaken all of yourself. If you want to eliminate the suffering in the world, then eliminate all that is dark and negative in yourself. Truly, the greatest gift you have to give is that of your own self-transformation." – Lao Tzu

For years we have been permitting the same attitude, beliefs, negative emotions, and pessimistic thought patterns to control our happiness. To resolve this problem, there is a simple solution. We make a pact that we will no longer enable clouds of misery to accumulate in our sky. We let go of the negative emotions before they create storms. We take a stand and declare that we are no longer going to be pitied, rejected, sad, or unworthy. We cannot delay our contentment for another day, or let it wait on hold for another hour. We have to fasten our happiness magnets now.

Most successful people reached a breaking point in their lives where they had to decide this was it, now or never. They were either going to go out and make things happen, or wait around all of their lives. They chose to take action. This is why they are happy today.

"The secret of change is to focus all of your energy, not on fighting the old, but on building the new." – Socrates

When you find the capacity within yourself to let go of the unnecessary worry you have been retaining, you free your ambition and confidence to germinate and grow. By constantly questioning whether or not others approve of you, or what they may think of your decisions, you are limiting your potential and restricting your free flow.

In this step, you are encouraged to let go of the habitual cycle of defeat that you have victimized yourself with for so long. This is the time to create the best version of you. Think of it as awakening your inner-child. Bring back the innocence, yet guide your ambition with the maturity and wisdom you have equipped yourself with over the years. Stop worrying about rejection. Pay no mind to getting laughed at if you fall down. Get back up and move forward always. Do not look around to see who witnessed you stumble. This is your life, not theirs. The moment has come for you to be courageous. Let your positivity be reflective of your attitude.

"On our deathbeds, none of us wishes we had more money in the bank or a bigger car sitting in the driveway. Instead, as we take our last few breaths, we wish that we had lived a life that was courageous, authentic, and remarkably loving." – Robin Sharma, *Daily Inspirations*

Attitude

"There is very little difference in people, but that little difference makes a big difference. The little difference is attitude." – W. Clement Stone

We know that two people who are equally oppressed almost always react differently to their situation. Some give up, while others persevere and turn their struggles into foundations for success. When afflicted with terminal illness, one patient might pull through and survive, while the majority of others will succumb to the disease. If two people are wrongfully convicted, or charged with breaking an unjust law, and they face prison time, they each have a choice of whether they will let the situation defeat them, or remain positive. If a group of people get fired from their jobs, those who immediately go out and find work elsewhere, or manifest another way to bring in income are going to be much happier than the few who decide they want to be pitied and feel sorry for themselves while sitting at home all day eating processed foods and watching television. The girl who moves on after being dumped in a relationship, deciding to embrace the good times and progress with her life, will always be in a better position than the guy who cannot accept the break-up, becomes abusive, and attempts suicide over it. The determining factor is attitude.

Attitude can be defined as *a feeling, or way of thinking, that affects a person's behavior.* If we deliver a positive attitude, and we carry this mindset through each obstacle we face, we are more than likely to be among those who find success through oppression, or survive a health scare. To generalize, you can maintain a good or bad attitude. You can be optimistic or pessimistic. Victor Frankl was a neurologist and psychiatrist who was imprisoned in a Nazi concentration camp during World War II. He was separated from his wife, mother, and father – losing them all before the war ended. After the war, Frankl was released and wrote the book, *Man's Search for Meaning*, in which he described the life of an ordinary concentration camp inmate from the objective perspective of a psychiatrist. In the book he explained how important it was to maintain a positive attitude. He described this by stating, *"We who lived in concentration camps can remember the men who walked through the huts comforting others, giving away their last piece of bread. They may have been few in number, but they offer sufficient proof that everything can be taken from a man but one thing: the last of the human freedoms – to choose one's attitude in any given set of circumstances, to choose one's own way."*

"The only disability in life is a bad attitude." – Scott Hamilton

I want to introduce you to two people: the *opportunistic optimist*, and the *problematic pessimist*. The optimist searches for the best in every situation. When confronted with potential gloom, she will pick it up, mold it into a useful tool, and continue on her journey with that gloom disguised as something beneficial. The pessimist points out the worst in situations and consistently finds himself in a hole, trying to climb his way out. At times an optimistic person may find herself in a dark place as well, but she will eventually create light. This is a good time for you to analyze which type of attitude you are emanating from within. If you notice that you are typically more negative and search for the worst in situations, or are quick to give up, use this lesson to change the patterns you have formed and let your optimism emerge.

"The pessimist sees difficulty in every opportunity. The optimist sees the opportunity in every difficulty." – Winston Churchill

To determine whether your thinking patterns are aligned more as an optimist or pessimist, I will share a couple of scenarios involving genetically-modified food and global warming. Knowing that *we cannot eat food that has been genetically altered (GMOs) without getting sick or increasing our chances of developing disease (saynotogmos.org)*, we face a dilemma. There are millions of acres of genetically-modified crops growing around the world. A fraction of these harmful crops are being processed into health-damaging ingredients that are added to the processed foods and beverages sold in grocery stores, markets, and restaurants. The remaining crops are used to feed livestock. A pessimist might say, *"Because there are so many genetically modified foods in circulation, nothing can be done now other than to continue abiding by the current system in place. We will never get rid of GMOs, so why even bother?"* Contrary to this, an optimist will think of a solution that benefits others. She might say, *"Okay, we will first raise awareness so that everyone knows of the dangers attached to eating food that is not real. Then we will use all of the GMO crops that are currently in transit to create biofuels and other energy alternatives so that they do not go to waste. There is no reason to continue poisoning people, wildlife, and the environment with food that is not substantial for sustaining life."* When approaching global warming, a pessimist would likely say, *"We cannot do anything about it. All of us are going to die eventually anyways. Why worry about it?"* An optimist, on the other hand, could provide a solution such as, *"Animal agriculture is responsible for fifty-one percent of all greenhouse gas emissions – more than all of the exhaust fumes from every mode of transportation in the world combined – and logging is decimating the forests which are the only solution for storing carbon and other greenhouse gases. If we simply banned factory farming and permanently prohibited logging, started growing our own organic fruits and vegetables, transitioned to vegan diets, and began planting trees to rebuild the forests, then we would reverse global warming."* Be the opportunistic optimist. Search for the best in all situations. As you start to adapt this change, you will likely notice everything around you transitioning. Where you once saw a dead end, you may now notice a lush forest of opportunity. Places that you thought were closed off might have secret openings that are now visible to you. It is amazing how simply adjusting our attitude can correct everything else in our life.

   "If we could change ourselves, the tendencies in the world would also change. As a man changes his own nature, so does the attitude of the world change towards him. We need not wait to see what others do." – Mahatma Gandhi

   When we identify the people, places, and things that entertain our happiness, we may notice that some of these entities are no longer within grasp. This is frequently a result of harboring a poor attitude. Positive people tend to avoid those who are pessimistic. By changing our demeanor, we might notice they are more accepting of our presence. It helps to contact them and sincerely apologize for our wrongdoings over the years. No matter the situation, we should always remain hopeful and keep our faith.

   "If you think you are beaten, you are;
   If you think you dare not, you don't.
   If you would like to win, but think you cannot
   It is almost a cinch that you won't.
   If you think you will lose, you have lost,
   For out in the world we find
   Success being with a fellow's will;
   It is all in the state of mind.
   If you think you are outclassed, you are:
   You have got to think high to rise.
   You've got to be sure of yourself before
   You can ever win a prize.
   Life's battles don't always go
   To the stronger or faster man,
   But soon or late the man who wins
   Is the one who thinks he can."

   – Walter D. Wintle

Jacoby

Mental Faith

"I have one life, and one chance to make it count for something. I am free to choose what that something is, and the something I have chosen is my faith. Now, my faith goes beyond theology and religion, and it requires considerable work and effort. My faith demands – this is not optional – that I do whatever I can, wherever I am, whenever I can, for as long as I can – with whatever I have – to try to make a difference." – Jimmy Carter, *former President of U.S.A.*

A component of optimism is having strong mental faith. This can be personal, religious, or spiritual. Having faith is trusting that the Universe will conspire to protect you and help you manifest all that you dream into reality. Your role is to believe that you are capable. Whether you aspire to be an actor, artist, athlete, attorney, author, business owner, CEO, doctor, engineer, entrepreneur, environmentalist, federal agent, musician, nurse, or to take on some other profession, you must first believe heartily that you can accomplish this. You have to envision yourself in the position, then give it your all and trust that your higher power, or fate, will guide you to the exact place you are envisioning. This is not difficult, however it is a fundamental. Once you nurture your mental faith so it is tenacious enough to carry you, whatever you are after will invite itself into your life. You put the energy out that you are ready to attain your goal, and nature brings you the resources you need to be successful.

"Nature loves courage. You make the commitment and nature will respond to that commitment by removing impossible obstacles. Dream the impossible dream and the world will not grind you under, it will lift you up. This is the trick. This is what all these teachers and philosophers who really counted, who really touched the alchemical gold, this is what they understood. This is the shamanic dance in the waterfall. This is how magic is done. By hurling yourself into the abyss and discovering it is a feather bed." – Terence McKenna

Sometimes we have to be bold and take risks. A major obstacle that most people who are afflicted with depression have a difficult time conquering is their fear of failure, or aversion of the unknown. They seem to be afraid of change. They are unwilling to go after the life they desire. If you are in a position where you know you are not happy, how can it hurt to take a chance that could result in affluence and joy? If you are retaining anxious thoughts, suspicions, or a lack of confidence, then you are clearly needing to strengthen your mental faith. Once you discover your passions, the desire to attain whatever is necessary to center your life around this infatuation drives you to succeed. This unhappiness you are being confronted by is likely a message for you to go out and change your life path. Your discomfort is challenging you to throw yourself out there and seek something new. If you put the pieces in place to manifest a new life, chances are, what you are seeking will find you. The key is believing. You have to place your trust in the Universe.

"Believe in what you want so much that it has no choice but to materialize." – Karen Salmansohn (*notsalmon.com*)

Thoughts Are Things

"Create the highest, grandest vision possible for your life, because you become what you believe." – Oprah Winfrey

To correct ourselves, it is paramount for us to be cognizant of our thoughts and how influential they are over our well being. When we think negatively, this attracts negativity into our life. If we think we are less than another, or see someone else as being superior, then we will always be less and remain inferior. If we cling to a dream and know that one day it can blossom into reality, then chances are we will accomplish this dream. I notice that many of our problems lie in our thinking patterns. We always stop where we are comfortable. We never embrace challenges. We are quick to agree to avoid confrontation. We settle too often, and for far too little. We frequently allow fear and uncertainty to impede on our aspirations. If we simply believe we can accomplish a goal, and we accompany this with zero doubt, then as long as it is a feasible goal, our chances of being successful are going to be high.

"Keep your thoughts positive because your thoughts become your words. Be sure that your words remain positive because your words become your behavior. Behave positively knowing that your behavior becomes habitual. Practice habits that are positive, as your habits become your values. Demonstrate positive values, they will become your destiny." – Mahatma Gandhi

It is wise for us to embrace positivity, maintain strong faith, and use our thoughts to uplift us. When Mahatma Gandhi wrote the majority of his writings, he was immensely oppressed. However, he was a man of his word and valuable person. He always maintained a positive attitude while retaining the belief that his people would prevail. Although Gandhi did not live to see the change he yearned for, his leadership inspired a nation to break free from oppression. He established a legacy built on compassion and non-violence.

"It is not what you have, or who you are, or where you are, that determines whether you are happy or unhappy; it is what you think about." – Dale Carnegie

If happiness is what you are seeking, then you must fill your mind with happy thoughts. I know this objective is not always easy to fulfill, especially if you are living in oppression, or if you are not producing the neurotransmitters in your brain that make this possible, but there are ways to generate happiness even in the most difficult situations. To begin, you can exercise your body and mind, fuel with organic plant-based foods that stimulate the production of neurotransmitters, expand your intellect, and spend more time in nature. If you are unhappy with your life, simply make changes to fill the voids. By refusing to alter your approach, you can never expect a different outcome.

"A man's mind can be likened to a garden, which may be intelligently cultivated or allowed to run wild; but whether cultivated or neglected, it must, and will, bring forth. If no useful seeds are put into it, then an abundance of useless weed seeds will fall therein, and will continue to produce their kind." – James Allen, *As a Man Thinketh*

84   Jacoby

Plant seeds of optimism in your mind. Fill your head with thoughts of abundance. Write yourself positive notes for affirmation. Sweeten your home with plants to liven it up. Hang motivational pictures or pieces of art on your walls. Pick up new hobbies. If you truly are not content with how you are living, embrace change. Do everything you can to attract positive people, thoughts, and things into your life. Transform yourself into the person you are seeking in others. Let your good intentions lift you to the places that you dream of experiencing. Use your kindness to attract miracles into your life.

"The first step to living the life you want is leaving the life that you do not want. Taking the first step forward is always the hardest, but then each step forward gets easier and easier. Then each step forward gets you closer and closer until eventually what had once been invisible starts to be visible, and what had once felt impossible starts to feel possible." – Karen Salmansohn

You may be wondering how you are going to shift your attention away from the things that are bringing you down, especially when they have been leading to your demise for so many years. A good first step is to write down a list of all of the people, places, and things that stimulate feelings of happiness. What brings contentment to your life? Are there certain people that make you feel happy? Is there a place where you can go that will generate good vibes? Are there certain memories that cheer you up? Does sunshine lift your spirits? Do you spend time in nature? Have you ever elapsed time observing animals in the wild, watching them move, and listening to them sing and communicate? Have you tried drinking fresh organic green juices? When was the last time you enjoyed a fresh organic apple, apricot, banana, handful of berries or cherries, mango, melon, orange, or pineapple? This is a good time for you to pinpoint all of the things that bring you joy, and once you do this, then you can transpire new thoughts, and expend your energy thinking of these components of happiness. You can summon the people who make you happy back into your life, and visit the places that bring you good vibes. Spending more time in the sunshine while embracing nature will make you more lively. Fueling with optimal raw foods will replenish your reserves of positivity. You have the power to make the corrections that are necessary to stimulate happiness. Do not doubt how powerful your thoughts really are.

"When you doubt your power, you give power to your doubt." – Honore de Balzac

In Society's Anonymous, we grasp the concept that within us lies the power to manifest the life we desire. When we correct our perception and carry a positive attitude, nothing can intimidate us to give up this capability. The power we harness within cannot be depleted without our permission. We choose whether or not we will utilize our strengths based from our beliefs, and from the actions and decisions we make over the duration of our lives.

After preparing our minds for change, we now move on to step three, where we learn the importance of maintaining a clean internal environment.

"Nothing with power is working against me. Everything with power is working for me. At the center of my being is that which cannot be intimidated, threatened, or oppressed." – T.K. Coleman

The 3rd Step: Cleansing Internally

"The ambition to grow our understanding and compassion, and to help the world is a wonderful energy that gives our lives genuine purpose. But it is important to remember that to realize this wonderful ambition we must first take care of ourselves. To bring happiness to others, we must be happiness, and this is why we always train ourselves to first take care of our own bodies and minds. Only when we are solid can we be our best and take good care of our loved ones. When we live without awareness, without the ability to truly see the world around us, our life is often like a runaway train."
– Thich Nhat Hanh, *The Art of Power*

Now that we have a better understanding of why we have been living at a low mental altitude for all of these years, and our bodies are ready for change, we can progress to the most important mechanism of reversing depression. Cleansing the body and mind of negative emotions, chemicals that have been added to the food and water supply, harmful microbes, and the combination of mucus and plaque that is hardened to the intestinal walls is vital when recovering from what brings us down. To *become* happiness, and to consider ourselves *solid* – as Thich Nhat Hanh suggests – it is necessary for us to cleanse internally.

As we dive deeper into Society's Anonymous, in the third step, *"We free our terrain of the toxins that are stimulating negative emotions by detoxing and cleansing internally. To successfully cleanse our system, we are introduced to internal cleansing services, juice fasting, parasite flushes, and other ways to rejuvenate the body and mind."* Remember the man named Joe Cross from *rebootwithjoe.com* who naturally reversed his depression and medical conditions by changing his lifestyle, cleansing, and juicing? Think similarly to what he did. Check out Kris Carr, and her *Crazy, Sexy, Raw* diet (*kriscarr.com*). She also reversed her ailments naturally. You can do the same. The most effective remedy for depression is a clean internal environment.

The question now is, how do we cleanse, and what exactly does it mean to detox the body? To summarize, when we detox, we are cleaning our bowels and purifying our blood. In the liver, we break down hormones, and transform harmful, fat-soluble substances into water-soluble compounds that can be excreted by the kidneys and colon. Knowing this, it becomes paramount for us to have a healthy functioning liver. We filter blood in our kidneys and expel substances into the urine, so it is important to be sure we are not placing too heavy of a burden on these organs with our diet and food intake.

Our lifestyle choices create the symptoms that make detoxing necessary. By cleansing, we clean up the intestines to be sure there are no harmful microbes inhibiting our digestion. We also flush the kidneys and liver. We remove the build-up of environmental toxins, food chemicals, negative emotions, and plaque that has been accumulating for years. When our digestive system is compromised, the impurities cannot be filtered efficiently, resulting in every cell in the body being adversely affected. Even if we eat relatively healthy, internal cleansing is beneficial.

Some common symptoms that require detoxification include:

- Allergies
- Appetite suppression
- Bloating
- Body odor or bad breath
- Chronic fatigue
- Constipation or infrequent bowel movements
- Depression
- Flatulence
- Frequent sickness (colds, flus, illnesses)
- Headaches or migraines
- Inability to sweat
- Irritated skin and skin conditions
- Lack of motivation
- Low-grade infections
- Menstrual problems
- Mental confusion
- Negative thoughts
- Puffy eyes or bags under the eyes
- Sleep disorders
- Stomach issues

By detoxing, we nourish the body with essential nutrients while removing the impurities. With fasting, we rest the organs and bypass the process of digestion – saving energy and diverting it towards repairing damaged cells and tissues. The process of cleansing internally stimulates the liver to drive endogenous and exogenous toxins from the body; promotes elimination through the intestines, kidneys, and skin; and improves the health and circulation of the blood. We want our gut to be healthy because the microorganisms that thrive in our internal environment communicate with the brain via the vagus nerve. They send signals that control our appetite and mood. By eliminating the harmful gut microbes through cleansing, we assure there is a healthy relationship established between the bacterium that are living inside of us, and our body and mind.

"I am always by profession a skeptic, but I do believe that our gut microbes affect what goes on in our brains. The bacteria in our digestive systems may help mold brain structure as we are growing up, and possibly influence our moods, behavior, and feelings when we are adults." – Dr. Emeran Mayer, *Professor of Medicine & Psychiatry UCLA*

During this phase in Society's Anonymous, we want to weed out the negative emotions we have been clinging to. To accomplish this task, we alkalize our bodies by removing acid-forming foods and reducing our toxin load. This requires cutting out alcohol, coffee, cigarettes, cooked oils, refined sugars, and saturated fats (meat, dairy, eggs) – toxins that are obstacles blocking us from the healing process. We take precautionary measures to assure we will not be exposed to chemicals, and if we have been exposed, we start eliminating the toxins we have stored within. This requires minimizing the use of common household cleaners and personal health care products that are saturated with harmful chemicals (cleaners, cosmetics, deodorants, lip balms, shampoos, soaps, toothpastes, and other chemical-based products), and finding alternatives that are truly natural. Most importantly, we cleanse our system from toxic debris and plaque buildup. We do this by undergoing internal cleansing procedures such as colon hydrotherapy, lymphatic drainage massages, and oxygen baths or infrared sauna sessions. If our body has been infiltrated by parasites – which is common in the average American – we will administer a parasite flush to remove these unwanted organisms. Then we will learn about juice fasting, before moving along to step four where we discover alternative fuels we can use to nourish our body, mind, and spirit outside of what we have been raised believing is best for us. Our goals are to freshen up internally, and rejuvenate the health of our internal environment.

Negative Emotions

"Anger is an acid that can do more harm to the vessel in which it is stored than to anything on which it is poured." – Mark Twain

Mark Twain was onto something when he introduced anger as being an acid. As humans we are a predominantly alkaline species. Eighty to ninety percent of our diet should consist of alkaline-forming foods, and the other ten to twenty percent that remains still must come from plant-derived food sources for us to balance our pH effectively. The Standard American Diet (SAD) consists of foods that are all acid-forming. The common meat and potato diet is dangerously acid-forming. In fact, all alcohol, dairy, eggs, fish, food chemicals, grains and bread products (unless sprouted), meat, meat products, nicotine, pesticide residues, poultry, refined sugars, soft drinks, and white flour products are acid-forming in the body. By eating at fast-food restaurants and casual diners, buying processed foods, and including animal proteins in our diet, we are creating an acid imbalance in our system. Choosing to drink alcohol and smoke cigarettes, and becoming dependent on prescription drugs also creates an acid/alkaline imparity.

To maintain homeostasis, our bloodstream remains slightly alkaline – in the range of 7.34 to 7.44. To keep this alkaline balance, our body fights to neutralize acid or alkaline compounds. We have buffering systems for bicarbonate, phosphates, and proteins. Our kidneys regulate acid and alkaline compounds which we excrete through the urine. Calcium is also used as a buffer to maintain blood pH – either from the alkaline calcium reserves in the bones, or from our diet. A high-acid diet therefore weakens the bones, damages the kidneys, and paves the way for health ailments. If our blood becomes acidic, our kidneys will start failing. The best counter to a high-acid diet is a plant-based alkaline diet, such as Dr. Cousens' *Live-Food Cuisine*. Animal foods do not have the alkaline minerals needed to buffer acidity. They simply create a more acidic terrain that attracts ailments, parasites, and viruses.

When we are ingesting, harboring, and storing all of this acid from our food intake, we tend to generate negative emotions that break down into more acids. Anger is likely the most common of these emotions. Other familiar acid emotions are aggression, agitation, anxiety, depression, envy, fear, hatred, jealousy, resentment, shame, and worry. These emotions arise from the microbiome in the gut, where bacteria send messages through the vagus nerve to the brain. The October 2012 *Nature Reviews Neuroscience* journal published a review, *Mind-Altering Microorganisms: The Impact of the Gut on Brain and Behavior*. In this review, it was determined that, *"The gut microbiota communicates with the central nervous system – possibly through neural, endocrine, and immune pathways – thereby influencing brain function and behavior."* Researchers were able to discover the role gut microbes play in the regulation of anxiety, cognition, depression, and pain. By introducing probiotics – healthy strands of bacteria – they could regulate these negative emotions. If we keep our gut healthy and free of acid wastes, chemicals, and other toxins, we can have an impact on the communication between the gut microbiota, our brain, and how it affects us. Based on these findings, we can assert that negative emotions could stem from poor dietary and lifestyle choices, congested bowels, and mucus and plaque-buildup. As we cleanse internally, remove the impurities and acids that attract negative emotions, and replenish our microbiome with beneficial strains of probiotics, we will notice that our outlook on life quickly transitions to being positive.

"Be vigilant; guard your mind against negative thoughts. You will not be punished for your anger; you will be punished by your anger." – Buddha

Anger is synthetic and hatred is not real. When we fuel ourselves with processed foods, prescription drugs, and other synthetic forms of energy, we tend to generate anger and allow hatred into our lives. Contrary to this, happiness is natural and love is real. When we fuel ourselves with raw, living plant-based foods; we refrain from using prescription drugs; and we enjoy nature; we more frequently generate love and allow happiness into our lives. Which would you rather have, anger and hatred, or love and happiness?

"Raise your words, not voice. It is rain that grows flowers, not thunder." – Rumi

When we are upset for any reason, the best approach is to nourish our body with a fresh organic green juice, exercise, and get out in nature. When I feel agitated, I often venture to the closest forest preserve and walk barefoot through the woods. The connection to Earth, the soil massaging my feet, and the sounds of wildlife drowned out any unwanted negative emotions. I fuel my body with organic greens, and stimulate my mind with happy thoughts. At other times I simply exercise or go running. I find that increasing my heart rate helps to decrease my tensions.

"For every minute you are angry, you lose sixty seconds of happiness." – Ralph Waldo Emerson

Anger will always succeed in reducing your happiness meter. If you are carrying anger, hatred, or resentment with you, this is practically guaranteeing an encounter with depression. Ask yourself what the source is for your agitated, angry, fearful, resentful, and shameful feelings. Could it be that your parents are pushing you to be something that you know you will never have interest in becoming? Are you simply living a synthetic life that lacks exposure to nature? What stirs up feelings of envy or jealousy? Do you feel like you are incapable of being successful or that you are not worthy of living the life you desire? Are all of the opportunities that you let pass by while being busy with life stimulating negative emotions? Are you hanging on to resentment from a tragedy or something that happened to you as a child? Do you need to get out of a relationship that is limiting you? Whatever you are harboring that is generating these feelings; it can easily be released by cleansing. As you let go of these memories, thoughts, and worries, you will also let go of your depression. Do not suppress these emotions, instead, release them so they can also seek change. By understanding that negative emotions are simply trapped stores of energy that want to be freed from your body, it becomes easier to let them go.

"One noteworthy study suggests that people who suppress negative emotions tend to leak those emotions later in unexpected ways. The psychologist Judith Grob asked people to hide their emotions when she showed them disgusting images. She even had them hold pens in their mouths to prevent them from frowning. She found that this group reported feeling less disgusted by the pictures than did those who had been allowed to react naturally. Later, however, the people who hid their emotions suffered side effects. Their memory was impaired, and the negative emotions they had suppressed seemed to color their outlook. When Grob had them fill in the missing letter to the word 'gr_ss,' for example, they were more likely than others to offer 'gross' rather than 'grass.' 'People who tend to [suppress their negative emotions] regularly,' concludes Grob, 'might start to see their world in a more negative light.'" — Susan Cain, *Quiet: The Power of Introverts in a World That Can't Stop Talking*

To clear away negative emotions, it is relevant to let them go. In order to do so successfully, we have to free the body of the acids, chemicals, microbes, and mucus that nurture these feelings and trap them inside. We start by removing chemicals from our diet and household. We follow this by cleansing internally. After cleansing, we replenish the gut with vegan probiotic strains. Finally, we complete a juice fast. Then we move on to step four, where we learn which foods we should be fueling with.

"We are all humans led astray by wrong ideas and united by common bonds, ready for improvement. Anger diminishes our power to distinguish right from wrong, and this ability is one of the highest human attributes. If it is lost we are lost." – Dalai Lama

In his book, *Being Peace*, Thich Nhat Hanh shares his meditation. He suggests when we need peace and tranquility to close our eyes, breathe in and out and repeat these words with each inhale and exhale: *"Breathing in, I calm my body and mind. Breathing out, I smile. Breathing in, I dwell in the present moment. Breathing out, I know this is a wonderful moment."* I encourage you to try this exercise the next time you want to clear your mind of anger, confusion, and uncertainty.

Being Chemical Free

"A 'Who's Who' of pesticides is therefore of concern to us all. If we are going to live so intimately with these chemicals – eating and drinking them, taking them into the very marrow of our bones – we had better know something about their nature and their power." – Rachel Carson, *Silent Spring*

The average person in modern society fills their home with dangerous chemicals, often unaware they are doing so. Their cabinets, pantries, and refrigerators are full of processed foods that contain cancer-causing chemicals and harmful ingredients. The majority of these foods are saturated with the chemical glyphosate, which has been linked in studies to several illnesses. Under the kitchen sink, and in their bathrooms, they store *beauty* products, cleaning supplies, cosmetics, detergents, and toiletries that are toxic. They do not add filters to their faucets or shower heads. Quite often, the water they consume is bottled and contains added ingredients. They use chewing gum, colognes, deodorants, and perfumes to cover up odors that are reflective of a backed-up digestive system, and poor bowel health. These cover-ups are also contaminated with industrial chemicals. They apply lip balms that contain parabens – which are strongly associated with breast cancer – to moisten their lips that are chapped from being deficient of essential nutrients. They coat their bodies with lotions that are saturated with chemicals. When Spring arrives, they are quick to spray their lawn with more chemicals. In Summer, they coat their skin with suntan lotions out of fear that the sun will give them skin cancer. In reality, it is the chemicals lurking in sunscreens and suntan lotions that are causing cancer. If sick, or ill, most people have a cupboard devoted to medicine which they label as the *medicine cabinet*. These pills and *medicines* are simply concoctions of more chemicals. This is the reality of our modern society. We are a chemical-nation. Sadly, cancer, depression, and an array of other illnesses are closely associated with chemical exposure. For the standard citizen, it is not common to be aware of the chemicals they are exposed to simply from drinking, eating, and maintaining normal hygiene. These chemicals sedate them, make them more passive, and contribute to depression and other health conditions. In this step I encourage you to remove all chemicals from your home. They are not necessary.

In the December 2013 issue of *Reproductive Toxicology*, a study, *Data gaps in toxicity testing of chemicals allowed in food in the United States*, was published. After extensive research into what manufacturers add to our food, the researchers discovered that *about one-thousand additives are in the food supply without the FDA's knowledge. For the eight-thousand additives that the FDA approves, fewer than thirty-eight percent of them have a published feeding study – comprising the basic toxicology test. For direct additives, added intentionally to food, only 21.6 percent of the almost four-thousand additives have undergone the feeding studies necessary for scientists to estimate a safe level of exposure, and the FDA databases contain reproductive or developmental toxicity data for only 6.7 percent.* A highlight of the findings signifies, *"In practice, almost eighty percent of chemical additives being intentionally added to the food supply lack the relevant information needed to estimate the amount that consumers can safely eat in the FDA's own database, and that ninety-three percent lack reproductive or developmental toxicity data – although the FDA requires feeding toxicology data for these chemicals."* To put this in layman's terms, food chemicals are dangerous.

On the website *foodkills.org*, it is noted, *"There are over fourteen-thousand man-made chemicals added to the American food supply today."* If you are buying fresh organic produce and preparing meals at home, you are minimizing your overall exposure to these chemicals lurking in the food supply. A new study published in the July 2014 journal *Environmental Research, Reduction in urinary organophosphate pesticide metabolites in adults after a week-long organic diet,* found that *eating an organic diet for a week can decrease pesticide levels, especially of organophosphates, by up to ninety percent in adults.* These phosphates are linked to many cancers and chronic conditions. During pregnancy, organophosphates are known to get into the amniotic fluid and are then passed to the infant, leading to childhood cancers. The best way to avoid these chemicals, as this study clearly shows us, is to eat organic and avoid conventional, processed foods. While we cleanse internally and complete this step in Society's Anonymous, it is required for us to free the body of toxins. This mandates us to temporarily eliminate comfort foods.

For this cleanse to be administered effectively, we have to avoid the following items:

- Refined sugars and any artificial, chemical sweeteners. This includes corn syrup, high-fructose corn syrup, sugar, aspartame, amino sweet, glucose syrup, Splenda, and any other type of refined sweetener. The only sweetness in our lives should come from fruits, our significant others, and keeping our children happy.
- Partially-hydrogenated or hydrogenated oils and trans-fatty oils. Any type of oil cooked at a high temperature, including in sauteed foods, becomes trans-fatty, even extra virgin olive oil. One of the most common myths is that cooking with olive oil is the most beneficial to our health, however when you cook these oils over 150 degrees Fahrenheit they become rancid and equivalent to trans-fats. It is best, and advisable, not to use any oils, cooked or raw, with the exception of organic virgin unrefined coconut oil used sparingly.
- Monosodium glutamate (MSG), sodium benzoate, other harmful preservatives, and chemical flavor enhancers. These are also referred to as enhanced flavoring agents and they are so poisonous they can be deadly in high doses.
- Food coloring and artificial dyes.
- Bleached flours and refined flours.
- All types of meat, be it mammal, bird, fish, reptile, or amphibian. When heated, meat produces carcinogenic chemicals known as heterocyclic amines and polycyclic aromatic hydrocarbons.

- Dairy products including whey, casein, ice cream, creamer, yogurt, butter, milk, or cheese. These items are often contaminated with the recombinant bovine growth hormone (rBGH).
- Eggs and egg products. In addition to heterocyclic amines, eggs contain arachadonic acid and the mammalian molecule Neu5Gc.
- Sodas and colas. They are loaded with coloring agents, genetically-modified sweeteners, and phosphoric acid.

When you choose to eat processed, or animal-based foods such as these listed above, you degrade your health and set the pace towards illness, even if it takes years for symptoms to show. When taking into consideration that they are also patterns that can be difficult to break, eating sugary, salty, oily, and fast and junk foods can safely be labeled as addictions. When you eat these things, you are not feeding your body nutrients, you are feeding addictions. You are nourishing unwanted microorganisms. Just as cocaine, heroin, and prescription drugs alter body chemistry and brain function, so do toxic foods. By upgrading our diet, our health also improves. We become much happier, and gradually shift to a healthier overall lifestyle. To successfully cleanse unwanted emotions, we have to eliminate these foods for at least ninety days.

When our diet is lacking in nutrients and we overload our bodies with chemicals in the form of acrylamides, alcohol, cigarettes, drugs, glycotoxins, industrial toxins, and synthetic food additives, we compromise our system. This results in toxemia. The blood becomes sticky, and then accumulates other toxins. The undigested foods ferment and decay into terrain for harmful bacteria. All of this shifts the pH from being alkaline to more acidic. This is a good explanation for how internal cleansing procedures are beneficial. The fermented and decayed foods are eliminated, toxins are expelled, and pH is shifted back to alkaline levels.

In addition to eating organic to avoid food chemicals and pesticide residues, it is wise to avoid alcohol, chemical cleaners, cigarettes, fluoridated and chlorinated water, most *beauty* products, a large percentage of cosmetics, lawn chemicals, psychotropic drugs, and suncare products that are not organic. If you are unsure of whether or not your health care, hygiene, and other *beauty* products and cleaners are safe, access the website of the *Environmental Working Group* (*ewg.org*). On the site you can type in the product you regularly use and it will present you with a grade for how safe the item is. You might be surprised when you search *FeBreze* – which contains ammonium and silicon compounds that are of high concern. If you have an air *freshener* in your home, I suggest you remove it. It is spraying chemicals at you that may very well be triggering your depressive symptoms. I can assure you that most common air fresheners, bathroom and kitchen cleaners, colognes, conditioners, deodorants, lotions, mouthwashes, perfumes, shampoos, shaving lotions, soaps, sun care products, and toothpastes are not safe. Look out for dangerous additives such as parabens, pthalates, and sulfates. If you are looking for a decent toothpaste, try *Earthpaste*. If you have bad breath, try chewing on mint leaves or an alternate fresh herb. For deodorant, the best choice is a clean internal environment. If this is not working, try an organic essential oil. You can also use these oils as natural perfumes. Dr. Bronner's soap varieties are an excellent choice for hand soaps and can also be used as body wash. Organic unrefined coconut oil is the best skin moisturizer. If you do not like coconut, try organic raw cacao butter. I use coconut oil on my skin to replace sunscreen, although I carefully moderate how long I spend in direct sunlight. You can also use coconut oil as a mouthwash by *oil pulling*. This is an Ayurvedic healing technique that draws toxins and bacteria out of the gums while cleansing the mouth. *Just Natural* sells a healthy variety of organic shampoos and conditioners. When cleaning your bathroom or kitchen, try diluting some organic vinegar in water and simply applying this to the surfaces. Vinegar is a highly effective cleaning agent, more powerful than any chemical. After all, dousing something with toxic chemicals is not exactly *cleaning*.

According to the *Environmental Working Group*, in April 2014, "*The EPA official responsible for reviewing the safety of chemicals used in thousands of every-day products was asked how many chemicals in use are so dangerous they should get a harder look by the agency to protect public health and the environment. The answer? One-thousand. Jim Jones, who runs the EPA office charged with reviewing the safety of chemicals that have been linked to everything from cancer to reproductive problems, told lawmakers that 'about one thousand' chemicals currently found in everyday products need to be reviewed.*" This news alone should be enough for us to question the safety of the everyday products we currently use.

Despite many technologically advanced countries banning the use of fluoride in water, the U.S. and Canada continue to promote water fluoridation. Fluoride – in the form of sodium fluoride, fluorosilicic acid, or sodium fluorosilicate – is added to many municipal water systems. Although a growing number of scientific studies suggest that fluoride is a health risk, we are still being exposed to this chemical. Most fluoride that is added to municipal water is an unnatural form of fluoride that contains sodium. Sodium fluoride is over eighty times more toxic than naturally-occurring calcium fluoride. This is one of the most deadly chemicals there is. The *Material Data Safety Sheet* (MSDS) for sodium fluoride shows the lethal dose (LD-50) that will kill fifty percent of a population of rats is 52 mg/kg. The LD-50 for calcium fluoride is 4250 mg/kg. We are exposed to this chemical each time we wash our hands, clean our dishes, and shower or bathe. One major problem that negatively impacts many people is the calcification of the pineal gland. When we drink water contaminated with chemicals, especially fluoride, and eat combinations of pharmaceutical drugs, along with farming chemical residues and chemical food additives, we calcify this gland. When the pineal gland is blocked, we no longer generate sufficient amounts of melatonin. This hormone keeps us happy and elevates our harmony. A lack of melatonin can dull our senses, lower our intellect, make us feel sluggish, and drain our desire to achieve more in life. To avert this it is important to avoid chemical contamination. There are many *YouTube* videos explaining the guidelines for decalcifying the pineal gland. You may want to access these.

"The sad irony here is that the FDA, which does not regulate fluoride in drinking water, does regulate toothpaste and on the back of a tube of fluoridated toothpaste it must state, 'If your child swallows more than the recommended amount, contact a poison control center.' The recommended amount that they are talking about, which is a pea-sized amount, is equivalent to one glass of fluoridated tap water. The FDA is not putting a label on the tap saying, 'Do not drink more than one glass of water. If you do, contact a poison center.' There is no question that fluoride can cause serious harm." – Paul Connett, *The Case Against Fluoride: How Hazardous Waste Ended Up in Our Drinking Water and the Bad Science and Powerful Politics That Keep It There*

To be safe, and to protect ourselves and loved ones from fluoride exposure, it is smart to install a reverse osmosis water filter in our home. In addition, be sure to place filters on your faucets and shower heads to protect from chlorine, lead, and other chemicals. When you drink water, always avoid tap water and stay away from bottled waters. The safest water to drink is distilled water because it is free of fluoride and all dissolved solvents. In fact, on the *Total Dissolved Solvents* (TDS) water meter, distilled scores a 000. This is practically pure. Once distilled, you can alkalize the water by adding cucumber skins, fresh herbs, lemon, or another type of fruit or vegetable.

Now that we know what chemicals we should be avoiding, we can discard of the health-damaging food products, household cleaners, and health care products that contain these toxins. Once our living environment is free from these health hazards, we can focus on cleansing our organs to be sure our internal environment is also waste-free.

Bowel Health & Digestion

"The bowel-wise person is the one who is armed with good knowledge, practices discrimination in his eating habits and walks the path of the higher life. His days are blessed with health, vitality, optimism and the fulfillment of life's goals. He is a blessing and source of inspiration to family and associates. His cheerful disposition comes from having a vital, toxin-free body made possible by the efficient, regular, and cleansing action of a loved and well-cared for bowel." – Dr. Bernard Jensen

At any age, it is always wise to be conscious of our bowel health and to keep our organs clean. Average Americans walk around each day with plaque hardened to their bowels. This is one reason why they wake up with bad breath. This is also a source of where body odor comes from, and where sickness may start to develop. If you have any sort of condition, disease, or sickness, or if you feel depressed, it is helpful to partake in internal cleansing regularly. When your internal organs are clean, you reduce the chance of having bad breath, are less likely to have body odor, and your skin will begin looking healthier. You also assist with the prevention and reversal of disease.

Many diseases can be directly linked to toxic residues in the system. Toxins in the colon stimulate the development of disease, and accelerate aging.

By keeping our colon and bowels clean, we feel happier, increase longevity, preserve our youth, and prevent disease. These poisons that are lingering within pollute the bloodstream and deteriorate every gland, organ, and tissue of the body over time. The accumulation of toxins that have clustered together over the course of our lives is known as toxemia. Chemical drugs, dairy, eggs, heat-generated chemicals, meat, and synthetic food additives present a toxic mix to the bowel. When our colon becomes over-intoxicated, it stagnates and assimilates these toxins into the blood. This leads to many degenerative diseases. The digestive organs, heart, immune system, lungs, and lymph also become tainted. As a result, we are left with feeling bloated, experiencing constipation and other bowel issues, having unhealthy skin and foul breath, and prematurely aging with arthritic conditions and low levels of energy.

Some of the symptoms of toxemia are: acne, anxiety, arthritis, constipation, cysts, depression, dull or pallid skin, eczema, headaches, insomnia, irritable bowel syndrome, psoriasis, sores, tumors, and worse.

"Dis-ease symptoms are an effort of the body to eliminate waste, mucus, and toxemia. This system assists Nature in the most perfect and natural way. Not the dis-ease, but the body, is to be healed; it must be cleansed, freed from waste and foreign matter, and from mucus and toxemia accumulated since childhood." – Professor Arnold Ehret

Dr. Thomas Lodi, founder of *An Oasis of Healing* in Mesa, AZ, established his own understanding of toxemia. His theoretic perspective is, *"Because the colon is five feet long and reabsorbs water, when we do not defecate up to five feet of waste daily, we retain a substance that is toxic in our system, being the feces. Then when the water is continually reabsorbed, the toxins are absorbed into the blood. Once they reach the blood, this becomes what is known as toxemia."* Disease comes from toxemia, as well as acidosis, a clogged detoxification system, excessive growth of candida, and insufficient enzymes. Professor Arnold Ehret's classic book, *The Mucusless Diet Healing System*, is an excellent read for those wishing to learn more about freeing the body of toxins. To avoid toxemia we have to cleanse our bodies of the toxic accumulation of alcohol, cigarette residues, dairy, drugs, eggs, meats, processed foods, sugars, and synthetic medicines. We have to cleanse the molecules of these substances, in addition to completely avoiding them.

It is the state of the blood that makes all disease possible. It is the quality of the condition of the internal environment that is the real disease. If you are experiencing issues with digestion – especially characterized by constipation – you will benefit from a cleanse, accompanied by a juice fast. By keeping our internal environment clean, we reduce the chances of developing the conditions that lead to most chronic diseases, and are more likely to experience health and happiness.

"Constipation can undermine the whole body, including the immune system, and it is now known that irregular bowel movements can be directly related to serious health conditions as well as emotional issues such as depression." – Loretta Lanphier, NP, CN, HHP, CH

Cleansing your colon is one of the more effective ways to start the detoxification process. This procedure alone can assist with weight loss and improve your mood. The health and vitality of the immune system is known to be dependent on the cleanliness of the colon. After cleansing your colon, the most efficient way to keep the weight off and stay healthy is to eat clean, mostly raw, low-fat, organic, and vegan.

"A successful therapy requires harmony of the physical and psychological functions in order to achieve a restoration of the body in its entirety." – Dr. Max Gerson, *M.D.*

There are several books on detoxification and cleansing that I recommend. *The 21-Day Superstar Cleanse*, by Rainbeau Mars is wonderful. *Soak Your Nuts,* written by Karyn Calabrese provides a twenty-eight day cleansing program. *Raw Food Cleanse,* by Penni Shelton, is about restoring health and losing weight by eating raw foods. Natasha Kyssa wrote a detox manual, titled, *The Simply Raw Living Foods Detox Manual.* Wherever you find your inspiration to follow through with this cleanse, use that source to guide you.

I will now introduce a few internal cleansing procedures that will speed up the process of detoxification.

Internal Cleansing Services

Perhaps the best way for maintaining clean bowels is to partake in internal cleansing services. These strategies speed up the detox course and help eliminate toxins faster. This equals to reversing depression more rapidly.

One procedure for cleansing internally is colon hydrotherapy. This is a simple procedure where a tube is inserted rectally and water is pumped into your colon to loosen up the hardened fecal matter for expulsion. When I go in for these services, I ask for organic chlorophyll implants. Adding liquid chlorophyll assists with detox and is a natural deodorizer. It may not sound like something we would jump for joy about having done, but I assure you it will improve your well-being.

"One autopsy revealed a colon to be nine inches in diameter with a passage through it no larger than a pencil. The rest was caked up layer upon layer of encrusted fecal material. This accumulation can have the consistency of truck tire rubber. It's that hard and black. Another autopsy revealed a stagnant colon to weigh in at an incredible forty pounds. When the bowel is this dirty, it can harbor an amazing variety of harmful bacteria and parasites." – Dr. Bernard Jensen

Another method for cleansing the colon is using an enema bucket. This can be much more cost efficient and can also be done in the privacy of your home without assistance. You can purchase an enema bucket and kit online for less than ten dollars and search on any online search engine for instructions guiding you through the process. If you go this route, be sure to use distilled water rather than the saline solution provided. If you have parasites, then you could try enemas using organic garlic water, or diluted organic apple cider

98   Jacoby

vinegar. If you use garlic as a medicinal food, always purchase organic to avoid the methyl bromide that is sprayed on conventional garlic. A simple *YouTube* search will provide you with instructions for implementing these enemas.

"The cell is immortal. It is merely the fluid in which it floats that degenerates. Renew this fluid at regular intervals, give the cells what they require for nutrition, and as far as we know, the pulsation of life can go on forever." – Dr. Alexis Carrell, *Nobel Prize winner*

Because the lymph fluid filters our cells, it is important to keep our lymph moving and clean from toxins. Many people who have been sedentary for years have tainted lymph fluid, and while exercise helps to move the toxins, there is also an internal cleansing service that will speed up the process for you. Most holistic health centers provide lymphatic drainage massages. This is a cost efficient and non-invasive procedure that moves mucus out of the lymph, making it easier to breathe, and revitalizing your energy. Anyone who has trouble with congestion or lung disorders would benefit by undergoing this procedure. By simply typing *lymphatic drainage* along with your zip code into an online search engine, you will find a place that offers this service. If you live on an island, or in a random place that does not offer this service, try jumping on a mini trampoline daily. This is known as *rebounding,* and also helps to move the lymph. Running uphill can be therapeutic for the lymph as well.

The oxygen bath is an internal cleansing service that submerges your body in ozone and draws toxins and heavy metals out of your system. Many people who do this service see the evidence of heavy metal toxins being expelled from their skin immediately after the procedure. When they dry off after each session, the white towels they use become discolored from the toxins being released. By typing *oxygen bath* into an online search engine, you should find a place nearby that offers this service. If you cannot find a location nearby, infrared saunas are similar. Try your best to sweat as much as you can.

Most internal cleansing services are non-invasive and rather simple procedures. After utilizing these services you feel terrific. They rev up your energy levels and provide a positive boost. Although I live in Northern California, I still prefer to fly to *Karyn's Raw Café and Inner Beauty Center* (*karynraw.com*) in Chicago, where they offer each of these internal cleansing services at affordable prices. I start with the lymphatic drainage, follow it with an oxygen bath, and finish with colon hydrotherapy. If you cannot find this service in your area, research skin brushing and try it out.

In addition to using these procedures, there are various flushes we can implement into our healing regime. Search for recipes that guide you through kidney, liver/gallbladder, and parasite flushes. Dr. Hulda Clark provides instructions for each type of cleanse on her web page (*drclark.net*).

"Step into a new world. A world without chronic diseases. Step out of your old world. It has kept you a prisoner. Try something new. The prison has no walls. It has only lines. Lines that mark the ground around you. Inside the lines are your old ideas. Outside are new ideas that invite you to step over and escape your prison. Dare to try these new ideas and your illness promises to recede. In a few weeks it can be gone." – Dr. Hulda Clark

After administering internal cleansing services, it is important to replenish our microbiome with healthy bacteria – or plant-based probiotics. Do not resort to eating yogurt or drinking Kefir. These probiotic strains are contaminated with animal-based proteins and sugars that are not health-promoting. I suggest a vegan probiotic – such as *Vitamineral Green* or *The Ultimate Probiotic* from *Healthforce Nutritionals*.

The August 2011 *PNAS* journal published a study, *Ingestion of Lactobacillus Strain Regulates Emotional Behavior and Central GABA Receptor Expression in a Mouse via the Vagus Nerve*. In this work, researchers demonstrated how probiotic treatment reduced anxiety and depression-related behavior in mice by regulating central GABA receptor expression. GABA is the main central nervous system inhibitory neurotransmitter and is significantly involved in regulating many physiological, and psychological processes. What they discovered is, *"The vagus nerve functions as a major modulatory constitutive communication pathway between the bacteria exposed to the gut and the brain. This finding highlights the important role of bacteria in the biodirectional communication of the gut-brain axis and suggests that certain organisms may prove to be useful therapeutic adjuncts in anxiety and depression."*

As we move forward with the detoxification process, and we have let go of negative emotions, removed chemicals from our diet and home, and actively engaged in internal cleansing services, it is our responsibility to carefully monitor what we are putting into our bodies. During the cleanse, we must nourish ourselves while also being sure not to disrupt the healing within. To do this effectively, I will familiarize you with juice fasting.

Juice Fasting

"After doing a juice cleanse, I am motivated to eat healthier and not emotionally. Cleansing is like my meditation. It makes me stop, focus, and think about what I am putting into my body. I am making a commitment to my health and hitting the reset button." – Salma Hayek

As Salma Hayek suggests, doing a juice cleanse is a lot like hitting the reset button. We flush toxins from our body, rejuvenate the cells and tissues, give our digestive system a break, and free up the energy that was being used for processing heavy foods. This free energy boosts our mental clarity, helps us to feel more vibrant, and promotes health and happiness. In the June 2014 edition of *Cell Stem Cell*, a study, *Prolonged Fasting Reduces IGF-1/PKA to Promote Hematopoietic-Stem-Cell-Based Regeneration and Reverse Immunosuppression*, found that, *"Fasting 'flips a regenerative switch' which prompts stem cells to create brand new white blood cells, essentially regenerating the entire immune system."* After only three days of fasting, study participants had reversed immune suppression and boosted their immunity. By fasting, we not only elevate our mood, we also strengthen our immune system. This can be done by juice fasting or water fasting. Fasting with only water is a little more intense, though highly effective, and should be done

Jacoby

at a supervised water fasting reservation. In *Society's Anonymous*, the juice cleanse is a vital component in recovering from what brings us down. This is the last step in the cleansing process.

There are four major inhibitors that block us from maintaining happiness. They are dehydration, malnutrition, resistance, and stagnation. With juice fasting, we expel stagnant energy, hydrate, nourish ourselves, and rejuvenate our spirit. This helps us to beat resistance and magnetize positivity.

To complete a juice fast, it is required that you only drink liquids for the set period of time you devote to your fast. To do so, you will need a juicer, plenty of organic fruits and vegetables, lots of distilled water, patience, and discipline. When you juice fruits and vegetables, the fiber is removed. Because we expend around seventy percent of our energy in a regular day digesting food, by drinking only the liquid – which contains the organic hydration, nutrients, vitamins, and enzymes – we give our bodies the opportunity to direct energy towards deep cleansing and eliminating acidic waste, plaque, and other toxins we may be storing. While fiber is definitely important in our diet, going without it for this short period of time will benefit us as we spend less energy on digestion.

"Infirmity and sickness, at any age, is the direct result of loading up the body with food which contains no vitality, and at the same time allowing the intestines to remain loaded with waste matter." – Dr. Norman Walker, *Pioneer of Juicing*

If you have been raised on the *Standard American Diet* (S.A.D.) – which consists of processed foods, fast foods, soft drinks, and animal products – you are carrying a toxic load in your system. These toxins that you have accumulated from cooked food, food processing, and abiding by this diet, are not easily released from the body – especially because the chemicals you are ingesting damage the organs used for elimination. This easily weakens your immunity and leads to depression. Imagine how run down your immune system has become from the toxins that have been infiltrating your bloodstream with every meal over the course of your lifetime. All of this havoc is interfering with the normal functioning of your organs.

If your colon, kidneys, and liver are not functioning appropriately, your body simply cannot remove toxins. If you are consuming toxins at a faster pace than your body is processing and removing them, you are inviting a toxin overload to take place. These impurities often remain burrowed in your bones, cells, organs, and tissues. By implementing a juice fast, and combining it with internal cleansing, you finally begin removing these toxins.

"When I am off the road, and I can really control my diet down to the calorie, I juice seven days a week. Every afternoon, whatever I have at hand, beets, carrots, ginger, whatever. I juice, literally, every single day. And on the road, I try to find fresh juice wherever I can." – Henry Rollins

If this is your first time fasting, I suggest you start with a three day juice fast. Even for a three day fast, this will require about five days of eating differently. On the first day, you begin by eating only raw fruits and vegetables. Day two is the first day of juicing, and this requires that you drink only liquids until day five. On the fifth day, you can again eat a simple combination of organic raw fruits and vegetables. By starting off with a three day fast, you avoid shocking your body, and prepare your body to enter the cleansing cycle safely. As you gain the discipline and experience you need to feel more confident about fasting, you can try longer cleanses, such as two week cleanse challenges, or thirty day juice feasts. I encourage you to start simple, then progress into the complex. I also recommend that you take twenty-four hours each week to give your digestive system a break and refrain from eating solids. An easy way to accomplish this is to eat lunch on a Monday afternoon, and then drink only liquids until you have lunch the following day on Tuesday.

It is important to keep in mind that when you start fasting and cleansing the body, you are eliminating years of toxins that have accumulated. Once your body starts releasing these toxins into your bloodstream, it is normal to feel a little *under the weather*, and to experience detox symptoms. Do not let the discomfort scare you away or cause you to halt the cleansing process. Fight through it. You may feel like you have the flu, experience back pain around your kidneys, notice you have bad breath or body odor, develop a rash or break out on your skin, and could even have headaches. You will likely feel hungry and be tempted to eat. Remember that your system has not had a chance to release these toxins before now, and since they are finally being eliminated, they are changing the chemistry of your body. As they pass through your bloodstream, your eliminative organs – especially your colon, kidneys, liver, and skin – can become overwhelmed. To assist the body with the process of detoxification, and ease the stress on these organs, I strongly suggest colon hydrotherapy, enemas, infrared sauna sessions, lymphatic drainage massages, and oxygen baths during the fasting period. It also helps to exercise, though not too vigorously – as you do not want to wear yourself out.

"Fasting is an effective and safe method of detoxifying the body. A technique that wise men have used for centuries to heal the sick. Fast regularly and help the body heal itself and stay well. Give all of your organs a rest. Fasting can help reverse the aging process, and if we use it correctly, we will live longer, happier lives." – James Balch, M.D.

Prior to starting your fast, go to your local organic farmer's market, or grocery store, and stock up on fruits and vegetables for juicing, as well as good quality drinking water. You may want to get apples, beets, blueberries, carrots, celery, cucumbers, ginger root, grapes, kale, lemons, limes, oranges, spinach, tomatoes, and turmeric root. By juicing a combination of these options, you will find success with your fast. Anything that you can eat raw, can also be juiced – do not attempt to juice beans, potatoes, or eggplant. Vegetables are best, especially beets, cabbage, carrots, celery, collards, cucumbers, kale, leafy greens, romaine lettuce, sprouts, and tomatoes. Freshly prepared raw, organic apple, grape, and melon juices are also tasty options.

"I love to create this green juice shake made from kale, spinach, cucumber and wheatgrass. The nutrients in the juice help me recover after a tough workout. The Kale Banana Smoothie at LYFE Kitchen is very similar to my recipe and is fantastic." – Troy Polamalu, *Professional Football Player*

In addition to shopping for your ingredients, you will also need a juicer. Having a high quality juicer is an essential for when you are completing your juice fast. Try to purchase a juicer that is at least seven-hundred watts. If you cannot afford this, any juicer will do. I used a Jack LaLanne power juicer that I found at a resale shop for years without a problem. It cost me around ten dollars.

If you feel like juicing is too difficult of a task, and you are overwhelmed by the thought of preparing juice for yourself daily, you can always find a local organic juice bar, or purchase juice cleanses online. Online cleanses are known as juice delivery cleanses. *Suja* juices (*sujajuice.com*) are organic, cold-pressed, unpasteurized, and affordable. They can also be delivered to your door. *Blueprint Cleanse* (*blueprintcleanse.com*) is another company that provides juice deliveries.

"I do not have any particular thing I do ritualistically. I do the same thing every day. I get up. Drink a lot of water. Have a wheatgrass shot. Drink some green juice. Eat as healthy as I can." – Erykah Badu

For support through your juice cleanse, or to find more information, try accessing Joe Cross' website (*rebootwithjoe.com*), or Kristina Carrillo-Bucaram's page (*fullyraw.com*). You may also want to search for Penni Shelton and scroll through her page (*rawfoodrehab.ning.com*). A few other sites I recommend are *juicefeasting.com*, *rawkinbodycleanse.com*, and *courtneypool.com*. There are plenty of resources online where you can gather more information about juice fasting. You can also search online for Steve Factor (*pureenergyfactor.com*), owner of *Rawkin' Juice;* Ronnie Landis (*ronnie-landis.com*), author of *The Live-It Lifestyle: Dropping Diets Forever;* Dan 'The Life Regenerator' McDonald (*regenerateyourlife.org*); Karinna Zarate (*goveganin30.com*) from *Eat Sunshine!;* or Carly Morgan Gross (*culinarykarma.net*). They are caring, compassionate, and knowledgeable health coaches who would happily assist you on your healing journey. Another option is to find a group of friends, family members, or peers who will join you on your fast.

"The ideal technique for successful fasting is the use of fresh, raw fruit and vegetable juices. On such a diet, the full spectrum of nutrients is supplied in an easily assimilated form, so the digestive tract is able to remain essentially at rest. It is only through the combined use of both cleansing processes, and a very good diet, that one will be able to reach her or his maximal level of physical health and an unclouded consciousness." – Rudolph Ballentine, M.D.

Now that we have accurately identified the causes for why we are experiencing depression, corrected our attitude and perception, and cleansed internally, we can move on to step four in Society's Anonymous. In this step we learn all about which foods fuel happiness, and how the majority of non-foods we have been filling our bellies with could be triggering our depression. We equip ourselves with nutritional knowledge that will help us break free from the sadness that brings us down.

The 4th Step: Choosing Alternative Fuels

"The greatest tragedy that comes to man is emotional depression, the dulling of the intellect, and loss of initiative that comes from nutritive failure." – Dr. James McLester, *Former President of American Medical Association*

At some point, we are going to have to accept the fact that *basic nutrition* has failed us. For far too long we have trusted in the *Food Pyramid*, counted calories, tried out *fad* diets, consumed animal proteins, allowed advertisements for food products to persuade us into buying them, and recognized FDA-approved foods as being healthy, safe, and unharmful. If these foods were truly safe, and if the basic nutrition guidelines were compatible with achieving optimal health, then millions of us would not be experiencing depression or other health conditions that disrupt our balance and well-being. As confirmed in the May 2012 review, *Natural Mood Foods*, published in *Nutritional Neuroscience*, *"Today we know that dietary factors have emerged as affectors of the brain that influence cellular energy metabolism and modulate the signaling pathways of molecules involved with brain plasticity."* The review recognizes our dietary choices playing more of a role in our level of happiness than we may have once believed.

To recover from what brings us down we cannot continue eating poorly, and filling up with sugary-drinks and chemical-laden foods. To invite happiness into our lives, this will require that we are aware of what we put into our bodies with each meal or snack we consume. We are going to have to consider the energy that the food items we rely on for fuel contain within. We want our food to provide living nutrients that are not damaged or denatured. In the fourth step of Society's Anonymous, *"We learn the difference between real foods and processed foods, and grasp how they contain either living nutrients or synthetic chemicals. We understand that the nutrients fuel positivity and happiness, and the synthetic chemicals stir-up negative emotions and depression. We are equipped with the knowledge needed to consciously choose how we nourish our bodies, and we do so by eating only the best available organic plant-based, whole foods."*

"Health is normal. The human body is a self-repairing, self-defending, self-healing marvel. Disease is relatively difficult to induce, considering the body's powerful immune system. However, this complicated and delicate machinery can be damaged if fed the wrong fuel during the formative years. Healthy living with nutritional excellence throughout life can slow the decline of aging. It can prevent the years and years of suffering in ill health that is so common today as people get older and become dependent on medical treatments, drugs, and surgery. Nutritional excellence is the only real fountain of youth." – Joel Fuhrman, *Disease-Proof Your Child: Feeding Kids Right*

To complete the fourth step on our adventure to happiness, we begin to remove certain foods, drinks, and fillers from our diet. This includes animal-based food products, gluten grains, GMOs, processed foods and beverages, and refined sugars. We are required to start adding organic juices, smoothies, salads, and raw fruits and vegetables. This may seem like a difficult task, and we might grimace at the thought of it, however we note that being depressed is also not an ideal way to live. Eating organic is important because we avoid the farming chemicals, glyphosate, GMO residues, phosphates, and other chemicals found in conventional produce. These chemicals are known to alter the neurotransmitters in our brain. Our goal should be to start enjoying the healthy foods we may not desire at the present moment, and to learn to appreciate the taste of fresh organic green juices. If we record the shift in our energy levels when we eat healthy, in comparison to when we eat poorly, we should notice a big difference.

To successfully invite happiness into our lives, and increase our odds of permanently erasing sadness, it is mandatory that we change our diet. Once we make the changes, we will be grateful that we followed through. Now we can learn about the relevance of choosing to eat organic.

"Raw food is the best way to have the cleanest energy. We take so much care about what kind of fuel we put in our car, what kind of oil. We care about that sometimes more than the fuel that we are looking at putting in our bodies. It is cleaner burning fuel." – Woody Harrelson

Eating Organic

In a June 2014 review published in the *British Journal of Nutrition, Higher Antioxidant, Lower Cadmium Concentrations, and Lower Incidence of Pesticide Residues In Organically Grown Crops*, an international team of researchers led by *Newcastle University* determined that *organic crops are up to sixty percent higher in a variety of health-promoting antioxidants than their conventional counterparts*. After analyzing 343 studies and distinguishing the compositional differences between organic and conventional crops, the team discovered that a transition to eating organic fruit, vegetables, cereals, and foods derived from them, provided additional antioxidants equivalent to eating between one to two extra portions of fruits and vegetables daily. The results also clarified a significantly lower level of toxic heavy metals in organic crops. Cadmium, which is one of only three metal contaminants, along with lead and mercury, for which the *European Commission* has set maximum permitted contamination levels in food, was found to be almost fifty percent lower in organic crops when compared to conventional. The lead researcher behind this project, Professor Carlo Leifert, explained: *"This study demonstrates that choosing food produced according to organic standards can lead to increased intake of nutritionally desirable antioxidants and reduced exposure to toxic heavy metals. This constitutes an important addition to the information currently available to consumers which until now has been confusing and in many cases is conflicting."* We now know with certainty that eating organic is healthier.

In step three I mentioned a study published in the July 2014 *Environmental Research* journal, *Reduction In Urinary Organophosphate*

Pesticide Metabolites In Adults After A Week-Long Organic Diet, which was conducted to determine whether an organic food diet reduces organophosphate exposure in adults. This study found that eating an organic diet for only a week can decrease pesticide levels – especially of organophosphates – by up to ninety percent in adults. These phosphates are linked to many cancers and chronic conditions. During pregnancy, organophosphates are known to get into the amniotic fluid and are then passed to the infant, leading to childhood cancers. The best way to avoid these chemicals, as this study clearly demonstrates, is to eat organic and avoid conventional, processed foods.

Many studies have been done proving that conventional crops produce far less phytochemicals than organic varieties. Phytochemicals are compounds produced by plants that are of great benefit to the body. In his book, *Life Force,* Dr. Brian Clement mentions a study from the 2002 *European Journal of Nutrition* which proved that *organic vegetables contain nearly six times as much salicylic acid as non-organic vegetables. The salicylic acid is disrupted by the pesticides used in non-organic farming.* Studies have been done both at *Rutgers* and *Tufts University* which have proven organic crops have up to eighty-eight percent more minerals than do conventional. According to the *Organic Consumers Association, organic food contains qualitatively higher levels of essential minerals such as calcium, magnesium, iron, and chromium, which are severely depleted in chemical foods grown on pesticide and nitrate fertilizer-abused soil.* U.K. and U.S. Government statistics indicate that *levels of trace minerals in (non-organic) fruit and vegetables fell by up to seventy-six percent between 1940 and 1991.*

Minerals, vitamins, and phytochemicals are nutrients, and among the most important nutrients for us to obtain. They are referred to as micronutrients. If you compare the macronutrient content of organic to conventional produce it remains the same. This is only comparing carbohydrates, fats, and proteins, not vitamins and minerals. What is most important is the micronutrient content. Organic fruit contains much higher amounts of these irreplaceable micronutrients than the opposing conventional produce. Micronutrients are responsible for manufacturing neurotransmitters that stabilize our mood and keep us happy. By eating foods deficient in these nutrients, we create chemical imbalances in our body that are linked to depressive symptoms. *A comprehensive review of ninety-seven published studies comparing the nutritional quality of organic and conventional foods revealed that organic plant-based foods contain higher levels of eight of the eleven vital micronutrients that were studied. This includes significantly greater concentrations of polyphenols and antioxidants. In this comprehensive review, the team of scientists concluded that organically grown, plant-based foods are twenty-five percent more nutrient dense, on average, and deliver more essential nutrients per serving or calorie consumed.* This review was published in the March 2008 edition of the *State of Science Review* by the *Organic Center* and is titled, *New Evidence Confirms the Nutritional Superiority of Plant-Based Organic Foods.*

Please purchase organic food. You are not only boosting your immunity and elevating your mood by eating it, you also help to build Earth's top soil back up to an adequate level. Without topsoil, little plant life is possible. Topsoil is the outermost layer of soil. Because it has the highest concentration of microorganisms and organic matter, the roots of plants obtain their nutrients from this layer. The conventional monocropping methods common today are destroying this vital layer of Earth. Conventional monocropping can be defined as growing an excess of one particular type of crop when it is not needed. These crops are often genetically modified (alfalfa, canola, corn, cotton, soy, sugar beets, and wheat) to withstand heavy application of pesticides, which damage the soil microorganisms and lead to desertification. The Earth and soil need a variety of crops for nourishment. Planting an assortment of organic crops, or polycropping, as organic farmers are more likely to do, helps to rebuild the topsoil. It feels good to protect the planet.

By eating organic, you are helping to save the environment. You are supporting the organic farmers who work hard day-after-day to be sure they are providing us with our optimal nutrients. We must thank these courageous farmers. They are the ones that are keeping our planet alive. They bring us hope. They keep our aspirations of coexisting with all of nature lingering around. A great way to get involved with the organic movement is to join an organic co-op. In Houston, TX you will find the largest co-op in the United States, *Rawfully Organic*. The organizer is Kristina Carrillo-Bucaram. She is beautiful, charismatic, charming, and incredibly inspiring. You can learn more about her and how she operates this business by accessing *fullyraw.com* or *rawfullyorganic.com*. If we could do what she is doing in Houston all over the country, and in every city around the world, we could cut our healthcare costs, improve the environment, and reduce the extinction of species and indigenous natives. We would also help many people overcome depression.

In most areas across the country there are *Community Supported Agriculture* (CSA) groups offering organic crop-shares where you pay a certain amount of money every couple of weeks and you get organic produce delivered to you, or have the option of picking it up locally. Check out *coopdirectory.org* to find one nearest you. This eliminates a trip to the supermarket.

What it comes down to is we can either pay the organic farmers a little extra for their hard work and dedication towards providing real food for us, or we can pay the hospitals a few years later a lot more to misdiagnose us, and give us erroneous treatments for our ailments that stem from eating foods stripped of their nutrients and loaded with toxic chemicals that destroy nature. The choice is ours. The *Pesticide Action Network* reported that *organic farmers in the U.S. produced more than $20 billion worth of pesticide-free food in 2007, and at a twenty percent annual growth rate, organics are the fastest growing agricultural sector*. Together we can keep this trend going. We do not need pesticides or GMO's to grow our own food, or to feed the world.

Visit the websites of the *Organic Consumers Association* (*organicconsumers.org*) and The *Organic-Center* (*organic-center.org*) to learn more about the many benefits of eating organic. Read actual books, such

108   Jacoby

as *Comfortably Unaware* by Dr. Richard Oppenlander, *The Food Revolution* by John Robbins, *Sunfood Diet Infusion* by John McCabe, and *Organic Manifesto* by Maria Rodale. Discover the truth about food. Taste the difference. Feel the elevation in energy as you indulge in the delights of organic produce.

Living Foods

"My refrigerator is powerful. In fact, it has a direct link to my overall well-being." – Kris Carr, *Crazy, Sexy, Raw*

I encourage you to take advantage of the power that your refrigerator can harness. Do this by filling it with raw fruits, vegetables, and health-promoting foods. In June 2012, the *Public Health Nutrition* journal published a study, *Frequent Consumption of Vegetables Predicts Lower Risk of Depression*. Researchers found that frequent consumption of vegetables appears to cut one's odds of depression by more than half simply by eating veggies three or more times a week. They concluded, *"More consumption of vegetables was protective against depressive symptoms."* The May 2012 review, *Natural Mood Foods*, suggests, *"Eating lots of fruits and vegetables may present a non-invasive, natural, and inexpensive therapeutic means to support a healthy brain."* Yes, the food we consume really does impact our health and happiness.

"When you nourish your own mind and your own spirit, you are really feeding the Soul of Life. When you improve yourself, you are improving the lives of those around you. And when you have the courage to advance confidently in the direction of your dreams, you begin to draw upon the power of the universe." – Robin Sharma, *Daily Inspiration*

When I mention *living foods*, I am referring to fresh organic fruits, vegetables, nuts, and seeds that have not been cooked, pasteurized, or altered in any way that could damage the nutrient content. If a food requires cooking, it is not ideal for eating. As I mention in, *The Raw Cure: Healing Beyond Medicine*, "When you eat food, you are inclined to be drawn to the source of the food. By choosing to eat fruits, vegetables, and other plant-based foods, this connects you to nature, the origin of that food. The living energy reunites you with more of life. When you eat meat (dead flesh) and other processed foods that lack living energy, you begin to require synthetic entertainment to activate an undernourished and understimulated mind. The dead energy from the food sucks you into TV, video games, celebrity gossip, mainstream media, and being an observer rather than a participant in the things you enjoy. Ultimately, you change the course of your evolution."

"Keeping your body healthy is an expression of gratitude to the whole cosmos – the trees, the clouds, everything." – Thich Nhat Hanh

The enzymes in live foods aid digestion. Living foods contain life within them and promote cellular longevity. A sprout is a perfect example of this type of food. All of the nutrients in sprouts are unharmed and ready to provide the body with nutrients. Other living foods are raw fruits and raw vegetables. Fresh, unpasteurized green juices and smoothies are also considered *living*.

We produce around two-hundred thousand new cells every second of our lives. Our bodies are made up of trillions of cells. Each one of these cells is an individual living organism. Only after its own survival, the cells main concerns are protecting and contributing to the health of other cells. Our cells keep us alive and we should do our best to nourish them for the span of time they live inside of us. When we fail to nourish our cells, they fail to provide us with optimal health. Think of owning a business. You have a group of employees working for you. In order to keep them happy, you must pay them. Now, say you stop paying them and keep making them work. How long do you reckon this will last? Imagine your cells as your employees that are battling to keep your business intact and their form of payment is good, nourishing food. Make sure you pay them well.

Even the cells of the healthiest people in the world die off at some point. Every minute their bodies are generating millions of new cells. These cells are constructed from the energy and substances that are present in their system at that particular time. Because of this, it is obligatory that we eat richly nourishing food. When we cheat and eat poor quality foods, we pay for it sooner or later.

People who commonly eat clarified sugars, cooked oils, dairy, eggs, fast and processed foods, meat, synthetic chemicals, and other food-like substances – while also drinking soda and alcohol – tend to have bodies that are constructed of up to trillions of weak cells that are prone to disease. Their bones are also being depleted of nourishment, and their organ tissues are accumulating the residues of these unhealthy foods. Those following such harmful diets end up being visibly depressed and unhealthy, with complexions lacking the vibrancy they would have from fueling with truly healthy foods.

To reverse sadness and stimulate happiness, we want to build cells using optimal fuel sources. These fuel sources are simply raw organic fruits, vegetables, and plant-based foods – or living foods. We want to avoid heavy, acid-forming foods. Acid-forming foods create acidosis in the body. Acidosis conditions nurture inflammation, sadness, stress disorders, and stress injuries. We always want to avert an acidic body condition. Be sure to avoid these foods as much as possible while you recover from what brings you down.

"We want foods with the most energy in them. Enzymes are the manifest form of energy. The only source of energy is to eat raw food." – Dr. Brian Clement, *Hippocrates Health Institute*

Acid foods to avoid: *alcohol, artificial coloring, artificial flavoring, aspirin, barley, beef, breads, cakes, candy, canned foods, cereals, cheeses, chicken, chocolate, coffee, condiments, cooked corn, corn starch, crackers, custards, dairy products, diet sodas, dressings, doughnuts, egg whites, eggs, fish, flours and flour-based foods, gelatin, gravies, grits, ice cream, jams, jellies, ketchup, mayonnaise, meats, gluten grains, pasta, pastries, pork, preservatives, processed oils, peanuts, refined sugars, rice cakes, rice, rice vinegar, salt, sodas, soybeans, soy products, spaghetti, sugars, tapioca, tea (conventional), vinegar, yogurt*

Some of you might be wondering how you could live without milk, meat, or cheese. It is quite simple once you discover plant-based alternatives. Making almond milk is fun, and takes about thirty minutes of your time. You need a high-speed blender, pitcher, nut milk filter, fresh raw almonds, hemp seeds, chia seeds, dates, cinnamon, and vanilla bean powder. Soak about two cups of almonds in water overnight. Be sure the almonds are fully submerged in water. After soaking, strain the water, and pour the almonds into the blender. Combine chia and hemp seeds if you would like. I add about three tablespoons of each. Throw in three or four pitted Medjool dates. Flavor it with cinnamon and vanilla, then fill the blender with distilled water. Let it puree for a few minutes, then pour it into the nut milk filter while the filter is resting inside of the pitcher. Squeeze the filter as if you are milking an udder until the liquid comes out. With the remaining pulp, you can make desserts or breads. I make a raw banana bread with mine in the dehydrator. If you feel you do not have time to prepare your own almond milk, you can purchase organic almond, hemp, or chia milks at most grocers. *Whole Foods* is always a reliable source.

By simply searching online for *raw vegan cheese* recipes, you will find several options. Plant-based cheeses are much healthier and taste surprisingly better than animal-derived cheeses. There are also a variety of mock-tuna, mock-salmon, mock-chicken, and veggie burger recipes that are vegan, delicious, and worth trying. To learn more about making plant versions of your favorite meals, check out the books, *Gorilla Food,* by Aaron Ash, or *Cooking With Amore*, by Maria Amore. John McCabe has a good recipe book out titled, *Simple Vegan Recipes*. Other great options are any of the books by Ani Phyo (*aniphyo.com*), Cherie Soria (*rawfoodchef.com*), Megan Elizabeth (*meganelizabeth.com*), Mimi Kirk (*youngonrawfood.com*), Chris Kendall (*therawadvantage.com*), or Sarma Melngailis (*oneluckyduck.com*).

Try starting your day with a fresh organic juice or green smoothie to replace coffee. With any blender, you can mix frozen bananas, fresh berries and other fruits, kale or spinach, chia seeds, flax seeds, hemp seeds, pitted dates, distilled water, and a scoop of some type of organic greens superfood powder. I prefer *Vitamineral Green* made by *Healthforce Nutritionals*. This powder is alkaline-rich, contains digestive enzymes and probiotics, and provides us with every nutrient on the spectrum. Be sure your ingredients are organic. If you prefer juice, use your juicer and start your day with a blend of powerful greens.

For lunch, eat a humongous salad. You want to aim for at least a pounds worth of organic romaine lettuce, kale, or some other type of leafy green, mixed with fresh organic vegetables, and a homemade organic vegan dressing. I often add avocado, bell pepper, burdock root, currants or figs, green onion, mango, shaved carrots, sliced radishes, and tomatoes. To replace dressing, I prefer to squeeze citrus over my salad and then season it with organic herbs and spices.

Dinner can be any combination of organic plant-based foods. If you crave grains, go for pseudograins as an alternative. These include amaranth, buckwheat, millet, and quinoa. Be sure you are not using cooked oils in your food. Snack on fresh juices, fruits, vegetables, nuts, seeds, and dried fruits throughout the day and after dinner if you are hungry.

By eating and drinking more living foods, we liven up, gain more energy, and tend to have more charisma. If we are sick and we introduce these foods, we notice almost immediately that we start to feel better. Living foods are for living people. If you want to be alive, I suggest you eat foods that are alive.

I challenge you to make the transition to a plant-based, living foods lifestyle. By replacing processed foods with vibrant, edible plant-matter, you will not only lose body fat and gain mental clarity, but you will also increase longevity, reduce your chances of developing disease, and significantly lower your risk of dying. By choosing to fuel yourself with edible plant matter that is chemical-free, non-GMO, fresh, and free from sugars and gluten, it is likely that you will soon notice improvements in your mood.

Why Plant-Based?

"The biggest change that comes with eating raw is how you feel physically. There are times of the day when I feel euphoria. A wash of happiness comes over me. I feel very clean, knowing I am not digesting a lot of additives. If you eat raw food, you are putting pure fuel into your body. I used to feel stuffed. Now I can be satisfied without overloading my system. Raw food is not a phase, it is a lifestyle. It is not something you can unlearn when you know about it, even more so when you have experienced it — you cannot forget the energy, how much better you look and feel, how much more inspired, connected and loving you feel. That stuff is with you for life." — Russell James, *Raw Food Chef*

The common widespread belief is that we must raise animals for food so we can get optimal amounts of calcium, iron, protein, and other important nutrients. I want to enlighten you with some life-saving information. This is false. Think about where these strong, lean animals are getting their nutrients. The answer is simple. Animals get their calcium, iron, protein, and other nutrients from eating a variety of grasses and plants. This generates lean muscle. The same is true for humans who restrict meat from their diet and only consume plants. They are naturally lean and strong. In *The China Study*, Dr. T. Colin Campbell points out that there are absolutely no nutrients we cannot obtain from eating a plant-based diet free of harmful animal proteins. Sure, we do get substantial amounts of protein and fat when we eat animals and their by-products, however, we miss out on antioxidants, fiber, phytonutrients, and other important micronutrients that are lacking in animal-based foods. We also ingest carcinogenic compounds such as heterocyclic amines and polycyclic aromatic hydrocarbons; damage our endothelial cells with trans-fats and dietary cholesterol; and disrupt our digestive and eliminative processes.

While cholesterol is paramount for our body to function, it is important to note that we create the healthy version of cholesterol as we nourish ourselves with plant-based foods. Foreign cholesterol that is obtained from eating meat, dairy, and eggs is not the cholesterol we want in our system. By eating a well-balanced vegan diet, our body will produce the healthy version in abundance.

112   Jacoby

"It is not the plant-based foods that will make you ill, it is the meat and the liquid meat (i.e.: dairy) that can lead to sickness and death. Consider this: If your food had a face or a mother (or comes from something that did), then it also has varying amounts of artery-clogging, plaque-plugging, and cholesterol-hiking animal protein, animal cholesterol, and animal fat. These substances are the building blocks of the chronic diseases that plague Western society." – Rip Esselstyn, *My Beef with Meat: The Healthiest Argument for Eating a Plant-Strong Diet*

Fiber is extremely important for maintaining an untainted bowel. Fibrous vegetables contain high levels of inulin, which feeds the healthy actinobacteria in our gut. Animal-based foods contain zero fiber. Antioxidants and phytonutrients help to maintain a healthy microbiome, eliminate free radicals, lengthen telomeres, and fight off harmful pathogens. These nutrients are non-existent in meat, dairy, and eggs. Because we get more than enough protein in our diet by eating a combination of raw fruits, vegetables, nuts, and seeds, it is unnecessary for us to continue eating animal-based foods. On a plant-based diet, we also receive sufficient amounts of calcium, iron, and other essential nutrients. The only vitamin we may need to supplement with is B-12. Keep in mind that more meat-eaters suffer from B-12 deficiencies than do vegans, so this is not simply a *vegan deficiency*. *Vitamineral Green* is a good choice of supplement for B-12. If you are curious about your blood levels and want to know whether or not you are getting the nutrients you need, access *rawfoodeducation.com* and elect to have a labwork consultation done with Dr. Rick Dina. He is an exceptional teacher, knowledgeable doctor, and wise man.

"I have been vegan for about ten and a half years. It has been all good. I am obviously much healthier" – Woody Harrelson

In step one, while reading about age, we learned that advanced glycation end-products (AGEs) tend to shorten telomeres, accelerating the aging process. I mentioned how glucose binds to cooked animal proteins, leading to the formation of AGEs, and by eating meat we damage our cells and shorten telomeres. In a September 2013 study led by Dr. Dean Ornish and published in *The Lancet Oncology* journal, *Effect of Comprehensive Lifestyle Changes On Telomerase Activity and Telomere Length In Men With Biopsy-Proven Low-Risk Prostate Cancer*, it was determined that changes in diet, exercise, stress management, and social support can result in longer telomeres – the parts of chromosomes that affect aging. For five years, the researchers followed thirty-five men with localized, early-stage prostate cancer to explore the relationship between comprehensive lifestyle changes, and telomere length and telomerase activity. All the men were closely monitored through screening and biopsies. Ten of the patients embarked on lifestyle changes that included: a plant-based diet (high in fruits, vegetables and unrefined grains, and low in fat and refined carbohydrates); moderate exercise (walking thirty minutes a day, six days a week); and stress reduction (gentle yoga-based stretching, breathing, meditation). They were compared to the other twenty-five study participants who were not asked to make major lifestyle changes. When the five-year study ended, *the group that made the lifestyle changes experienced a significant increase in telomere length of approximately ten percent.* Researchers found that *the more people changed their behavior by adhering to the recommended lifestyle program, the more dramatic their improvements in telomere length.* Meanwhile, *the men in the control group who were not asked to alter their lifestyle had measurably shorter telomeres – nearly three percent shorter.* This study demonstrates how we can slow the aging process by choosing to eat plant-based, exercising, and eliminating stress.

In addition to accelerating aging, eating animal-based foods such as meat, dairy, and eggs, is strongly associated with depression. This is likely because of the arachadonic acid that is contained within these foods – along with the low-level energy, and harmful pathogens. A February 2012 *Nutrition Journal* study, *Restrictions of Meat, Fish, and Poultry In Omnivores Improved Mood*, found that simply eliminating animal products from the diet of omnivore subjects improved their mood within two weeks. The researchers discovered that arachadonic acid – found primarily in chicken and eggs – was to blame for their initial depression before the elimination of these foods. They acknowledged arachadonic acid as a compound that can *adversely impact mental health via a cascade of brain inflammation.* High intakes of this acid began to promote changes in the brain that resulted in disturbed mood and this was demonstrated with the group of subjects who continued to eat fish for the duration of the study. Fish-eaters reported significantly worse moods than vegans. The conclusion was that *restricting meat, fish, and poultry improved short-term mood state in modern omnivores.*

"I try to stick to a vegan diet heavy on fruit and vegetables." – Clint Eastwood, *Hollywood Actor and Producer*

In a 2010 *Nutrition* journal cross-sectional study, *Vegetarian Diets are Associated with Healthy Mood States*, vegetarian test subjects reported significantly less negative emotion than omnivores. The researchers concluded that arachadonic acid – a key substrate for the synthesis of pro-inflammatory eicosanoids and downstream cytokines that can adversely impact mental health via a cascade of neuroinflammation – was to blame for the anxiety, depression, mood disturbance, and stress experienced by those who included meat in their diet. Miraculously, by eliminating chicken, fish, and eggs, their symptoms improved within two weeks. The top sources for arachadonic acid are chicken, eggs, beef, processed meats (sausage, hot dogs, bacon, and ribs), fish, burgers, cold cuts, pork, and pizza. If you are unhappy, and your diet is abundant in these foods, perhaps it is time for you to make some dietary changes. Try skipping meat once or twice a week to start, and then progress to removing it entirely from your diet. You will be thankful once you transition.

A major cause of inflammation is a cellular-surfaced molecule found in red meat and milk products. Scientists label this *Neu5Gc,* or the *mammalian meat molecule.* Once ingested, this compound absorbs into our tissues, stimulating an immune response. Our immune system creates antibodies to resist the molecule and begins to attack our organs where the molecule is hiding as our blood cells try to eliminate it from our system. The result is inflammation. We avoid Neu5Gc altogether by choosing to eat plant-based.

Jacoby

In the January 2014 Nature journal, a study, *Diet Rapidly and Reproducibly Alters the Human Gut Microbiota*, explains how long-term dietary intake influences the structure and activity of the trillions of microorganisms residing in the human gut. These same microorganisms communicate with our brain and have an impact on our appetite, behavior, feelings, and mood. Researchers studied the impact that animal-based diets and plant-based diets have on the gut microbiota by dividing the groups into vegan, or strictly meat-based diets. In the study, it was found that, "*Short-term consumption of diets composed entirely of animal products alters the microbial community structure and overwhelms inter-individual differences in microbial gene expression. The animal-based diet was found to increase the activity of bilophilia wadsworthia, showing a link between dietary fat, bile acids, and the outgrowth of microorganisms capable of triggering inflammatory bowel disease.*"

Bilophilia are microbes that love bile. Because bile helps to digest fats, more bile is produced when the diet is rich in meat, dairy, and eggs. When extra bile is produced, we generate more of these microbes. Blooms of bilophilia are known to cause inflammation and colitis — conditions that are closely associated with depression. In this study, researchers observed fifty clustered, species-level bacterial phylotypes and how each diet had an impact. They found that among those eating plant-based diets, only three of these bacterial clusters were altered, while twenty-two of the phylotypes on animal-based diets were changed significantly. *The microbiome of those on meat-based diets had clusters composed of putrefactive microbes, bilophilia wadsworthia, increased lactic acid bacteria, staphylococcus, increased enteric deoxycholic acid concentrations (DCA), and several other potentially damaging organisms.* DCA is a secondary bile acid that promotes liver cancer, DNA damage, and hepatic carcinomas. A high level of bilophilia wadsworthia is known to cause inflammation in the bowel. This alteration in the gut microbiota could also explain symptoms of anxiety and depression.

"You cannot expect to reform the healthcare system, much less expand coverage, without confronting the public health catastrophe that is the modern American, meat-based diet." – Michael Pollan, *Omnivore's Dilemma*

There are many reasons why I promote a plant-based diet. It is not only because I disagree with the way animals are treated. I should not have to get into detail about why it is wrong to enslave, rape, torture, and kill billions of animals that possess the ability to feel, think, and love (please see the film *Earthlings*). Sadly, I have learned over the years that there will always be people who simply do not care about the feelings of other sentient beings, and who think torturing, slaughtering, and abusing animals is justified as a part of some perverse cycle of life. This is mostly a result of industry propaganda, misleading advertisements, and miseducation. What we are blinded by is collective karma. We do not recognize that for as long as we keep treating animals poorly and inflicting suffering on them, we are going to live with controversy, depression, pain, and suffering. Our actions against the animal kingdom reflect on our well-being.

"The act of regularly eating foods derived from confined and brutalized animals forces us to become somewhat emotionally desensitized, and this numbing and inner armoring makes it possible for us as a culture to devastate the earth, slaughter people in wars, and support oppressive social structures without feeling remorse. By going vegan, we are taking responsibility for the effects of our actions on vulnerable beings and we are resensitizing ourselves. We are becoming more alive, and more able to feel both grief and joy." – Will Tuttle, PhD, *The World Peace Diet*

Aside from the ethical reasons, I also promote veganism because of the environmental impact eating animals and their by-products has on the planet. With billions of animals being raised in cages, forced to eat chemically saturated GMO feed, and being poisoned with antibiotics, we have to question where all of the feces end up, where they are getting the feed, and where they are finding land to raise these animals. On the *EarthSave* website (*earthsave.org*), it is noted that one-half of the Earth's landmass is grazed by livestock – making this land unlivable for humans or wildlife. We also know that over seventy percent of all U.S. grain production is fed to livestock. For those who worry about carbon dioxide emissions from humans, it seems odd to me that they are not considering the enormous population of caged farm animals that are also emitting greenhouse gases in much larger quantities. It may be a surprise for some to learn that the rainforests all around the world are being destroyed to clear land for growing GMO alfalfa, corn, soy, and wheat, which feeds the livestock. More forests are being decimated for factory farms and cattle ranches. It may be news to you learning that up to five million pounds of animal excrement is produced every minute in the U.S. alone in factory farms. This is confirmed in, *Livestock's Long Shadow,* a 2009 *United Nations* report released by the *Food and Agriculture Organization*. With this excrement comes methane gases, and excess nitrogen. This animal waste is dumped in our lakes, oceans, rivers, and streams, leading to ocean dead zones and habitat destruction for many wild animals. The methane gases, nitrous oxide, and carbon being emitted from the mass breeding of farm animals, the clear cutting of the forests, and the animal excrement is the number one contributor to global warming – responsible for over fifty-one percent of all greenhouse gas emissions. Please see the film *Cowspiracy* (*cowspiracy.com*) to learn more. This is an environmental disaster. In addition to not respecting the animals right to live (*nonhumanrightsproject.org*), some people also do not appreciate the environment. For those who have been raised in a city, or in suburbs that lack nature, I see why they care so little. They have not experienced the beauty of nature, and are not informed that their eating choices are destroying what remains of our non-renewable natural resources.

Because I am aware that many people do not consider nature, or the mistreatment of animals, my main emphasis when promoting a plant-based, vegan diet is the undeniable impact this way of eating has on improving health. I have many friends who eat poorly. My intention is to help them see that removing animal products and refined, processed foods from their diet is a necessity for maintaining happiness. I do not mean to attack anyone when I

116   Jacoby

advocate for veganism, I simply want to assist them. While they play the devil's advocate, or respond by regurgitating pro-meat propaganda, they woefully do not see they are fueling their poor health by choosing ignorance. We have all been lied to for the majority of our lives and misled into believing that eating meat, dairy, and eggs is somehow beneficial and health-promoting. False advertisements, industry propaganda, erroneous studies, and billions of dollars spent on marketing by the meat, dairy, and egg industries are the reasons for why so many people still believe eating dead body parts of animals is healthful. This is not the truth. Eating animal products does not promote good health, it nurtures depression and disease. I have worked with several people who are seriously ill, and who spent the majority of their lives believing that eating animals was health-promoting. Each one wishes they had transitioned to a plant-based diet sooner. After removing animal products, they were shocked by how fast their bodies responded, how much happier they became, and how rapidly their health improved from fueling with foods derived from plants. Prior to doing so, they were the same as my other friends. They laughed at the idea of veganism and countered by claiming that their ancestors ate meat and lived long lives. They told themselves that saturated fat and cholesterol are indeed healthy, simply because they read it in a magazine promoting the meat industry. They chuckled at the thought of eating vegan because they believed somehow they were not going to get the adequate protein they need – as if animal protein is advantageous for human health. Then, their illnesses kicked in, and depression soon diffused their smiles.

"Nothing has changed my life more. I feel better about myself as a person, being conscious and responsible for my actions, and I lost weight and my skin cleared up and I got bright eyes and I just became stronger and healthier and happier. I cannot think of anything better in the world to be but be vegan." – Alicia Silverstone, *Hollywood actress*

We know that eating animals is not only an environmental disaster. It does not only promote the suffering and abuse of animals all over the world. Eating animals is killing us. It is creating trillions of dollars in profits for the medical industry while we are suffering, watching our loved ones suffer, and each day inching closer to our own death. Today it is so well-known that eating meat, dairy, and eggs is a major contributor to sickness and disease that *Kaiser Permanente* is promoting a plant-based diet for physician's to *prescribe* to patients. In the Spring 2013 edition of *Permanente Journal*, they include an article, *Nutritional Updates for Physicians: Plant-Based Diets*. In the article they encourage physicians to prescribe plant-based diets to patients by stating, *"Healthy eating may be best achieved with a plant-based diet, which we define as a regimen that encourages whole, plant-based foods and discourages meats, dairy products, and eggs as well as all refined and processed foods. We present a case study as an example of the potential health benefits of such a diet. Research shows that plant-based diets are cost-effective, low-risk interventions that may lower body mass index, blood pressure, and cholesterol levels. They may also reduce the number of medications needed to treat chronic diseases and lower ischemic heart disease mortality rates. Physicians should consider recommending a plant-based diet to each of their patients, especially those with high blood pressure, diabetes, cardiovascular disease, or obesity."*

For more information on the dangers of eating animal-based foods, please watch the documentary, *Forks Over Knives*. If you are unaware of the way animals are being treated, see the film *Earthlings*.

"We have never treated a single patient with protein deficiency; yet the majority of patients we see are suffering from heart disease, diabetes, and other chronic illnesses directly resulting from trying to get enough protein." – Dr. Alona Pulde & Dr. Matthew Lederman, *Forks Over Knives*

Processed Foods & Drinks

"The modern food and drug industry has converted a significant portion of the world's people to a new religion—a massive cult of pleasure seekers who consume coffee, cigarettes, soft drinks, candy, chocolate, alcohol, processed foods, fast foods, and concentrated dairy fat (cheese) in a self-indulgent orgy of destructive behavior. When the inevitable results of such bad habits appear—pain, suffering, sickness, and disease—the addicted cult members drag themselves to physicians and demand drugs to alleviate their pain, mask their symptoms, and cure their diseases. These revelers become so drunk on their addictive behavior and the accompanying addictive thinking that they can no longer tell the difference between health and health care." — Dr. Joel Fuhrman, *Eat to Live*

According to Dr. Robert S. Harris in his *Nutritional Evaluation of Food Processing*, *"Nutrients are destroyed when foods are processed because many nutrients are highly sensitive to heat, light, oxygen, and the pH of various substances and additives used in the process. There is no question that processing food reduces the amount of nutrients that are contained within."* These nutrients that are destroyed when food is processed are the antioxidants, minerals, phytonutrients, and vitamins that are responsible for producing the neurotransmitters that keep us happy. They are endangered in processed foods and drinks.

Surveys conducted by the *USDA Economics Research Service* (ers.usda.gov) reveal that around seventy percent of the calories in the *Standard American Diet* (S.A.D.) come from processed foods. These consist of all foods that have been altered. When cooked, especially with high heat, the proteins become denatured, the enzymes are inactivated, the vitamins are damaged, and the biophotons fade or vanish. Many of these foods have been *fortified* with synthetic nutrients. These nutrients have very little, if any, positive effect on the body. A November 2009 study of 3,456 middle-aged civil servants, published in the *British Journal of Psychiatry*, *Dietary Pattern and Depressive Symptoms In Middle Age*, found that, *"Those who consumed a diet rich in processed foods had a fifty-eight percent increased risk for depression, whereas those whose diet could be described as containing more whole foods had a twenty-six percent reduced risk for depression."* Examples of foods that

118

may be in your pantry that are fortified would be cereals, crackers, pasta, toaster pastries, and frozen microwaveable food products. To nurture happiness, if you have cabinets full of processed foods, I encourage you to dispose of them and replenish your cupboard with high-quality organic foods provided by nature and free of synthetic nutrients and chemical additives.

"Paradoxically, Americans are becoming both more obese and more nutrient deficient at the same time. Obese children eating processed foods are nutrient depleted and increasingly get scurvy and rickets, diseases we thought were left behind in the 19th and 20th centuries." – Dr. Mark Hyman

Melanie Warner – author of *Pandora's Lunchbox* – explains, *"There are an estimated five-thousand different additives that are allowed to go into our food, but the FDA does not know how many additives are truly going into our food. This is in part because regulations are not only self-regulatory – so the food industry is doing the testing – but they are also voluntary. The ingredient companies do not have to tell the FDA about a new ingredient. If they choose to, they can simply launch it into the market. The FDA does not know about them, and nobody else really knows about them."* Judging from her statement, we know that when we opt to eat processed foods, we are potentially ingesting thousands of chemical additives. This is damaging our health and emotional well-being.

I am sure you have heard the statement at least a hundred times in your life, but you really are what you eat. You become what you eat because the cells which your body generates during the moments you are eating are constructed of the substances you have eaten. To be at an optimal level of health, fast food cannot be included in your diet. It is not okay to have it once a week. It is not okay to have it once-in-a-while. You should never consider fast food as nourishment. I know it can be convenient to stop at a drive-thru and grab that quick stomach filler, but think about how much more convenient your good health will be if you avoid these food choices and eat only high quality foods containing actual nutrients. Fast food restaurants, grocery stores, and most sit-down diners serve processed meats containing nitrites and nitrates which have been identified as cancer-causing, as well as heterocyclic amines and other cooked meat carcinogens. They also offer breads containing bleached, refined gluten grain flours and bromide; soft drinks loaded with artificial sweeteners, chemicals, phosphoric acid, and the ever so dangerous sodium benzoate; fruits and vegetables that are often genetically modified; and dairy products that are full of growth hormones, low-quality proteins, and antibiotics. In addition, the chains promote their foods as being healthy, when they are truly hazardous combinations of all of the worst food groups that are saturated with chemicals.

In independent laboratory tests conducted by the *Physician's Committee for Responsible Medicine (PCRM.org)*, it was found that KFC's grilled chicken items contain alarming amounts of PhIP, one of the most abundant heterocyclic amines in cooked meats. This carcinogen is known to bind directly to DNA, causing mutations. DNA mutation is considered by many experts to be the first step in cancer development. Although these tests were carried out to specifically target menu items from KFC, this does not single them out as the only fast-food establishment serving items containing these cancer-causing compounds. Several fast-food chains serve menu items containing these carcinogens. It is a widespread belief that all meats cooked at high temperatures contain some form of heterocyclic amines.

The seven worst categories of foods are cooked oils, dairy, eggs, gluten flours, meat, processed salts, and refined sugars. Fast food joints serve all of these and they often combine each of them together in one meal. This is not proper food combining. Each of these items requires different digestive juices to be broken down and digested. When the food products are mixed, as they are with any sandwich, the digestive juices neutralize each other and the food does not digest well. This is why many people carry around extra pounds of weight and have excess plaque coating their intestinal walls. It is the animal protein, fermentation, gluten grains, putrefactive bacteria, rancid oils, sugars, and slew of added chemicals that leads to cancer, depression, diabetes, heart disease, obesity, and many other diseases.

Have you ever seen the videos where burgers from the most popular fast food companies were left out to rot and they did not decompose? Because of the additives and preservatives, many of these foods do not break down. French fries could sit out for decades and the structure of them would not change much. Have you ever imagined what happens when you allow these items to enter your body? How do you expect your body to break down these compounds? We cannot consider anything that will not decompose in nature to be food. Fast food *restaurants* serve *plasticized* food. Why are we eating it?

"Millions upon millions of Americans are merrily eating away; unaware of the pain and disease they are taking into their bodies with every bite. We are ingesting nightmares for breakfast, lunch, and dinner." – John Robbins, *Diet for a New America*

What we need to realize is that calories are not everything. When eating at places such as *Subway* because of the *low calorie* count in their menu items, or similarly, with following a diet such as *Weight Watchers* to count calories, one can still become unhealthy and eat their way to sickness. The problems we face in this country do not relate to eating excessive calories as much as they do with eating animal proteins, chemical additives, farming chemical residues, and GMOs. Cancer is more likely to develop from eating one-thousand calories a day of processed, chemically-laden foods than it will from eating three-thousand calories of raw, organic plant-based foods. We have to make the connection and not be so gullible to believe everything we are told.

Heart disease is mostly attributed to poor diet. Dietary cholesterol is found only in animal-based foods. In the *China Study,* Dr. T. Colin Campbell studied the dietary effects on blood cholesterol levels and determined that *animal protein consumption by men was associated with increasing levels of 'bad' blood cholesterol, whereas plant protein consumption was associated with decreasing levels of this same cholesterol.* This tells us we should avoid animal products if we want to lower our cholesterol levels and prevent heart disease. Simply restricting calories will not prevent disease from occurring. We have to abide by clean diets that are free of chemicals to assure good health.

120   Jacoby

The worst of the animal products are the processed meats and cheeses. *The University of Hawaii executed a study that followed nearly 200,000 men and women for seven years. The results concluded that people who consumed the most processed meats showed a sixty-percent increased risk of pancreatic cancer over those who did not consume processed meats.*

"Every year, the average American eats as much as thirty-three pounds of cheese. That's up to 60,000 calories and 3,100 grams of saturated fat. So why do we eat so much cheese? Mainly it is because the government is in cahoots with the processed food industry." – Michael Moss

The staple of the *Subway* diet is processed meat. It depends on what the customer orders, but other than the few vegan options they offer, each sub they serve is piled with processed meat and offers the choice of adding cheese. Cheese and meat are major contributors to cancer and heart disease. The flours and gluten grains used in the bread contain compounds that are known to trigger a variety of health problems. The farming chemical residues, food coloring, GMOs, refined sugars, and sodium benzoate hidden in the bread, condiments, *fresh* fruit slices, peppers, pickles, and/or soft drinks can compromise the function of the pancreas. The margarine made from palm oil that is in the cookies, and soybean oil in the bread, both have the capacity to oxidize the cells and cause inflammation, leading to weakness and fatigue. Partially because celebrities and athletes promote fast-food chains as being healthy, there is a societal epidemic of irritable bowel syndrome and diverticulitis. Because of the junk sold by fast foods corporations, we are witnessing degenerative diseases such as diabetes and obesity becoming increasingly common. These garbage foods also lead to arthritis, cancer, emotional disorders, erectile dysfunction, heart disease, and stroke.

If you are a stellar athlete, or someone who is well known and well respected in society, please consider that you are promoting corporations that are selling toxic foods which are robbing your fans and those who look up to you of good health. Do you realize how many children idolize you because you inspire them? You are misleading them into a life of illness. I urge you to end any contracts you have with corporations promoting toxic products and start endorsing lifestyle changes that truly are healthy.

If the current diet you are consuming includes processed fillers and sugary beverages, I encourage you to familiarize yourself with how to prepare your own meals. It may not be as convenient to do it yourself, however you will notice a difference in your energy levels soon after eliminating processed foods that will overshadow the minor inconveniences. For every processed food item that you enjoy, there is a way to revise the recipe using ingredients that are healthier, and do not play a role in planet degradation. It is likely that what you create will taste far superior and feel better going in and coming out. By filling your shopping cart, counter tops, and refrigerators with fresh organic produce and truly nourishing foods, you can elevate your mood and increase your longevity. If you would like to watch demos for how to prepare your own delicious meals and snacks, access *YouTube* videos of Fully Raw Kristina (*fullyraw.com*), Dara Dubinet (*daradubinet.com*), Yovana Mendoza (*rawvana.com*), Jason Wrobel (*jasonwrobel.com*), Chef BeLive (*chefbelive.com*), and Chris Kendall (*therawadvantage.com*), to name a few. You also have the option to attend classes at a vegan culinary school. Check out the *Living Light Culinary Institute* (*rawfoodchef.com*) in Fort Bragg, CA.

GMOs

"Our food system belongs in the hands of many family farmers, not under the control of a handful of corporations." – Willie Nelson, founder of Farm Aid (*farmaid.org*)

One of the hazards attached to eating processed and animal-based foods is the likeliness that you are ingesting genetically modified organisms (GMOs) with each bite. Beginning in 1996, the U.S. Government began approving ingredients that are genetically altered by scientists to be added to the food supply. Today, over eighty-eight percent of all corn, ninety-three percent of the soy, ninety percent of the canola and sugar beet crops, and a large percentage of the cottonseed, alfalfa, and papayas being grown in the United States are genetically modified. It is estimated that close to eighty percent of all processed foods on supermarket shelves contain genetically modified ingredients, as do the majority of school lunch items being served to our children in cafeterias. Although research links GMOs to allergies, organ toxicity, and other health issues, the *U.S. Food and Drug Administration* does not require safety testing for GMOs.

So, what are GMOs? Genetically modified organisms are created when biotech companies insert foreign genes into the DNA of seeds so the crops can withstand a number of conditions as they grow. After they alter the seeds, they obtain a patent for them. Then they get farmers under contracts. Their plan is likely to monopolize the global food supply. Most GMO crops contain the Bt toxin, *bacillus thuringiensis*. As the crop grows, it emits this toxin, which acts as an insecticide. The problem associated with this toxin is that once we eat the crop, or when the livestock eat these GMO foods, the Bt toxin is still active and can damage our intestinal flora. This alters our gut microbiota, leading to depressive symptoms – among several other health ailments. GMO seeds also have a foreign gene inserted into them from a strand of bacteria that can tolerate the chemical glyphosate, which is added to *Roundup* herbicide weed killer. Once this gene is inserted, the crops become resistant to the chemical. The result is that millions of pounds of this health-depleting chemical are applied to these GMO crops annually. Glyphosate has been linked to multiple health conditions in several studies.

"The companies that are genetically engineering and patenting seed are chemical companies. They have interest in selling more chemicals. They do not do genetic engineering to reduce chemical use; they do genetic engineering to increase chemical use." – Vandana Shiva, author of *Soil Not Oil, vandanashiva.org*

Interestingly enough, the same company selling this herbicide that the crops are resistant to, also sells the seeds. So now they control the food supply, and provide the chemicals that kill weeds and protect these mutant plants. In addition, they have a pharmaceutical sector that supplies the medicine for people once they get sick. If you want to learn more about this *business model*, go to an online search engine and type in *Monsanto Pfizer merger*. You will see this statement on the *Monsanto* webpage, *"Prior to Sept. 1, 1997, a corporation that was then known as Monsanto Company (Former Monsanto) operated an agricultural products business (the Ag Business), a pharmaceuticals and nutrition business (the Pharmaceuticals Business), and a chemical products business (the Chemicals Business). Former Monsanto is today known as Pharmacia. Pharmacia is now a wholly owned subsidiary of Pfizer Inc., which together with its subsidiaries operates the Pharmaceuticals Business. Today's Monsanto includes the operations, assets, and liabilities that were previously the Ag Business. Today's Solutia comprises the operations, assets, and liabilities that were previously the Chemicals Business."* So you see, the same company selling genetically modified seeds also sells the chemicals being applied to the crops, and additionally sells the pharmaceutical drugs that serve a purpose of combating sickness and disease. This should be a concern to us all, and each of us should be more vocal about requiring food companies to label GMOs. We should demand that we know what is in our food. Please access *organicconsumers.org/monsanto/* to learn more about the dangers attached to the GMO epidemic.

The *American Academy of Environmental Medicine* (AAEM) now encourages physicians to prescribe diets that do not contain genetically modified foods to their patients. They called for a moratorium on genetically modified organisms (GMOs), long-term independent studies, and labeling, stating, *"Several animal studies indicate serious health risks associated with GM food, including infertility, immune problems, accelerated aging, insulin regulation, and changes in major organs and the gastrointestinal system. There is more than a casual association between GM foods and adverse health effects. There is causation."*

Going back to the dangers of glyphosate, an April 2013 study published in the journal, *Entropy*, by Anthony Samsel and Stephanie Seneff, titled *Glyphosate's Suppression of Cytochrome P450 Enzymes and Amino Acid Biosynthesis by the Gut Microbiome: Pathways to Modern Diseases*, explains how this chemical harms human health. The study links GMOs to Alzheimer's disease, anxiety, autism, cancer, depression, diabetes, gastrointestinal disorders, heart disease, infertility, and obesity. The results show us that, *"Glyphosate inhibits cytochrome P450 (CYP) enzymes, and CYP enzymes play crucial roles in biology – one of which is to detoxify xenobiotics – so the chemical enhances the damaging effects of other food-borne chemical residues and environmental toxins."* Citing recent studies, the review coauthor, Stephanie Seneff, PhD, senior research scientist at Massachusetts *Institute of Technology's Computer Science and Artificial Intelligence Laboratory*, explains how, *"Glyphosate acts as a potent bacteria-killer in the gut, wiping out delicate beneficial microflora that help protect us from disease."* Seneff describes how, *"Glyphosate can disrupt the gut's ability to create tryptophan,*

123

the building block of serotonin, and important neurotransmitter linked to happiness and well-being. Low serotonin levels have been linked to suicide, depression, obsessive-compulsive disorder, and other ailments. Not only is glyphosate hampering tryptophan production in your gut, but it is also lowering levels in plants, causing even more deficiency." The study concludes, "The toxin Glyphosate found on GMO food prevents the breakdown of other toxins; kills beneficial bacteria in your gut, reducing vitamin and mineral absorption; destroys the wall between your gut and your bloodstream, allowing toxins to enter your bloodstream, where they are attacked by your immune system, creating inflammation, which releases cytokines that enter your brain, causing inflammation in your brain and brain cell damage, resulting in depression anxiety." This information is alarming. Knowing how damaging GMO foods can be to our health, and seeing how abundant they are in the food supply, can we question why so many of us are sick, depressed, and living below our happiness threshold?

Most developed nations do not consider GMOs to be safe. In more than sixty countries around the world – including Australia, Japan, Russia, and all of the countries in the European Union, there are significant restrictions or outright bans on the production and sale of GMOs. In the U.S., the government has approved GMOs based on studies that were conducted by the same corporations that created them and profit from their sales. The companies claim there is no difference between a GMO crop variety and a natural crop variety. If there truly was no difference, then why do they own patents for the seeds that rule them as being unique? Fortunately, many Americans are catching on and refusing to buy products that contain these unnatural ingredients. We simply do not want to be part of an experiment any longer. We do not want our children to be experimented on either. I have a beautiful daughter, and there is not a chance in the world that her mother or I would allow food that has been genetically engineered in a lab to be served to her.

"Any scientist who tells you they know that GMOs are safe and not to worry about it, is either ignorant of the history of science or is deliberately lying. Nobody knows what the long-term effect will be." – David Suzuki, Geneticist

What I find scary about eating genetically modified food is that we introduce foreign microorganisms to our gut microbiota. These organisms could seriously impact our health. Since GMOs were introduced to the food supply, there has been a steady rise in chronic conditions, diseases, mental health disorders, and profits for the medical industry. Mark Lyte, a researcher from *Texas Tech University* who studies how microbes affect the endocrine system, explains that new microorganisms could alter the mind. He is quoted as saying, *"I am seeing new neurochemicals that have not been identified before being produced by certain bacteria. These bacteria are – in effect – mind-altering microorganisms."* When we eat food that is unrecognizable by nature we cannot predict the effect it will have on our body. The wise choice is to eat truly organic foods that are heirloom and free of GMOs. The non-GMO project (*nongmoproject.org*) is adding their stamp of approval to packaged food items that are GMO free. Look for it. To be sure you are avoiding GMOs, do not purchase food items that contain sugar, corn syrup, high-fructose corn syrup, cornstarch, aspartame, canola oil, soybean oil, soy, soy lecithin, or any corn or soy derivatives – unless they are labeled as organic.

Avoiding Gluten & Sugar

"Government-sponsored guides to healthy eating, such as the USDA's food pyramid, which advocates six to eleven servings of gluten grains daily for everyone, lag far behind current research and continue to preach dangerously old-fashioned ideas. Because the USDA's function is largely the promotion of agriculture and agricultural products, there is a clear conflict of interest inherent in any USDA claim of healthful benefits arising from any agricultural product. Popular beliefs and politically motivated promotion, not science, continue to dictate dietary recommendations, leading to debilitating and deadly diseases that are wholly or partly preventable." – Ron Hoggan, *Dangerous Grains*

The *gluten-free* trend is becoming more common each year as people are finally beginning to understand the negatives of gluten on health. As Jimmy Kimmel showed us in a segment on his late-night talk show, most of us do not know what gluten is – all we know is that we do not want to be eating it. Gluten is a protein contained in barley, rye, spelt, and wheat, and these grains are not necessary in our diet. Gluten contains two protein fractions known as gliadins and glutenins. Gliadin has been shown to cause inflammatory bowel disease. Glutenin is not easily digestible. They both contribute to diverticulitis, celiac disease, and dermatitis herpetiformis. They break down the ileum to the point where problems with absorption start to occur. Gluten grains are also high in lectins and when the lectins bind to insulin receptors, they interfere with glucose metabolism, causing intestinal damage and protein and carbohydrate malabsorption. Gluten has been linked to several symptoms, including ADD, arthritis, bi-polar disorder, depression, fatigue, headache, irritability, and inflammation in the blood vessels, heart, liver, and kidneys.

"Outside of gliadin, few things share such a lock-picking, intestinal-disrupting talent. Other factors that trigger zonulin and disrupt intestinal permeability include the infectious agents that cause cholera and dysentery. The difference, of course, is that you contract cholera or amoebic dysentery by ingesting feces-contaminated food or water; you contract diseases of wheat by eating some nicely packaged pretzels or devil's food cupcakes." – William Davis, *Wheat Belly*

Whole gluten grains are associated with high levels of the bacteria prevotella – a gut microbe that is linked to inflammation and arthritis. This could explain why too much gluten in the diet can cause celiac disease. This disease is commonly thought of as a GI disorder, but can also cause profound psychological symptoms – such as depression or anxiety. The highlight of this disease is that the small intestine is damaged, producing symptoms such as abdominal cramps and swelling, constipation, diarrhea, gas, pain, and vomiting. Once damaged, the small intestine may not absorb essential vitamins, minerals, and proteins efficiently. This is likely a result of the overabundance of the bacteria prevotella.

For decades now, researchers have associated celiac disease with depression. A March 1998 study in the *Scandinavian Journal of Gastroenterology, Depressive Symptoms in Adult Celiac Disease*, confirmed, *"Close to one-third of those with celiac disease also suffer from depression."* The *Journal of Psychosomatic Research* published a study in December 2003, *Recurrent Brief Depression in Celiac Disease*, which found, *"Adolescents with celiac disease have a thirty-one percent risk of depression, while only seven-percent of healthy adolescents face this risk."* Depression is related because the intestinal damage caused by celiac disease prevents the absorption of essential nutrients – many of which keep the brain healthy. Some of these nutrients include zinc, tryptophan, and the B vitamins. These nutrients are necessary for the production of neurotransmitters in the brain – one of these being serotonin. A serotonin deficiency is linked to depression.

By avoiding gluten, there is a chance we could improve our mood and decrease depressive symptoms. It is still wise to be cautious of some of the gluten-free products being sold on supermarket shelves. Many of these contain dough conditioners, eggs, GMO sugars, harmful preservatives, and other food additives that are better off not entering your body.

"Sugar suppresses activity of a key growth hormone in the brain called BDNF. BDNF levels are critically low in both depression and schizophrenia." – Dr. Joseph Mercola

Sugar comes in many forms. There are refined sugars, brown sugars, sugar crystals, cane sugar, evaporated cane juice, beet sugars, high-fructose corn syrup, glucose, sucrose, maltose, lactose, fructose, agave nectar, heated honey, and synthetic sweeteners. All sugars are deleterious to our health, unless they are eaten in their natural state, coming from raw fruits or vegetables.

Sugar is acid-forming and leads to an imbalance in the ratio of phosphorus to calcium. Sugar causes excess calcium excretion, and when we lose this calcium, the pH level in our body tilts toward acidity. Because we store alkaline minerals in our bones, we then draw calcium from them to buffer our pH level so it becomes slightly alkaline. This process weakens our bones and contributes to osteoporosis.

"Some studies show that sugar is eight times more addictive than cocaine. Sugar is the new nicotine. Sugar is the new fat – except fat is not addictive in the way that sugar is. What is worse, is that sugar actually causes diabetes and obesity." – Dr. Mark Hyman, *10-Day Detox Diet*

Knowing that sugar is genetically modified, it is wise to stay away from it. All refined sugars that are not specifically labeled as cane sugar, or organic, are likely GMO. Sugar is associated with depression because the process of converting sugar to energy requires B vitamins. These vitamins are responsible for producing neurotransmitters that stabilize our mood. By eating too much sugar, or drinking sugary drinks, we are depleting our body of nutrients.

126

Because many of us crave sweets, it would be difficult to completely wean ourselves from everything sweet in our diets. Fresh organic fruits, or dried fruits are the only sources of sugar we should be consuming. Contrary to the common widespread belief, eating low-glycemic raw fruits, especially berries and cherries, has been documented to help reverse diabetes – assuming that the diet is also free from animal-based fats, cooked oils, and trans-fats. Eating fresh organic fruits is among the greatest choices we can make for fueling good health. Check out *Freelee the Banana Girl* (*thebananagirl.com*). She began eating up to thirty bananas a day (*30bananasaday.com*), cut out all other sugars and junk foods, and was able to reverse her depression and significantly improve her life. Her book, *Go FRUIT Yourself*, explains how you can follow a similar program to achieve optimal health.

In addition to eating fruits, truly raw dates are a source of food helpful in overcoming a craving for sweets. If you feel like you must add sweetener to your food, use raw organic coconut nectar, raw organic date syrup, or organic Stevia. A small amount of organic maple syrup is more beneficial to your health than a small amount of sugar. Remove all processed sugar from your life and your health will likely improve.

Hydration

"It is chronic water shortage in the body that causes most diseases of the human body." – Masaru Emoto, *The Healing Power of Water*

Staying hydrated is crucial for good health. This requires that we drink plenty of clean water daily. Even mild dehydration has been linked to cognitive impairment. Aim for at least half of a gallon each day. Be sure the water you drink is not from a bottle, and is not tap water. You want to be confident that your drinking water is free of chlorine, lead, fluoride and other harmful contaminants and solvents. The safest water is distilled water. When water is distilled, all of the fluoride and other chemicals are removed. You can alkalize the water by adding cucumber skin, citrus slices, or even fresh herbs. Another healthy option is drinking water from a reverse osmosis filter. Although the water contains few dissolved solvents, it is still considered clean.

Often when we feel mentally imbalanced, and depression starts to creep its way into our lives, the reason is because we are dehydrated. To function efficiently, our cells and organs must be hydrated. Some of us think we are well hydrated, but we are drinking water with a high TDS count, making it more difficult to absorb. If your head feels cloudy, or you are generating negative thoughts within, please force yourself to drink as much distilled water as you possibly can. Drink until you cannot tolerate a drop more. After a few minutes, repeat the process. Keep filling with water until you flush out the stagnation.

Drinking alcohol or soda is not in any way hydrating. In fact, these substances will dehydrate your organs further. Do you know that for each eight ounce serving of soda you drink, you add so much acidity to your body that you will need anywhere from thirty to thirty-five eight ounce glasses of water simply to dilute the acidity? Soda is ten thousand times more acidic than distilled water. If you pour soda over a piece of the flesh of an animal, the tissues will eventually deteriorate. When your diet is too acidic, your body becomes a breeding ground for disease. You gain extra weight, your bones weaken and become brittle, your complexion fades, your mood declines, and you tax your digestive organs.

Soda contains high amounts of phosphoric acid, which inhibits our ability to absorb calcium and magnesium. When we are consumers of these unhealthy drinks, our bodies use the calcium in our bones to buffer the acidity. This weakens our bones and leads to osteoporosis. The sugars in sodas also feed candida yeast, and trigger weight gain, even when a person is drinking diet sodas. *Researchers found that the risk for becoming overweight increases by forty-one percent with each can of daily diet soda.* These findings were a result of eight years of data collected by Sharon P. Fowler, MPH, and her colleagues at the *University of Texas Health Science Center* in San Antonio. It really is sad to know that misinformation is being spread suggesting that drinking *diet soda* will help us lose weight. This is far from being accurate. Bone mineral density loss, compromised cellular health, and a shortened lifespan are more likely to happen for those who consume these colas and sodas, sweetened or not.

"Soft drinks have long been suspected of leading to lower calcium levels and higher phosphate levels in the blood. When phosphate levels are high and calcium levels are low, calcium is pulled out of the bones. The phosphate content of soft drinks like Coca-Cola and Pepsi is very high, and they contain virtually no calcium." – Michael Murray N.D. and Joseph Pizzorno N.D., *Encyclopedia of Natural Medicine, Revised Second Edition*

If you drink diet soda, or any soda at all, I urge you to quit immediately. Let the habit go and watch how fast you will see improvements in your health and life. Soft drinks are referred to as *soft* drinks for a reason. They soften your bones, teeth, and your chances of maintaining good health and experiencing happiness. If you want to be healthy, you simply cannot drink sodas, colas, caffeine-loaded *energy* drinks, or other highly-acidic, sugary, chemically-saturated beverages. There can be no exceptions. Even most *fruit* juices sold in stores are not healthy. To hydrate, drink clean water or fresh organic, cold-pressed juices.

By eating more raw fruits and vegetables; drinking plenty of water; removing animal products, processed junk foods, GMOs, gluten, and refined sugars from our diet; and by making healthier lifestyle choices, we provide our body with the fuel it needs to thrive at an optimal level of health.

We have come a long way so far. Steps three and four will likely be the most difficult for you to incorporate into your life, yet they are of utmost importance for recovering from what brings us down. If you have setbacks with your diet, and you find it is difficult for you to maintain, please feel free to email me, find a health coach, or seek some other source of inspiration. Do not get discouraged or down on yourself. The transition requires discipline and patience that you will acquire soon. You are on your way to a much happier life.

It is now time for us to move on to step five, where we will remove ourselves from the same stagnant environment and explore the outdoors.

Jacoby

The 5ᵗʰ Step: Engaging in Outdoor Physical Activity

"Look at the trees, look at the birds, look at the clouds, look at the stars, and if you have eyes you will be able to see that the whole existence is joyful. Everything is simply happy. Trees are happy for no reason; they are not going to become prime ministers or presidents and they are not going to become rich and they will never have any bank balance. Look at the flowers – for no reason. It is simply unbelievable how happy flowers are." – Osho

After learning about nutrition, we now begin to appreciate all of nature equally. We awaken to the certitude that everything is connected. From the microorganisms to the plants; the mycelium and the soil to the roots, the trees, and their leaves; the winds and the rains to the fruits, the grasses, and the grains; the sun and the rivers, to the beautiful species on this land; all of life is merged with nature. By living in accordance with the cosmos, we are also a part of this alliance. Our decisions have an impact on everything around us. Once we make this connection, we compile evidence that a happier world awaits us.

As we venture into the domain of happiness, the fifth step in Society's Anonymous is, *"We activate our body, mind, and soul by engaging in physical activities such as exercise, gardening, meditation, and yoga. We understand the importance of removing ourselves from the synthetic world, and reclaim our relationship with nature by spending more time appreciating the natural environment."*

We know that this disconnect from our earthly surroundings which we have been experiencing as a result of residing in big cities and suburbs that lack nature is partly to blame for our melancholy, so in this step we nurture our relationship with the green earth and outdoor world. We understand our lack of movement, and sedentary lifestyle is inhibiting our potential to reach the level of happiness we desire, so we combat this by engaging in physical activity. To establish a balance between our synthetic habitat at home, or in the office, and the lush ambiance of the wild, we compromise by walking barefoot, adventuring through state parks and forest preserves, admiring the wildlife, hugging trees, gardening, growing our own food, and appreciating all that Gaia – the Earth Mother – offers. To be sure we are equipped for when weather conditions are not up to standard, we replicate a natural environment in our home using house plants, and we join a local gym so we can remain active all year – not only seasonally.

The reason why we consolidate the outdoors with physical activity is to validate that we are pursuing an equal proportion of the two. Too frequently, when we decide to start exercising, we buy a gym membership and work out indoors. This leaves us with little time leftover to enjoy the outside world. We want to move away from functioning inside as much as possible so we can breathe fresh air, absorb the rays of the sun, and begin to appreciate the joys of nature. To accomplish this objective, we can try doing our exercise routines at a park. We also have the free will to run or hike the trails in local forest preserves. Practicing yoga outdoors is an additional way for us to connect with the cosmos. Another attractive option is to meditate with sounds from the natural environment resonating through our soul. We should strive to be at one with the plants, trees, and wildlife so we are more in-tune, and are provided a better opportunity to elevate our consciousness.

We have been conditioned to live in fear of the natural world for so long that we have accepted depression as a natural part of our evolution. We are commonly afraid of forests because we worry wild animals are out to get us, or that bugs will bite us. This is not true. Sure, we might get a few bug bites, but this is not a deal breaker. We should be cautious of animals, but we cannot let their presence restrict us from celebrating the forest ecosystem. What we will notice as we embrace our connection with everything around us, is discontent can easily be excluded from our lives. This is our chance to explore the lushness of the woods, start our own gardens, get involved in yoga, practice meditation, engage in physical activity, and participate in exercise classes. By doing so, not only do we elevate our happiness and improve our relationship with nature, we also strengthen our cardiac muscles – assuring good health, high stamina, and increased endurance.

Connecting With Nature

"There is no Wi-fi in the forest, but I guarantee you will find a better connection." – pureinsight.org

Being outdoors allows us to step outside of the synthetic environment that commercialization, industrialization, and the Western lifestyle has structured as a foundation for us. Before depression, we were seeds formulated from nature. Over the course of our lifetime, many of us are drawn away from anything that is natural. We are born in hospital rooms with artificial lights, and injected with a slew of harmful pathogens, heavy metals, and toxins that are lurking in vaccines. We play with plastic toys, suck on plastic pacifiers, and drink from plastic bottles filled with genetically modified infant formulas that nurture a terrain for childhood disease. Once we start the education process, we occupy the majority of our days being locked in synthetic buildings learning different ways to help increase the profits of industries, while failing to ignite our passions, or expand on our interests in the arts and music. As students we are not even offered real food for lunch. The stuff they serve us on cafeteria trays is genetically modified, saturated with chemicals, and fosters sickness. Once dismissed from class, we then choose to watch television, or play video games over spending time outside. Our meals at home likely come from a package and are often microwaved, meaning they do not provide us with the antioxidants and phytonutrients needed to produce the neurotransmitters responsible for maintaining our happiness. We are targeted by corporations selling health-depleting food items, and unnecessary products that we do not need on advertisements that are aired during commercial breaks from our *favorite shows*. We use artificial products to poison our skin. We spray chemicals all over our homes to *kill* bacteria, germs, and viruses that are waiting dormant in the foods we commonly eat. We repeat this cycle for years until we finally graduate from school and are ready to start our career. This is

Jacoby

when most of us resort to working in offices where we are again void of nature. Knowing all of this, how can we be surprised that depression is so common? In this step, we exert our energy escaping the artificial, technological life that we have been sucked into, and begin to establish a balance with nature.

According to the *Kaiser Family Foundation*, it is estimated that the average teen aged eight to eighteen in the U.S. spends seven to eight hours a day in front of a media device. A March 2014 study published in *World Psychiatry* journal observed more than 12,000 adolescents and determined, *"Youngsters who spend more than five hours a day surfing the net, playing video games, and watching television suffer more commonly from depression, anxiety, and suicidal thoughts than others."* An August 2013 report, *How Healthy Behavior Supports Children's Well-Being*, published by *Public Health England* found, *"Excessive screen time – more than four hours a day – was linked to anxiety and depression and was responsible for limiting a child's opportunity for social interaction and physical activity. It was determined in the report that, "Too much screen time limited a child's opportunities for physical activity and face-to-face social interaction with friends and family, which are key factors in reducing childhood anxiety."* A February 2011 study published in *Pediatrics* journal, *Pathological Video Game Use Among Youths: A Two-Year Longitudinal Study*, found excessive gaming may lead to depression, anxiety, and poor grades in school. Judging from these three sources, we can safely conclude that a major contributor to depression among children is the amount of time they spend playing video games, surfing the internet, and watching television. Perhaps if they invested more of their time adventuring through the woods they would not be so commonly depressed. As parents we have to be the enforcers and lead our children away from media devices by keeping them active and engaging their minds using other sources of stimulation. We can accomplish this by encouraging them to read books, get involved in group activities they enjoy, spend more time outdoors, pick up an instrument, and participate in sports. The best way to convince them is to lead by example.

"The best remedy for those who are afraid, lonely or unhappy is to go outside, somewhere where they can be quite alone with the heavens and nature. Because only then does one feel that all is as it should be and that the Great Spirit wishes to see people happy, amidst the simple beauty of nature. As longs as this exists, and it certainly always will, I know that there will always be comfort for every sorrow, whatever the circumstances may be. And I firmly believe that nature brings solace in all troubles." – Anne Frank, *The Diary of a Young Girl*

A study published in the January 2014 *Environment & Behavior* journal, *Happiness and Feeling Connected: The Distinct Role of Nature Relatedness,* concluded there is a highly significant relationship between nature and happiness. Their research suggests, *"Nature relatedness has a distinct happiness benefit, beyond the more generalized advantages of feeling connected to family, friends, and home."* What this confirms is our connection to nature is correlated with most measures of human well-being. This indicates that spending time outside may play an extremely important role in maintaining positive mental health. Knowing this, there are no legitimate excuses that can justify us staying indoors. We are summoned to acknowledge the importance of escaping the same stagnant environment.

"I only went out for a walk, and finally concluded to stay out till sundown. For going out, I found, was really going in." – John Muir, *founder of Sierra Club (sierraclub.org)*

In the book, *Last Child in the Woods: Saving Our Children from Nature-Deficit Disorder*, author Richard Louv found ways to link the lack of nature in today's younger generation to troubling childhood trends, including the rise of obesity and depression. He informs us that the condition many physicians and psychiatrists label as *Attention Deficit Disorder* (ADD) is more appropriately termed *Nature Deficit Disorder* (NDD). His discoveries lead us to believe that for all of these years we have witnessed kids being poisoned with drugs to control and dictate their behavior, a much cleaner, safer, and more simple approach would have been allowing them to spend time in nature. There is no reason for us to continue following the dangerous trend of feeding kids chemicals simply because they want to play. We can instead opt to give them this freedom.

In 2005, the *California Department of Education* teamed up with the *American Institutes for Research* to conduct a study on at-risk students in the Fresno, Los Angeles, and San Diego areas. The study focused on the educational and social-emotional impact that outdoor environmental education programs would have on these children. After only a week of taking outdoor classes, researchers found that the kids improved their science scores by twenty-seven percent. In addition to boosting these scores, students who participated in the programs showed significantly higher gains in cooperation and conflict resolution skills, compared with those who opted out. In the six to ten weeks following their program participation, parents of these children observed them engaging in positive environmental behaviors at home. Among the children who attended the program, teachers reported significantly larger gains in self-esteem, conflict resolution, relationships with peers, problem-solving skills, motivation to learn, and positive classroom behavior. All of these changes were a result of simply being in nature for one week. Prior to being outside and having the opportunity to connect with the natural environment, many of these same kids had low self-esteem, an inability to resolve conflicts, troubled relationships with peers, and generally lacked motivation. This all changed simply from spending one week being educated in a more natural environment.

What if every person who is currently experiencing depression was to spend more time in nature? Imagine if all children were given the opportunity to learn in a natural environment. Think about how much happier society would be. I cannot depict in words how revolutionary this would be for our well-being. All of the people I pass by on city streets who normally wear grim faces would likely be smiling again. We would definitely notice a difference.

will be much happier. Try learning the *P90x* routine, or the *Insanity* workouts and practice them outside. Condition your body so you can run with ease. You can start off with brisk walking, then progress to a light jog, and eventually, as long as you keep at it, you will pick up the pace more and more with each attempt. Find group exercise classes that motivate you to keep coming back. Take your bicycle out more frequently. Participate in recreational sports with other groups of people. Push yourself to be a more active person and create the best version of you.

"I run because if I did not, I would be sluggish and glum and spend too much time on the couch. I run to breathe the fresh air. I run to explore. I run to escape the ordinary. I run, to savor the trip along the way. Life becomes a little more vibrant, a little more intense. I like that." — Dean Karnazes, *Ultramarathon Man: Confessions of an All-Night Runner*

Gardening

"The single greatest lesson the garden teaches is that our relationship to the planet need not be zero-sum, and that as long as the sun still shines and people still can plan and plant, think and do, we can — if we bother to try — find ways to provide for ourselves without diminishing the world." — Michael Pollan, *The Omnivore's Dilemma*

Now is a better time than any to plant your own garden. While you restore nature in doing so, you also could save yourself from depression. An article written by Robyn Francis and published on the website for *Permaculture College Australia (permaculture.com.au)* reports, *"Getting our fingers dirty and harvesting our own food can trigger our natural production of 'happy chemicals' that suppress depression."* The article cites research revealing contact with soil, and a specific soil bacteria known as *mycobacterium vaccae*, triggers the release of serotonin in our brain. Serotonin is a neurotransmitter that acts as an anti-depressant and strengthens the immune system. A lack of this chemical has been linked to depression.

Every home should have a garden. In cities, rooftops of buildings could be equipped with gardens. Abandoned parking lots would be much more resourceful if they were transformed into gardens. Growing our own food is empowering in many ways. Not only are we connecting with nature, we are breaking free from the corporate dictators who are trying to monopolize the food chain. By gardening, we give back to the Earth. To complement having a garden we should also have compost piles, or food-waste bins for our food scraps. This minimizes our trash load.

"A garden should make you feel you have entered privileged space — a place not just set apart but reverberant — and it seems to me that, to achieve this, the gardener must put some kind of twist on the existing landscape, turn its prose into something nearer poetry." — Michael Pollan

When we decide to plant our own organic gardens, we guarantee that our food does not contain pesticides or other chemicals that deplete the neurotransmitters which are needed to fuel happiness. We also raise our

137

dopamine and serotonin levels. These two *happy chemicals* can free us from depression. In addition to creating vivacity, gardening rebuilds our top soil and contributes to a healthy environment. I urge you to make an attempt to get your own garden started. Create art with the space you dedicate to this project. Turn your garden into a masterpiece. Share your soul with this special piece of land. You will be rewarded as you do so.

"*My garden is my most beautiful masterpiece*" — Claude Monet

I also recommend placing house plants in each room of your home. I repeat this several times throughout the book for a reason. Filling your home with plants is adding life to materialism; you are providing living energy. You may discover that you are a much happier person by doing so.

Meditation

"*If every eight year old in the world is taught meditation, we will eliminate violence from the world within one generation.*" – Dalai Lama

I once witnessed a photo of a Buddha with a caption that read, "*Meditation: Because some questions cannot be answered by Google.*" In society today, it seems that we rely on *Google* and other search engines for answers to every question we have. Technology has gained control of our minds. To meditate, we have to shut down our computers, turn off our cell phones, and block out the anxiety, depression, struggles, and worries that are invading us. This becomes an antidote for the technological intrusion. We do not have to meditate all day, by simply meditating for thirty minutes daily, we can greatly improve our health, mood, and overall well-being.

According to a January 2014 study published online in the *Journal of American Medical Association (JAMA) Internal Medicine*, meditation appeared to provide as much relief from anxiety and depression as antidepressants were shown to provide in other studies. The study focused on forty-seven clinical trials performed through June 2013, and involved 3,515 participants. Using mindfulness meditation, they found evidence of improvement in symptoms of anxiety, depression, and pain, after subjects underwent what is typically an eight week meditation program. In a January 2012 study published in the *Cognitive and Behavioral Practice* journal, "*Mindfulness in the Treatment of Suicidal Individuals*," mindfulness meditation was found to show promise in reducing thoughts of suicide.

"*Mindfulness helps you go home to the present. And every time you go there and recognize a condition of happiness that you have, happiness comes.*" – Thich Nhat Hanh

I mention in step one how we often blame depression on biology. Well, there is evidence supporting the notion that meditation can alter our brain chemistry – relieving depression. In his book, *The Emotional Life of Your Brain (2012)*, Dr. Richard Davidson describes the biochemical interaction between the limbic system and the frontal lobes. Using functional MRI (fMRI) technology, Davidson demonstrated that *the left side of the frontal lobe – known as the left prefrontal cortex – tends to be more active when people*

138

express feelings of happiness. In contrast, the right side of the frontal lobe – the right prefrontal cortex – is more active when people feel sad. Based on these findings, he proposes, *"From learning what stimulates the left prefrontal cortex, we can then find ways to help people become happier."* He also suggests, *"By learning what slows the activity in the right prefrontal cortex, we can find ways to eliminate sadness."* In the book, Davidson provides studies showing that meditation strengthens the activity of the left prefrontal cortex, and reduces the activity in the right prefrontal cortex, making it a perfect remedy for depression.

To understand how meditation works in the body to relieve depression, I will reference to Murali Doraiswamy, a professor of psychiatry at *Duke University Medical Center*. He suggests, *"Some forms of meditation have been found to activate the parasympathetic nervous system, which stimulates the body's relaxation response, improves blood supply, slows down heart rate and breathing, and increases digestive activity. It also slows down the release of stress hormones, such as cortisol."* Dr. Doraiswamy recommends meditation for people with depression, panic or anxiety disorders, ongoing stress, or for general health maintenance of brain alertness and the cardiovascular system. If you are afflicted with anxiety, depression, or stress, I encourage you to practice meditation.

"The soil in which the meditative mind can begin is the soil of everyday life, the strife, the pain, and the fleeting joy. It must begin there, and bring order, and from there move endlessly. But if you are concerned only with making order, then that very order will bring about its own limitation, and the mind will be its prisoner. In all this movement you must somehow begin from the other end, from the other shore, and not always be concerned with this shore or how to cross the river. You must take a plunge into the water, not knowing how to swim. And the beauty of meditation is that you never know where you are, where you are going, what the end is." – Jiddu Krishnamurti

Being active does not always mean we have to exercise vigorously, it could also include meditating. Knowing that simple meditation can provide relief from depression, why is it that so few partake in this activity? In this step, we can begin practicing meditation. Try meditating for twenty minutes each morning, and again every evening. If you can, practice in nature. If this is not an option, as you clear your mind from clutter, technology, and worries, choose nature as a setting for your practice. Visualize yourself in a beautiful redwood forest, with no worries, away from stress and struggles. You could also play peaceful music in the background, listen to recorded sounds from nature, or follow guided meditations. Find a setting that is comfortable for you, and try to conquer the art of meditating. After practicing regularly, you will likely notice improvements in your life.

In addition to meditation, yoga is also known to be beneficial for relieving depression. If you can incorporate both meditation and yoga into your busy life, I guarantee you will find a calmer, more relaxed version of you. This will help reduce stress, eliminate anxiety, and generate happiness.

139

"To the mind that is still, the whole universe surrenders."
– Lao Tzu

Yoga

"Yoga is the martial art of the soul, and the opponent is the strongest you have ever faced: your ego."

Yoga provides us the opportunity to connect with inner peace, intention, and spiritual love. It is a chance to unite with nature and find harmony. Practicing yoga helps to cleanse of all deadening foods, negative thoughts, and slothful energy. Feelings of lethargy and unwanted emotions escape our bodies as we participate. Yoga simply works in tune with following a clean vegan diet rich in raw fruits and vegetables. It helps to align with nature and the vibe of our spirit, which can improve through a clean diet. Practicing yoga helps us to be more aware of our energy levels and to clear the mind of negativity. If you are not yet aware of who you are, this practice could help you discover your identity. If you still have not gained a relationship with nature, yoga is a perfect starting point.

A study published in the 2007 *Evidence-Based and Complementary Alternative Medicine* journal, *Yoga as a Complementary Treatment of Depression: Effects of Traits and Moods on Treatment Outcome*, found yoga to be a, *"Promising intervention for depression."* As a complementary treatment during the study, yoga was shown as being highly beneficial and an effective remedy to reduce depression, anger, and anxiety – as well as neurotic symptoms and low frequency heart rate variability. I am certain that some mental health *professionals* may not agree that yoga on its own has the power to heal psychiatric disorders, but most will recognize that yoga can be advantageous for reducing the symptoms of depression. The April 2010 *American Family Physician* journal published a review, *Exercise, Yoga, and Meditation for Depressive and Anxiety Disorders*, which found all three activities – exercise, yoga, and meditation – to be effective treatments for depression.

"Yoga is the unifying art of transforming dharma into action, be it through inspired thought, properly nurturing our children, a painting, a kindness or an act of peace that forever moves humanity forward." – Micheline Berry

Incorporating yoga into our life is an intelligent way to bring balance between body, mind, and spirit. There is always a place somewhere within each community where yoga is practiced. If you are having trouble locating a practice near you, there is the option of purchasing yoga DVDs, or participating from a live webstream in the comfort of your home.

When we change our diet, correct our attitude, cleanse internally, and start incorporating physical activity into our everyday lives, it is amazing how fast our sadness is transformed into glee. We discover there is little reason, if any, to resort to dangerous anti-depressants or other pills. A lifestyle change is the most powerful remedy. Now we can start expanding our intellect, picking up new hobbies, and exploring our talents.

The 6ᵗʰ Step: Gaining Substance

"Don't gain the world and lose your soul, wisdom is more powerful than any silver or gold." – Bob Marley

In the May 2013 *Morbidity and Mortality Weekly Report* – released by the *Centers for Disease Control and Prevention* – it is noted, from 1999-2010 there was a forty-nine percent increase in suicide rates among men aged fifty to fifty-nine, and a fifty-nine percent increase among women aged sixty to sixty-four. The *National Center for Health Statistics* reports, men aged sixty-five and older have the highest suicide rate of all age groups. As I comprehend these numbers, I concentrate on the correlation between the age groups of those most likely to commit suicide, and the average age for retirement. Statistics reveal people are more likely to lose their joy of living once they have retired.

The average person dedicates the first half of their lifespan chasing a simulated path to success. As children, we spend the majority of our days in synthetic buildings, being fed genetically-modified food, and drinking hormone and chemical-laden milk from another species, while we are educated to fit into a system that governs our economy. We are forced to leave our imaginary world of magic, mystery, and adventure, to prepare for *the real world*. In doing so, we disconnect from our true calling.

"Some people are afraid of what they might find if they try to analyze themselves too much, but you have to crawl into your wounds to discover where your fears are. Once the bleeding starts, the cleansing can begin." – Tori Amos

Bearing that we make it through the early education years without being afflicted with some type of serious illness from eating the deleterious foods we are served in school cafeterias, we continue with more education. Now we are driven to succeed. We follow the patterns of the system in place, and live with the impression that we must work to make a living, often leaving our dreams behind. We long for entitlement, fame, material wealth, money, and power. In order to pay for this education, we settle for less than ideal jobs, or take out loans we may not ever be capable of paying back, and between work and school, we have little or no time to nurture our emotional, mental, physical, or spiritual growth. Often we give up art, music, sports, and other talents or things we are passionate about to simply make a living. It becomes more important to have a better paying position, drive a fancier car, and live in a larger house.

Once the education process is complete, the time comes to immediately seek employment, and again we give up the freedom to nurture our personal growth by dedicating our time to proving we are *hard workers*, and are worthy of a pay raise or promotion. This pattern of working so we can afford to eat, live, and provide for our families takes over our lives, and as a consequence we live with no substance. We are evolving into a generation of men and women with weak character, who do very little to help better the world by instead choosing to spend the little free time we find drinking alcoholic beverages, dining out at overpriced restaurants, and looking to party. After twenty, thirty, forty, or fifty years of living this way, our health begins to fail from the habitual alcohol, drug, food chemical, and sugar abuse; we retire from the job which we devoted our lifespan to securing; and we suddenly crash. We realize the prime of our life has passed and we have nothing to show for it, aside from a nice house, fancy car, and poor health. We panic. We question why we did not take time to adventure, create art, draw, paint, play music, sing, spend time with those we love, travel, write books, or take care of our health. Now that our position of power and entitlement is expired, we have little substance that shapes the fabric of who we are. When there is no one left to impress with our house and car, we no longer see the value in owning them. Since our health is failing, we cannot travel the world as we always planned we would once retired. This facade of a happy retirement soon unravels into a disaster.

To prevent being a victim of the *retirement facade*, it is wise to establish a legacy for yourself beyond corporate affairs, ego, materialism, and work. The sixth step in Society's Anonymous is, *"We devote more time and energy to acquiring new talents, building character, expanding our intellect, nurturing our personal growth, and pursuing our passions. In doing so, we gain substance and establish a legacy."*

"I have come to believe that each of us has a personal calling that is as unique as a fingerprint and that the best way to succeed is to discover what you love and then find a way to offer it to others in the form of service, working hard, and also allowing the energy of the universe to lead you." – Oprah Winfrey

I am not recommending you to quit your job or lose your drive. What I want is for you to achieve balance. Do not let school and work prevent you from doing the things you truly enjoy. In this step, I encourage you to get involved. Volunteer and be active with organizations that are improving the planet and welfare of others for the sake of doing good, not merely to benefit your bank account or reputation. Acquire new talents. Find new hobbies you have fun with. Pick up a musical instrument. Learn a new language. This is your chance to build your character and gain substance so you do not become another statistic that gave up on life after retirement. Make sure you are alive during this lifetime.

"The real question is not whether life exists after death. The real question is whether you are alive before death." – Osho

Do you ever wonder how much more enjoyable life would be if only you had more money, more time, less stress, and less worry? Do you pass time at work each day waiting for your shift to expire, so you can lug your mind, and the sluggish body attached to it back to your comfortable home where you will eat, watch television, and fall asleep, only to wake and repeat the same schedule you have been controlled by for years? Do you think about your past and wish you had done certain things differently so you could be living a more abundant life in the present? Are there certain activities, events, hobbies, or talents you enjoy, possess, or would like to participate in, but find yourself too busy being bored, or dedicating your energy to a boss, company, or corporation so you opt to leave these entities which you enjoy out of your life? If the life you

142

lead derails you into a less than perfect reality, I challenge you to correct your perception. You are permitting yourself to be a person who never truly lives before they die. When you allow your thoughts to align with the entities that are supplanting voids in your life, this is a precursor to discontent.

We are trying to go above and beyond being normal. We each have the capacity to be extraordinary. Sometimes we simply do not tap the valuable resources we carry within. Ellen DeGeneres once said, *"Normal is getting dressed in clothes that you buy for work and driving through traffic in a car that you are still paying for – in order to get to the job you need, to pay for the clothes, the car, and the house you leave vacant all day so you can afford to live in it."* How is this to be considered living? To me, being normal is struggling while we sit on gold mines that could help us live more comfortable lives if we only thought to look beneath us, or to explore our surroundings more diligently. To mine our potential and make use of it, the only choice we have is to build our character and add substance to who we are.

"Empty pockets never held anyone back. Only empty heads and empty hearts can do that." – Norman Vincent Peale

What you are going to discover, if you have not already is money does open up opportunities for us, however it cannot buy us happiness. Real wealth comes in the form of knowledge. We cannot acquire this knowledge in public school systems, textbooks, or through mainstream media outlets. True knowledge is embedded in us through experience. For every struggle, hardship, and loss we are confronted with, or each generous act, loving gesture, and heartfelt intention we release from our being, we gain truth and understanding. Sometimes depression is a direct result of confusing quantity with abundance. If you have a head full of wisdom and truth, you have more than the man who has too many numbers on his bank account balance and drives his ego around in fancy cars while stuffing himself with unhealthy foods, and seeking to impress as many women or men as possible with his emptiness. I am encouraging you to allow your drive to be stimulated by your passions, not money or income. You will build a more appreciative foundation for your life.

"Many people die with their music still in them. Why is this so? Too often it is because they are always getting ready to live. Before they know it, time runs out." – Oliver Wendell Holmes

We all have a song that is harvesting inside of us. Too often our pineal gland is closed from calcification, so we cannot recognize the words. We lose the rhythm. This gland closes from food chemicals, fluoride in the water supply, negative thoughts, and poor lifestyle decisions. Now that we have cleansed and experienced our spiritual awakening, we can share this music with society. We are free to live away from negativity. We can branch out and expand. We deepen our character. We broaden our values. In this step, we define our legacy – what others will remember us for. We do our part to make the world a better place than it was before our birth. These are the fundamentals of gaining substance. This is an opportunity for us to discover our purpose and use it to improve society.

"One thing I want to tell you is that you are a unique individual with a specific purpose in life and if you do not live that purpose you will have a constant gnawing stress eating you away on the inside. This stress is a foundation of human disease. It is the consequence of not living our life purpose. As part of the natural world we are governed by its laws. The amount of disease we see in the world today is a consequence of being out of harmony with those laws. No matter what we do, no matter how powerful we consider the blocks, no matter how strong the resistance, no matter how conditioned and molded we have become, unless we uncover and become the embodiment of our life purpose, our mission, our destiny, we deny ourselves access to the deep abiding peace within that is a natural consequence of being in harmony with Life. This wonderful inner peace is the basis of health, prosperity, happiness and optimal creative expression. We call it Living In Natural Magic." – Nick Good

Acquiring New Talents & Hobbies

"Life is painful. It has thorns, like the stem of a rose. Culture and art are the roses that bloom on the stem. The flower is yourself, your humanity. Art is the liberation of the humanity inside yourself." – Daisaku Ikeda

Talent is another word for intelligence. If we are exceptionally good at something, this means we possess an amazing ability to learn, or acquire technique. To be talented, you do not have to be a famous artist, athlete, or musician. Most importantly, you retain qualities others are inspired by. Something as simple as showing kindness to all people is an admirable talent. Other talents include the skill of loving others unconditionally even when they do not express love to you; always being friendly; extending compassion to people who appear less fortunate or to those who are hateful and mean; leading by example and staying true to your morals and values; having the competence to verbalize your feelings to others; maintaining courage and strength while facing adversity; or speaking publicly. Many of these character traits are rare, and if you carry them, you are definitely talented.

By simply seeking out new hobbies, we may stumble across an activity we are passionate about and this could become a talent. If you are unsure about what talents you may be harboring, simply ask family or friends. Once you decide on them, start practicing. Read articles and books about them. Do what you must to attract these talents into your life. If you feel like you may be passionate about art, join an art class or take free lessons online (*jerrysartarama.com*). If you desire to learn the guitar, there are several free lessons on *YouTube*, or you can access Justin Sandercoe's webpage where he offers free lessons (*justinguitar.com*). If you have a nice voice and think you would benefit from voice lessons, you can also find free lessons online from Justin Stoney of the *New York Vocal Coaching* school (*voicelessonstotheworld.com*). There are even piano lessons online at no charge (*zebrakeys.com*). Personally, I was never the best dancer. For some reason, I never found a passion for it. I took lessons with my mother on a

144   Jacoby

couple of occasions, but still never picked it up. Recently I discovered free lessons online (*learntodance.com*). There are so many options, and as humans we are naturally inclined to learning new things. There is no reason why we should not take advantage of all the world has to offer.

"Every artist was first an amateur." – Ralph Waldo Emerson

Whatever your new hobbies may be, whether they are beekeeping, birdwatching, bowling, chess, cooking, dance, diving, drawing, extreme sports, gardening, hiking, knitting, martial arts, modeling, mountain biking, painting, permaculture, photography, preparing raw food, reading, recreational sports, veganism, or writing – make time for them in your life, and be patient. You cannot expect to be a master at any of these activities overnight. Most often when we start including new leisurely happenings into our lives, we meet new people who share similar interests. This is how positive friendships are born.

"Your life is not worth anything until you do something that challenges your reality." – Morgan Freeman

Character Building

"Be more concerned with your character than your reputation, because your character is what you really are, while your reputation is merely what others think you are." – John Wooden

Character can be defined as, *"The mental and moral qualities distinctive to an individual."* At the *Josephson Institute Center for Youth Ethics* (*charactercounts.org*), children are taught the *Six Pillars of Character*. These include Trustworthiness, Respect, Responsibility, Fairness, Caring, and Citizenship. For us to be trustworthy, we should be honest at all times; loyal to our friends, family, and loved ones; and always follow through with what we say we are going to do. To be treated with respect, we follow the *Golden Rule* and live as reflections of the way we treat others around us. As responsible individuals, we emanate self-discipline, hold ourselves accountable for our actions, and set good examples in doing so. Fairness is associated with being open minded, always hearing both sides, and giving everyone a chance. To be caring, we should be kind, compassionate, and genuine. Finally, citizenship requires that we obey our conscience, and get involved in the community. By learning these foundations of character, we establish morals and values.

"To educate a person in the mind but not in morals is to educate a menace to society." – Theodore Roosevelt

One thing I take pride in is being honest. In my writings I deliver the truth. When I share information with other people, I am open with them and I do not hold back. In doing so, I feel like my intentions are pure. I aim to live my life in a fashion where I could leave my door open, windows up, and have someone watch my every move and I would not have to hide a thing. When we cleanse the negativity away from our lives so we can claim the same attitude, the feeling is indescribable.

"Character, the willingness to accept responsibility for one's own life, is the source from which self-respect springs." – Joan Didion, *On Self-Respect*

You can determine a lot about someone by observing how disciplined they are and examining whether or not they take responsibility for their actions. Most pessimistic people will blame others for their problems, and shift this negativity towards everyone around them. If you catch yourself being this way, please practice optimism. Remember, the best way to solve a problem is to handle it to the best of your ability without bringing other people down in the process.

"You can easily judge the character of a man by how he treats those who can do nothing for him." – Johann Wolfgang von Goethe

Although I am not rich – or even close to being considered rich in monetary value – I often donate money to organizations that are improving the planet. Some of these include, *Cofan Survival Fund, EarthSave, EarthFirst, EPIC, In Defense of Animals, International Anti-Poaching Foundation, Mercy for Animals, PETA, Save America's Forests, Save the Redwoods, Sea Shepherd*, and *Survival International*. I also find myself sending donations to artists and musicians who are out traveling the world and could use extra money to eat and survive. I do this because I want to see them succeed. I support these artists and organizations because they are using the funds to do good things. Most of the charities we commonly donate money to these days are fraudulent, and are using the money to fuel greed. Cancer walks and pink ribbon scams are a part of the problem. That money being donated is not going to a cancer cure, but rather it is going to creating more drugs that make the cancer worse. Please read, *The Raw Cure: Healing Beyond Medicine*, to learn more. Choose carefully which organizations you donate to. Most of the health-related charities are doing nothing to help.

I spent years in the *Big Brothers, Big Sisters* program helping children who were in need of male role models in their lives. I volunteered my energy and heart to this program because I expect these children to grow up and return the favor to other children. Leading by example is the best way to share kindness and speak truth. I do not expect anything in return when I do good deeds, but I cannot deny the good vibrations I feel, and positivity that is attached. Treat everyone with love and respect even when they may not return the gesture. You will be much happier this way.

"Money simply makes you more of what you already are. If you are a well-intentioned human being, money will magnify that." – Jordan Belfort, *The Wolf on Wall St.*

To strengthen your character, you must break out of your shell, adventure, and take risks. Get out in nature. Be bold. Help others. Do things that take you out of your comfort zone, and force yourself to struggle a little to find your way back. Use your life as a powerful message that will resonate well with others.

"Character cannot be developed in ease and quiet. Only through experience of trial and suffering can the soul be strengthened, vision cleared, ambition inspired, and success achieved." – Helen Keller

Expanding Our Intellect

"A good head and a good heart are always a formidable combination. But when you add to that a literate tongue or pen, then you have something very special." – Nelson Mandela

As we strengthen our character, and build a solid foundation, education is one of the fibers that binds the roots. Taking courses on topics we are passionate about allows us to venture more freely into our purpose. Reading books can increase our understanding of the concepts related to these topics. There are two websites that offer free college courses from universities and institutions all over the world. They are *coursera.org*, and *edx.org*. Knowing you have an opportunity to build your knowledge-base and absorb the information you are seeking at no charge is worthy of embrace. Please take advantage of this option.

"The more that you read, the more things you will know. The more that you learn, the more places you will go." – Dr. Seuss, *I Can Read With My Eyes Shut!*

In addition to expanding our knowledge with classes, it would be advantageous for us to pick up a new language. By learning a second language, we also learn another culture. We can then communicate worldly. Statistics show, a child who learns to speak in a bilingual household has a greater capacity to resolve internal conflicts. In the September 2012 issue of *Cerebrum* journal, a study, *The Cognitive Benefits of Being Bilingual*, examined Spanish-English bilinguals. The scientists – led by the neuropsychologist Tamar Gollan of the *University of California*, San Diego – found individuals with a higher degree of bilingualism, measured through a comparative evaluation of proficiency in each language, were more resistant than others to the onset of dementia and other symptoms of Alzheimer's disease. They discovered the higher the degree of bilingualism, the later the age of onset. On *duolingo.com*, you can learn a new language for free. The software is said to be more effective than *Rosetta Stone* or *Instant Immersion*.

"Some people think only intellect counts: knowing how to solve problems, knowing how to get by, knowing how to identify an advantage and seize it. But the functions of intellect are insufficient without courage, love, friendship, compassion, and empathy." — Dean Koontz

If we want to climb higher up life's ladder and explore new horizons, education is important. The good news is we can teach ourselves by reading books and researching, taking courses at institutes or universities, or even online. Remember, people do not grow old. When they stop growing, they become old. Every day, each of us should grow. Whether it is spiritually, emotionally, or in accordance with the cosmos and laws of nature, we must blossom. As we infuse our brain with knowledge, we can also practice being caring, compassionate, loving, and supportive.

"A room without books is like a body without a soul." – Cicero

Pursuing Our Passions & Leaving A Legacy

"Our lives are mere flashes of light in an infinitely empty universe. In twelve years of education the most important lesson I have learned is that what we see as 'normal' living is truly a travesty of our potential. In a society so governed by superficiality, appearances, and petty economics, dreams are more real than anything in the 'real world.' Refuse normalcy. Beauty is everywhere, love is endless, and joy bleeds from our everyday existence. Embrace it. I love all of you, all my friends, family, and community. I am ceaselessly grateful from the bottom of my heart for everyone. The only thing I can ask of you is to stay free of materialism. Remember that every day contains a universe of potential; exhaust it. Live and love so immensely that when death comes there is nothing left for him to take. Wealth is love, music, sports, learning, family and freedom. Above all, stay gold." — Dominic Owen Mallary

In this fast-paced world where we have been manipulated into working our lives away hoping we will retire rich at an old age, we have left our passions inside of the childhood homes we were raised in that have now been bulldozed to the ground. We are forgetting we each have a magical child within us that needs to be nurtured, loved, and stimulated. We hide from our beauty by covering up with Botox treatments, cosmetics, and surgeries. We all want to *fit in* so badly that we forget we were born in the most abundant, accepting, beautiful entity known as nature. We simply fight our way out of happiness as we chase materialism and superficiality. This resistance, and our urge to get away from who we really are fuels depression.

"The saddest people I have ever met in life are the ones who do not care deeply about anything at all. Passion and satisfaction go hand in hand, and without them, any happiness is only temporary, because there is nothing to make it last." — Nicholas Sparks, *Dear John*

To pursue our passions, it helps to practice them. We nurture our spirit by keeping them attached. This is why I encourage you to acquire new talents and expand your intellect. None of these materials we thrive for will remain with us for the duration of our spiritual journey called life. What we should go after then is knowledge, and elevation of consciousness. It never hurts to embrace the items we truly cannot lose.

"He is no fool, who gives up what he cannot keep, to gain what he cannot lose." — Jim Elliot

What defines you? Is it your character, or your job title? Is it your fancy car, nice house, designer clothing, and social status; or is it your art, creativity, love, and passion? Do you attract others into your life through your appearance, or are they drawn to you simply from the energy you exude? Are you living to please others, or is your life pleasing you? Are you happy with how you manage your time each day; or do you feel like work, school, or other activities and events are consuming all of your hours? Who is the person you want others to see when they glance your way? What is your legacy? To be fulfilled with happiness, we should have answers for each of these questions.

Remember, the main focus in this step is adding substance to who we are – away from work, school, and our professional lives – by utilizing our talents, exploring our hobbies and interests, adventuring the world, embracing our imagination, forgetting the illusion that we need to impress everyone around us, and pursuing the opportunity to bring out our true identity. We want to be remembered for something other than our cars, houses, and net worth. Our mission is to define our legacy.

"We can make it a saner and happier world if we slow down and have less focus on wanting or needing more stuff. If stuff made you happy, there would be nothing but happy people living in Bel Air, and unhappy people living in Fiji, where they have nothing. I have been to Fiji, and there are plenty of happy people there. I have never seen a hearse with a luggage rack on top. We have got to get away from stuff and appreciate what is here." – Ed Begley Jr., *Environmental activist and actor*

There was a man named Earl Manigualt – nicknamed *The Goat*. He grew up in Harlem during the *sixties* and *seventies*. He is still a legend to this day for his signature move on the basketball court known as, *The double dunk*. He would dunk the ball, catch it with his left hand, switch the ball to his right hand, bring it back around to the top of the basket and jam it through again – all done while still in the air on a single jump, and without hanging on the rim. While some people remember him for that move, his amazing leaping ability, and his basketball skills; his legacy will remain a mystery to future generations because he never utilized his talent and used it to elevate to the next level. He got sucked into the Harlem street life, struggled with addiction to heroin, and spent his life in and out of prison. His legacy though, did not end there. He cleaned himself up later in life, after acknowledging he did indeed have power and control over this inanimate object – being heroin – and he devoted the remainder of his days on Earth transforming abandoned lots into playgrounds, and teaching kids how to play the game of basketball.

I reference to *The Goat* because his story is a perfect example of a life that took unexpected turns, and a talent that was not fully utilized, but of a passion that always remained until the end. He struggled through the prime of his life, suffered some of the worst pain imaginable, and still reclaimed his legacy before he passed.

We do not have to struggle any longer. We should not accept pain into our lives. We can start building our legacy today, at this very moment, by adding substance to who we are.

"I was born with music inside me. Music was one of my parts. Like my ribs, my kidneys, my liver, my heart. Like my blood. It was a force already within me when I arrived on the scene. It was a necessity for me – like food or water." – Ray Charles

When you have a talent, skill, athletic ability, or anything you feel is a part of you, that completes you, it should be your duty to never let it go. If you have certain hobbies you can no longer enjoy, or interests you feel like you will never get a chance to explore, then you may need to assess some critical components of your life – beginning with time management – and allow

149

yourself the opportunity to engage in these activities. As the Zen saying goes: *"You should meditate for thirty minutes every day. If you do not have thirty minutes, then meditate for an hour."* If you are too busy to pick up the guitar, take piano lessons, learn to speak another language, get involved in the community, learn a craft, or do something that will help you gain substance, then you need to make time. If your job is keeping you from doing the things you love most, consider that you are allowing it to do so. You have accepted a position that is trapping you in the wage economy.

Whether we are at the executive level – in a position of power – running the show, or chasing our way to the top of the corporate ladder, there is something meaningful that many of us too often disdain giving thought to. Sooner or later we will have to retire and move on. When that day comes, what will be our next move? Once our life expires, we will be remembered by our legacy. What will yours be? If you cannot answer these questions with confidence and certainty, and you have not mapped out your future, today is a good day to figure it out and get started. Create a vision board. Find pictures of the things you desire, the places you would like to travel to, the people you always want in your life, those things you are passionate about, and your hobbies and interests; and make a collage out of them on a poster board. Hang it up on a wall somewhere in your home or office where you can always see it, and manifest these things into your life. The last thing you want to do is retire empty, lonely, and unhappy.

We are now ready to move on to step seven where we shift the focus to who we communicate with – our sphere of influence – and what kind of an impact we are allowing them to have on our dharma, or purpose in life.

"So many people walk around with a meaningless life. They seem half-asleep, even when they are busy doing things they think are important. This is because they are chasing the wrong things. The way you get meaning into your life is to devote yourself to loving others, devote yourself to your community around you, and devote yourself to creating something that gives you purpose and meaning." – Morrie Schwartz

The 7th Step: Acknowledging our Sphere of Influence

> Surround yourself with the dreamers and the doers, the believers and thinkers, but most of all, surround yourself with those who see greatness within you, even when you don't see it yourself.

As Edmund Lee explains in this quotation above, it is important for us to be aware of who we associate with, and how their presence has an influence on us. There are going to be three types of people who are brought into our lives. Those who bring us joy and happiness, those who we can tolerate in moderation, and those who bring us down. Our job is to do our best to keep those who bring us joy around as much as possible; the ones who balance us out in moderation; and to remove the ones who bring us down permanently, or more appropriately, help them to change. Sometimes the people who bring us down the most are family members, friends, or loved ones. It can be challenging to leave them behind, but if we are hurting ourselves more by hanging on to them, we have to accept that they are not worthy of keeping around. Refusing to let them go is simply taking from who we are and lessening our chances of establishing peace of mind.

The seventh step in Society's Anonymous is, *"We acknowledge our sphere of influence and choose our friends and companions wisely. We understand that many people will enter our lives, but we have the authority to distinguish between the positive and negative. As we filter through our contacts, we recognize those who we want to keep around, and we let go of the ones who bring us down. We accept that we simply cannot climb out of despair by remaining attached to people who enable our depression."*

I am confident that you have heard the phrase *guilty by association*. A guilty feeling relates to having done something we know was not morally acceptable, or clinging to the perception that we did something wrong. Being guilty by association applies to when we personally abide by good ethics, morals, and values, but we go wrong by choosing to associate with people who are guilty of possessing poor character and committing unlawful acts. A perfect example is the film, *Guilt By Association* – which is inspired by a true story. The movie is about a single mother named Susan Walker who moves in with her new boyfriend, and unbeknownst to her, he is selling drugs. After their home gets raided, she is sentenced to a twenty year mandatory-minimum sentence for her small involvement. She then has to fight to prove her innocence and regain control of her life. Things like this do happen.

We are judged by the company we keep, so we can easily be viewed as guilty because of our association with wrongdoers. Therefore, it is important for us to be aware of their intentions, choose to interact with positive people, and cling to those who smile frequently and radiate positivity. If we are depressed, there is a good chance we could be guilty of associating with others who are also feeling discontent. As Lao Tzu states, *"Highly evolved people use their consciousness as pure law."* If you feel that the energy is not favorable, or that someone may be belittling your ambitions, let them go. If you know a situation is not right, avoid it at all costs. I have experience with guilt by association and I am a better person today for sticking to my core instincts and values, and deciding to broaden my sphere of influence.

Awareness

"Keep away from people who try to belittle your ambitions. Small people always do that, but the really great ones make you feel that you too can become great." – Mark Twain

This step is often challenging, especially for those of us who are trying to walk a new path. We are so comfortable in our old shoes that we can easily revert back to scavenging the same dirt roads and following the trails we are familiar with. If we grow up around a group of friends, and when we enter adulthood they are still behaving the way we did as adolescents, we have to be aware of the likelihood that they are never going to change. If a family member constantly berates us, hurts us, or puts us down, we have to find a way out from the abuse. There is always an escape if we truly know in our hearts that we need revision. Sometimes we simply need to be brave and walk away if we want to step into a new adventure, pursue our passions, and fulfill our destiny. We cannot go about embracing this change if certain people we are associating with are holding us back. It takes courage to break free and make the decision that we are going to do something more with our lives. I challenge you to be authentic, courageous, and driven to succeed.

Once you take the steps necessary for creating your new life, often your family and friends will notice how successful and happy you have become, and they will follow your lead. This way you do not have to remove these people permanently from your life, but rather, you take a break, correct yourself, and invite them to also embrace change. You turn those who bring you down into motivators for improving your well-being.

Jacoby

You will know which types of people you want to associate with because when you are around them, you feel comfortable, happy, and at peace. Even when you are feeling low, they will stimulate good vibes within. Positive people deliver cheerful energy that is recognizable in their appearance. Their eyes are clear, skin glows, and they smile big. As you awaken your happiness, correct your attitude, and seek like-minded friends, you will notice that your personality becomes a magnet for attracting other jubilant people like yourself.

Positive People

"Anybody can be unhappy. We can all be hurt. You do not have to be poor to need something or somebody. Rednecks, hippies, misfits—we are all the same. Gay or straight? So what? It does not matter to me. We have to be concerned about other people, regardless." – Willie Nelson

No matter where we descend from, or from which walk of life we emerge, we all cherish affection, value good friendships, and yearn for companionship. We need positive people in our lives. Being around others who are happy stimulates radiance and excellence. A positive person will accept us for who we are. They look past mistakes, stereotypes, and wrongdoings. They help us evolve into leaders. They cherish our uniqueness. They are examples of who we want to be associating with.

"Eyes are the mirror of the soul. One of the most difficult things in the world is to express a positive soul through a negative personality and eyes express personality. When we have a positive personality, we are in control of life." – Dr. Norman Walker

You will know a positive person when you look them in the eyes. They emanate truth. They express an enlightened soul. You will feel welcome around them and their presence will comfort you. Positive people are compassionate, loving, and optimistic. They are grateful for everything. They seek out new opportunities and possibilities for themselves and their friends. They smile a lot, communicate well, and refuse to play the role of the victim looking for pity. When we are positive, we are concerned about our friends and family, and we extend good fortunes their way. We convert sadness to joy.

Negative people tend to bring us down. They live in fear of the unknown. They blame others, are stuck in their limitations, and dwell over the past. Sometimes, they may not intend to harm us, but they do. Some parents or grandparents act as if they want their child or grandchild to succeed, but all too often when these kids start finding success away from home, or they find opportunities that make them happy in a new environment, they try to shift them towards a different path that will keep them close to home. This is an example of a situation where we would choose to walk away in order to preserve our happiness. We only want happy people in our lives. If we notice that someone we love is not happy, we can work with them to help them correct their attitude and perception, improve their diet, cleanse internally, and connect with nature, but we cannot let their depression fuel ours. If it does, we have to let go and walk away.

Success Measures

Our sphere of influence has an impact on how others perceive us, and also plays a role in how we blossom and mature through life. In the landmark book, *Think and Grow Rich*, Napoleon Hill suggests that if we take the top ten most influential people in our lives and average out their salaries, this will give us an approximation of how much our salary should be. His idea is that the more successful our friends and family are, the more successful we will be. I want to take this a step further and shift away from the monetary value attached to the people in our sphere of influence, and see how their attitudes and beliefs impact us. What if we take the ten most influential people in our lives and average out their overall levels of happiness? Judging from how happy those we associate with are, we can get an idea for how happy we will be. We determine whether we are happy or sad in our choice of friends and companions, and who we idolize or look up to. It is imperative that we choose wisely who these ten influential people will be.

"The best way to become a person that others are drawn to, is to develop qualities that we are attracted to in others." – John C. Maxwell

As you live your life, think about what kind of person you would have to be in order for your friends and family to place you on their list of the ten most influential people in their lives. You will need to be accepting, affectionate, caring, charming, communicative, compassionate, driven, encouraging, friendly, happy, inspiring, loving, motivating, optimistic, respectful, successful, and trustworthy. Live each day developing these qualities. Lead by example. Build relationships with people so they can always rely on you to feel good. Turn yourself into a person that others idolize. You want to set the standard for excellence and positivity. This can be reflective of your attitude, character, diet, and lifestyle you lead. If each of us will embrace the lessons in this book, and we carry these components with us into everyday life, we can inspire the change that we wish to see in this world.

"Some of the biggest challenges in relationships come from the fact that most people enter a relationship in order to get something: they are trying to find someone who is going to make them feel good. In reality, the only way a relationship will last is if you see your relationship as a place that you go to give, and not a place that you go to take." – Anthony Robbins

As we progress into the eighth step, we pay close attention to the understanding that we each have a purpose in life. The feelings that we generate as a result of living stem from our actions, food choices, perceptions, and thoughts. We cannot live only to make others happy, we must do what we enjoy to satisfy our heartfelt desires within.

The 8ᵗʰ Step: Living Without Expectations

"We are raised on comparison; our education is based on it, so is our culture. So we struggle to be someone other than who we are." – Jiddu Krishnamurti

I admire anyone who goes above and beyond normalcy, discovers their passions, breaks free from limitations and restrictions, and lives the duration of their life doing exactly what they want to do. I have passed up so many opportunities to be somebody else in my lifetime, that I finally had to settle for being no one other than myself. I have had countless numbers of opportunities to be successful – doing things I simply do not enjoy. I worked a corporate job, climbed the rungs of the ladder to the top, got pretty high up, then decided this was not for me. I gave up a pretty significant salary in doing so. The reason why I am not financially well-off today, or living in an oceanfront home driving a fancy car, is because I will not sell my character to the highest bidder. I want to be a man of substance. I want to continue my pursuit to learn, travel the world, and appreciate the simple, still treasures of nature. Many of us struggle with this battle. It takes a lot of courage, discipline, and strength to depart from the expectations that have been placed on us, branch out on our own, and find success.

The eighth step in Society's Anonymous is, *"We reach a breaking point where we decide that we no longer want to live life for our friends, guardians, loved ones, or parents. At this moment of change, we begin living to satisfy our needs, keep our children happy, and to accomplish personal goals. This is our chance to break away from the boundaries, limitations, and restrictions that expectations have bottled us up in. We can now free our minds from the mental prison that has been holding us back, and follow a path that leads to happiness, health, and success."*

I have watched too many friends permit their parents and grandparents to control their future by living life according to their expectations and standards. This is not right. I have friends who allow their fans to dictate their actions because they want to please them. I have seen relationships go sour because of jealousy, and one person attempting to change the others life. Let us be honest, not one of us wants to live our life as a shadow of someone else. I do not care how wonderful that person is. To emerge as leaders and find our true identity, we have to be ourselves. Too often we choose careers based from what our parents want for us. We decide on a college that they think is best for us. We make decisions growing up that stem from their acceptance of each action. At times we may do things that go against our morals and values for the sake of pleasing and satisfying others. Living according to expectations that restrict us – or shape us in an unfavorable way – stirs up depressive symptoms, and frankly, it brings us down. Growing up, I did my best to be a trendsetter, and I avoided following others footsteps. We all have the capacity to set trends, and let our uniqueness blossom.

"To be beautiful means to be yourself. You do not need to be accepted by others, you need to accept yourself." – Thich Nhat Hanh

155

When I was a kid, a man approached my mother and father, pointed at me, and said, *"That boy will be a millionaire one day."* After this encounter, I always held on to that expectation. I started doing everything I could to try to make money. By the age of eleven, I spent hours in the library reading books on how to accumulate wealth. None of this paid off for me. I wish I would have spent that time researching and reading about some of the many things I am passionate about today. Sometimes expectations can lead us astray and take us further away from our calling. The wise choice is to follow our dreams and go after what interests us, not what our father wants for us, our mother expects from us, or what we think will make us the most money.

"My mother said to me, 'If you become a soldier, you will be a general. If you become a monk, you will end up as a pope.' Instead, I chose to be a painter, and I wound up as Picasso." – Pablo Picasso

As parents, our actions can play a huge role in our children's development. There are safe ways to encourage our kids to do things that we know will lead them to success, and there are ineffective ways that can be dangerous. The famous physician and author, Deepak Chopra, shared the story of how his father motivated him to become a doctor. A young Deepak wanted to be a writer when he grew up, and literature fascinated him. His father knew that becoming a doctor would pave a successful road for him, so he started buying him important pieces of literature written by other doctors and physicians. He used this technique to persuade him that as a doctor he will write books that are more credible. Deepak is now a very successful author, doctor, and leader who helps thousands of people around the world find their purpose in life.

Albert Einstein once said, *"The principle art of the teacher is to awaken the joy in creation and knowledge."* As parents we are teachers. Our actions deeply influence our children's thought patterns and play a role in shaping their future. By means of encouragement, we inspire confidence in them. To fuel their creativity and desire to learn, we should lead them in the right direction, but not tell them what they should expect to find. We must nourish them with healthy organic plant-based meals, and spoil them with love and affection. This is how we raise beautiful, creative, and intelligent families. We should not teach our kids cruelty, hatred, racism, or separation. We must refrain from forcing our views on them, and instead opt to let them be free-minded, and demonstrate this freedom by loving them unconditionally. Make time for your children. Learn with them. Get involved with their schooling and education. The youth of today will determine the level of happiness in society tomorrow.

"If you hate your parents, the man, or the establishment, do not show them up by getting wasted and wrapping your car around a tree. If you really want to rebel against your parents, outlearn them, outlive them, and know more than they do." – Henry Rollins

I am fortunate to have loving parents. There are many things they do however, which infuriate me with a desire to succeed. I feel like sometimes I cannot pass information along to them by simply repeating it to them over and

Jacoby

over, so I speak it in my actions. I live a pure life. I practice what I preach. I use my character and individuality as a statement. I feed on knowledge. The reason I do so is because I am not seeking to be right, I only want them to be more aware, health-conscious, positive, and self-empowering. If you feel suffocated by your parents, do not hurt yourself to despise them. Build your character and strengthen your will to demonstrate in your actions the changes you wish to see in them.

Mental Prison

"Lock up your libraries if you like; but there is no gate, no lock, no bolt that you can set upon the freedom of my mind." – Virginia Woolf
     As I dabbled with depression over the years, I noticed a reoccurring pattern. The more restricted I was, the more depressed I would feel. My mind was confined in fear, stress, and worry that was always attached to how others would perceive me, expectations they placed on me, and financial obligations. In a sense, I was a slave to acceptance and money. I locked myself in a mental prison. In today's world where accurate information, and books that reveal things to us that some people do not want us to know are being suppressed, we can all agree that we have had experience with this mental confinement. We are prisoners to an economic system that is stealing our dignity, individuality, passion, and pride by forcing us to work an exhausting amount of hours each week simply so we can afford to survive. This is dulling the joys of living.
     "Mental slavery is the worst form of slavery. It gives you the illusion of freedom, as you trust, love, and defend your oppressor, all while making an enemy of those who are trying to free you or open your eyes." – Miss Fiyah
     We all live under the guise of freedom, yet if we quit our jobs, and go after what we truly enjoy, there is a chance we will face severe consequences for our actions. We must pay for energy, shelter, and water. To fulfill these financial obligations, it requires that we are employed. This repeats the cycle of working long hours to simply eat, live, and survive. The uncertainty attached to walking away from our old life often inhibits us from proceeding. In Society's Anonymous, I am not encouraging you to quit your job, or revolt against the system in place, I am only asking that you free yourself from this mental prison. We cannot allow thoughts or worries to limit us. We can grow our own food. We can learn skills and acquire new talents that help others. We can live in communes that will reduce our financial obligations. We can start communities where we do not rely on corporations, but rather, we all contribute to building artistic gardens that will feed everyone around us. This will make fast food and processed foods obsolete. We can penetrate the abundance in simplicity. We do not need fancy cars, high-paying jobs, or large homes to be truly happy. We need good health, laughter, and love.
     "If you always put limits on everything you do, physical or anything else, it will spread into your work, and into your life. There are no limits, there are only plateaus. You must not stay there. You must go beyond them." – Bruce Lee

To find your inner child and let the best version of you blossom, it is important to remove all limitations. If you are in a situation where this seems impossible, try meditating and practice yoga. Channel your emotions through exercise. Hug the trees. Do something kind for someone you do not know. To be truly happy, we have to diminish boundary lines and follow our calling.

Follow Your Own Path

"If you believe in what you are doing, then let nothing hold you up in your work. Much of the best work of the world has been done against seeming impossibilities." – Dale Carnegie

Not many things inspire me more than seeing or reading about young minds who are pursuing their passions and using them to promote positive change in the world. Elif Bilgin is a sixteen year old from Turkey who won the 2013 *Science In Action* award at the *Google Science Fair*. Her invention is a bioplastic that is made from banana peels. This could eventually be used to replace petroleum-based plastics, and ultimately save the oceans. Most of us are unaware of the fact that there is a ten-to-one plastic to phytoplankton ratio in the oceans today, and in some areas of the Pacific, there is a seventy-to-one plastic to phytoplankton ratio. Without marine phytoplankton, this planet will perish. Eighty to ninety percent of the oxygen on land comes from the plankton in the oceans. Elif is following her own path and also doing her part to save this beautiful planet.

At the age of nineteen, Boyan Slat (*boyanslat.com*) unveiled his plans to create an *Ocean Cleanup Array* that he claims could remove up to 7,250,000 tons of plastic waste from the world's oceans. This device consists of an anchored network of floating booms and processing platforms. The concept would span the radius of a plastic patch in the ocean, act as a giant funnel, and then the angle of the booms would force plastic in the direction of the platforms, where it would be separated from plankton, filtered, and stored for recycling. The plastic waste could then be dispatched to garbage patches around the world. Boyan was inspired by the idea after diving in Greece. He noticed more plastic bags than fish, and wondered, *"Why can't we clean this up?"* This motivated him to dedicate half a year of research to identifying the sources of plastic pollution and the problems associated with cleaning it up. His research led him to this clean-up project which he presented at the *TEDxDelft* in 2012. This same year, the *Ocean Cleanup Array* was awarded *Best Technical Design* at the *Delft University of Technology*. Boyan Slat has been recognized as one of the twenty *Most Promising Young Entrepreneurs Worldwide* (Intel EYE50).

The reason why Elif and Boyan both found success at a young age is because they acted on their passions. They spent a vast amount of time and energy researching and finding ways to manifest their ideas into strategies for implementing change. They are following their own path, and not allowing other people to influence or dictate how they choose to live their lives. In this step, we are encouraged to start shifting our passions away from what other people expect of us, and to set our focus on what drives our happiness. You will notice that the more you do to help empower others, or to save wildlife and improve the environment, the happier you will be.

"Be yourself; everyone else is already taken." — Oscar Wilde

It is easy to look up to others and admire them for what they have accomplished. We each have idols and heroes who we draw inspiration from. Throughout my life, the person I idolized most was Nelson Mandela. In fact, one of the first non-fiction books that I read was his autobiography, *The Long Walk To Freedom*. He was an advocate for freedom and eventually became the President of South Africa. He lived through the *Apartheid* regime — which was similar to the *Civil Rights Movement* here in the United States. As a political prisoner, Mandela spent twenty-seven years locked up for his outspoken passions, and for his desire to see his people freed from the injustices they were facing. As someone who I looked up to, I understood the difference between wanting to be like him, and embracing some of his morals, qualities, and values. I have no interest in becoming the President. What I idolized in him was his determination to succeed, intelligence, positive attitude, undying passion, will to never give up, and wisdom. I acquired some of these qualities from familiarizing myself with his character. I think it is important for us all to have idols, however we should be able to distinguish between what sets us apart from them. We should not attempt to copy those we look up to, or follow their footsteps. We can pick up pieces from each idol, and use these new acquisitions to solidify our individuality. As you begin living your life without expectations, find idols or heroes of your own, then absorb the qualities from them that you admire, and use them to build the ideal version of you.

"Do just once what others say you cannot do, and you will never pay attention to their limitations again." — James Cook

In many situations, we will be told that *we cannot* accomplish certain things, or that we are incapable of achieving our dreams. The perpetrators that are filling our minds with this nonsense have given up on their dreams and are allowing limitations to belittle their ambitions. Simply because they are not capable of conquering something, this does not mean you do not harness the capacity to do so. You do not always need a degree, or years of experience to be competent enough to attain what you desire. The future hall of famer and NFL quarterback, Peyton Manning, once said, *"Remind your critics when they say you do not have the expertise or experience to do something that an amateur built the Ark, and the experts built the Titanic."* This quotation resonates well with me. The Titanic, which was built by experts, ended up sinking in the ocean, while the Ark lasted. Sometimes all it takes is for us to garner enough confidence to step up and conquer an obstacle that is holding us back before we will go on to achieve greatness. Always believe that anything is possible. This makes life more interesting.

For all successful people, there came a time when they had to decide that they were tired of living ordinary lives. At this *breaking point*, they made the decision that they would take a leap forward into the extraordinary. There is a quotation that motivates me and it reads, *"I choose, to live by choice, not by chance. To be inspired, not manipulated. To be useful, not used. To excel, not to compete. To act, not to excuse myself. To love myself, not pity myself. I choose to listen to my inner voice, not to the random opinion of others."* Our inner voice tells us when we love what we are doing. It assures us that we are on the right path. We can always confide in this voice. If you feel like you are following a life path that does not suit your needs, and you are understimulated, this is your opportunity to choose an alternate route.

Life Is Not A Competition

"My philosophy is: It is none of my business what people say of me and think of me. I am what I am and I do what I do. I expect nothing and accept everything, and it makes life so much easier." – Anthony Hopkins, *Famous Actor*

Can you imagine how much happier we would be if we lived according to Anthony Hopkins' philosophy? Too frequently we worry about how everyone around us judges our appearance and actions. We strategically map out our future so that our final destination will please them, while neglecting our own happiness. As we pursue this path, we find ourselves competing against masses of other people who are also racing to satisfy everyone but themselves. We need to go after what ignites our passions. There is no reason to compete.

"The best day of your life is the one on which you decide your life is your own. No apologies or excuses. No one to lean on, rely on, or blame. The gift is yours – it is an amazing journey – and you alone are responsible for the quality of it. This is the day your life really begins." – Bob Moawad

It is not wise to undermine our worth by comparing ourselves to others. Competition is everywhere. If we go through life trying to one-up everyone around us, or feeling inferior to people who might have more than us, this fuels envy and jealousy, which both trigger depression. Why should we allow competition to dictate our well-being? In the wage economy, there always seems to be someone looking to take our job. My philosophy is, if we have to worry about losing employment due to competition, we are better off letting that other person have it. If our work environment creates stress for us about job security, our job is likely not worthwhile. Contrary to this, if we are doing what we love, and are passionate about our job, we have no reason to worry. As leaders, we should always help those around us to be the best that they can be. Sometimes this includes equipping them with the knowledge or skill sets they need to qualify for our position, or even greater, to surpass us and become our successors. We can still find happiness in knowing that we paved the way for someone else to succeed. We cannot extend ourselves beyond what we are capable of. Sometimes the inevitable cannot be avoided. There is humbleness in knowing this.

"Maybe you are searching among the branches for what only appears in the roots." – Rumi

The reason why most of us compete with others is because we want to live up to expectations that have been placed on us. Sometimes we set unrealistic goals and we try with everything we have to accomplish something, or be someone, that simply is not a part of our destiny. We *search among the branches for what only appears in the roots*. This is another explanation for why we need to break free from the expectations that limit and make less of us.

We each have unique ambitions, dreams, goals, and visions. Simply because someone else may have more success or material wealth than we do, this does not make them better. It also does not justify us trying to compete with them. The best thing we can do is honor the qualities and talents that define us, and be proud of who we are. The richest man in the world is equal to you and me in the sense that we each have emotions, needs, and wants. These common bonds unite us as a species. We can choose to live equally by thriving independently, knowing that our material differences do not separate our unity. By accepting tradition, failing to explore our creativity, following others, setting boundaries on our imagination, and becoming someone who we do not freely decide we would like to be, not only do we fall as less than equal, we do not qualify as being complete. Individuality allows for us to discover the essence of our character, and reach the pinnacle of love. Through our attitude, composure, generosity, lifestyle, and talents, we define our legacy. We only discover equality when we acquire the strength and wisdom to accept difference as being equivalent, held together by these commonalities.

"There is only one way to avoid criticism, do nothing, say nothing and be nothing." – Aristotle

When we choose to pursue our passions and break free from the expectations that have been imprisoning us for so long, we will likely be criticized for doing so. As with anything we do or say in life, not everyone will agree. This is okay. We should move forward anyways. What we are being confronted by is the decision to keep ourselves trapped in depression, or to emerge as leaders, follow our own path, and demand happiness. Do not let criticism belittle you.

"Let others lead small lives, but not you. Let others argue over small things, but not you. Let others cry over small hurts, but not you. Let others leave their future in the hands of someone else, but not you." – Jim Rohn

When we listen to our inner voice, and ignore the expectations that others have placed on us, we lead enriching lives. We make arguing points for the things we disagree with in our everyday actions. We channel our emotions freely, knowing that each struggle makes us stronger. Most importantly, we control our future. We do not permit others to dictate our life path. These are major components of happiness.

"Making a difference in the world most times requires that you stand alone, away from the herd and with the willingness to stand powerfully for your truth despite popular opinion. This is leadership. Transformation is never made by the masses, it is always ushered in by the few willing to think and see beyond the mentality of the herd." – Judah Isvaran Rscp

161

You are a leader now. This means you no longer have to do things to fit in. You have no reason to compete. You are paving your own path to happiness. When others see how positive you are, they may choose to follow you. Embrace them, and encourage them to go after what excites their soul. Teach them how to branch off on their own. Show them the way to their roots so they can find what stimulates their drive. When we expend energy helping people around us understand how important of a task erasing expectations truly can be, we ignite the torch that sparks the change we wish to see in the world.

Clint Smith is a tenth grade English Teacher at *Parkdale High School* in Prince George's County, Maryland. He is also a spoken word performance artist (*clintsmithiii.com*). He encourages his students to rise above expectations. In his *TedX* speech, *The Danger of Silence*, he informs us that he has four core principles posted on the board in front of his class that are always visible *in an effort to create a culture in his classroom where students feel safe sharing the intimacies of their own silences.* His four fundamentals are to, "R*ead critically, write consciously, speak clearly, and tell your truth.*" He teaches his kids to become statisticians, not statistics. He instructs them that their ideas are no less profound, insights are no less enlightening, and values are no less important than those of Aristotle, Plato, or Socrates. He explains that their *Mt. Olympus is standing right in front of their faces, and it is now up to them to pick up their heads and start climbing.* He is relentless in helping them visualize their potential. We need more teachers like Mr. Smith.

"There is only one thing which makes a dream impossible to achieve; the fear of failure." – Paulo Coelho

As we escape limitations, elude competition, and erase melancholy, we must remain confident in our ability to find success doing what we enjoy. A major setback that limits us is clinging to a fear of failing. When we compete with others, this uneasiness becomes much greater, often preventing us from accomplishing our goals. When we live to impress others, and are constantly trying to exceed expectations, this fear is driven by our will to not fail these people. We are only hurting ourselves by living this way. Now we can go after what makes us happy. If we fail, we choose another angle. There is no reason to compete or live in fear.

We are now ready to progress to the ninth step. Think about how far we have come along on this adventure. Remember that everyone around us is also experiencing their own joys and sorrows. They are living through accomplishments and struggles. We are each fighting our own personal battles through this journey of life. It is important to appreciate, respect, and understand this as we come in contact with them. Therefore, we should always extend compassion and do our best to be non-judgmental. We need to recognize the impact that each decision we make has on everything around us.

"Find out who you are and figure out what you believe in. Even if it is different from what your neighbors believe in and different from what your parents believe in. Stay true to yourself. Have your own opinion. Do not worry about what people say or think about you. Let the naysayers nay, until they grow tired of naying." — Ellen DeGeneres

Jacoby

The 9ᵗʰ Step: Elevating Our Consciousness

"From my own experience I have found the greatest degree of inner tranquility comes from the development of love and compassion. A close, warmhearted feeling for others automatically puts the mind at ease. This helps remove whatever fears or insecurities we may have and gives us the strength to cope with any obstacles we encounter. It is the ultimate source of success in life. Kindness and compassion are extremely important in every area of life. It is futile to harbor hatred and ill-will even toward those who abuse us. Cooperation, trust, and consideration are far more constructive." – The Dalai Lama

As we go about the recovery process and heal from what brings us down, it is normal for us to release repressed memories. This may challenge us and test our character. We so casually hang on to anger, bitterness, hatred, and other feelings that are attached to painful occurrences from the past, that we do not recognize the role these emotions have played in our inability to feel completely satisfied. While we cleanse these unwanted emotions, it is imperative that we forgive those who have done us wrong, even our abusers and oppressors, and generate feelings of acceptance and love for everything and everyone that has had an impact in shaping our lives. We have to understand that wrongdoings are not intentionally directed at us. They are stimulated by confusion, disorientation, lack of compassion, and misunderstanding. Those who perpetrate against us are often seeking acceptance, compassion, love, and understanding. Because they lack these components of positivity, they develop negative qualities as they grow. They may not be aware that they have hurt us due to their own suffering. This is our chance to let go of any ill-will we are harboring.

The ninth step on our journey into the heart of Society's Anonymous is, *"We elevate our consciousness by understanding that depression, hurt, pain, and suffering are not feelings that are exclusive to us. These emotions are present everywhere, and each of us fights our own difficult battle. To eradicate this unnecessary negativity, we extend our compassion to all of life. This includes people in general, animals, plants, trees, and all of nature. We raise our awareness in order to appreciate the impact each decision we make has on everything around us."* Once we recognize that all living creatures generate emotions, feel pain, and are capable of suffering – similarly to how we do – we awaken to the injustices that are taking place all over the world, and learn how we can make a difference.

Have you ever considered the quotation that reads, *"The boy you punched in the hall today – he committed suicide a few minutes ago. The boy you called lame – he has to work every night to support his family. That girl you pushed down the other day – she is already being abused at home. That girl you called fat – she is starving herself. The boy you made fun of for crying – his mother is dying. You think you know them. Guess what? You do not."* For these reasons, among many others, we must always be compassionate, kind, and understanding. When we bully others out of their

163

happiness, we mask our own perception of what being happy is truly comprised of. By accepting these behaviors, we fail to examine the role we are playing in creating disharmony. This results in a society that embraces pain and suffering by disregarding how easily it can be reversed. Do we ever acknowledge this pain and suffering that takes place everyday, all around us, or are we too caught up in our own lives to notice it? This is a question we should seriously contemplate. While we go about our personal journeys fulfilling our egos, too many of us see past the unnoticeable costs that are attached to our lifestyle choices. Our lack of awareness, and blatant ignorance, both pose threats to our well-being, the safety of others, the survival of species, and the health of our landbase.

"We are all islands shouting lies to each other across seas of misunderstanding." – Rudyard Kipling, *The Light That Failed*

Every purchase we make has a ripple effect on the world. Raw materials that are used to manufacture goods come at expenses that often go beyond what we are aware of. Food products contain ingredients that inflict suffering on other living beings in order to be obtained. In other countries, children are sometimes forced into slave labor to get the materials needed to make new cell phone models, laptops, new cars, and other electronics we enjoy as consumers, and often take for granted (*raisehopeforcongo.org*). Mining for phosphates that are used as herbicides and pesticides for conventional agriculture has more of an impact on other cultures and the environment than you might expect (*thephosphaterisk.com*). Entire forest ecosystems are collapsing, and indigenous cultures are being killed (*survivalinternational.org*) so we can continue to eat at fast-food restaurants and serve animal products to those who choose to include animal-based foods in their diet. Deforestation is leading to climate change, and the majority of forests being decimated are destroyed to clear land for raising animals as food (*onegreenplanet.org*). Orangutans are being burned alive and driven to extinction in exchange for palm plantations, so we can add palm oil to processed foods and other consumer products (*saynotopalmoil.com*). Genetically modified crops (GMOs), animal agriculture, conventional monocropping, and deforestation are contributing to desertification in areas of the world that were once fertile and lush. Fracking chemicals, radioactive waste, and mercury from coal mines are accumulating in the oceans, rivers, and streams, creating dead zones, and causing mass fish deaths. Dolphins, sharks, whales, and other forms of marine life are washing up dead on shorelines all over the world. Starfish are disintegrating from ocean acidification. This beautiful planet is crumbling from our ignorance.

Despite these grave warnings, we continue to avoid the transition to solar energy, and we choose to heat our homes with propane, the end-product of fracking (*earthjustice.org/fracking*). The oceans are full of discarded plastic waste because we have nowhere to put it all, yet we still buy products that are packaged using petroleum-derived plastics (*projectaware.org*). Oil companies are pushing for the construction of the tar sands XL pipeline despite knowing that the process will likely cause irreversible damage to our homeland (*tarsandsblockade.org*). The state of California is experiencing a water

Jacoby

shortage because the majority of the water goes to factory farms and fracking, and they are suffering from drought because the logging industry continues to clear-cut the redwood forests which are responsible for moderating rainfall in the state. The planet is dying, and our daily decisions have a tremendous impact on whether or not we will save ourselves from the sixth mass extinction.

"Think about it this way. We are killing people in foreign lands in order to extract 200-million-year-old sunlight. Then we burn it, in order to boil water to create steam to drive a turbine to generate electricity. We frack our own backyards and pollute our rivers, or we blow up our mountaintops just miles from our nation's capital for an hour of electricity, when we could just take what is falling free from the sky." – Danny Kennedy, *former Greenpeace Activist and founder of Sungevity Inc. (sungevity.com)*

New research from a May 2014 study, published in *Science* journal, found that plant and animal species are going extinct at a rate between one-hundred and one-thousand per million annually. The study is titled, *The Biodiversity of Species and Their Rates of Extinction, Distribution, and Protection.* The lead researcher, Stuart Primm, announced, *"Before humans came on the scene, the typical extinction rate was likely one extinction per every ten million each year."* This study shows that our actions are speeding up extinction to a rate that is one-thousand times faster than normal.

According to a June 2014 report from the *American Psychological Association* and *ecoAmerica*, titled, *Beyond Storms & Droughts: The Psychological Impacts of Climate Change*, effects from the damage we have done to the environment, and global-warming related disasters are contributing to anxiety and depression. Researchers found that the increasing frequency and severity of climate change-related natural disasters, the impact on the environment, and unpredictable weather patterns have a significant negative impact on our well-being. They predict, *"As the effects of climate change accelerate, we are likely to see growing numbers of people suffering from post-traumatic stress disorder, anxiety, depression, and increased feelings of loss and helplessness."* What we are beginning to understand is that the less we appreciate nature, and the more we take it for granted, the greater the shadow of gloom that grows over our happiness.

In this lesson, I am urging that we recognize the impact our food choices, the purchases we make, and the lifestyle patterns we embrace each have on these rates of extinction. By making simple alterations we can drastically reduce the devastation taking place. With every dollar we spend we are casting a vote for the type of world we live in. We should be aware that the choices we make each day go beyond satisfying our desires and wants. Our decisions dramatically alter the ethnosphere of the planet. Once we come to this realization, our consciousness can awaken to a new level of understanding. When we can live knowing that our lifestyle choices have a minimal impact on other peoples way of living, there is happiness attached to this. In this step, I want to help raise awareness about some of the atrocities taking place in the world and share how easily we can get involved, work together, and do our part to stop them. I want us all to recognize that something as simple as changing our diet can ease suffering worldwide, improve the health of the environment, and save many innocent lives.

"A child raised to believe that a mountain is the abode of a protective spirit will be a profoundly different human being from a youth brought up to believe that a mountain is an inert mass of rock ready to be mined." – Wade Davis, *Light At The Edge Of The World*

I remember going on field trips as a kid to local mining operations and being taught that the hills, mountains, and elevated pieces of land were simply rocks and other resources that were there for us to level and use for building materials so we can *make progress* as a civilization. In areas along the Northwest Pacific, for decades now, schoolchildren have been taking field trips to logging operations where they are misinformed that the redwood trees and forests are here for us to cut them down and that without *proper* logging services, the forests would not grow back *the way they are supposed to* – as if they would need to grow back if they were not cut down in the first place. They are failing to inform these kids that trees are families and that they communicate through the mycelium networks underground. When they are cut down, forest ecosystems are destroyed. From memory, I recall being told that meat and dairy come from *happy* cows and that they are only here for us to consume them. I was never aware of the fact that these animals are being abused, raped, tortured, and slaughtered – or that they possess feelings, emotions, and loving personalities. Nowadays, we see advertisements supporting fracking as a clean energy source that does no damage to the environment. However, what they are failing to disclose is the truth revolving around how many chemicals are being used in the fracking cocktail mix, how dangerous they are, and how seriously damaging they are to our health and the health of the environment. Pharmaceutical drugs are everywhere, and the common widespread belief is that these pills will help cure us when we are sick. The truth is that most of these chemical drugs are restricting us from being healthy, keeping us ill, and damaging our microbiome.

I do not have any recollection of ever being told the truth. Everything was always fabricated. Children all over the world are still being deceived to this day with misinformation. No one ever seems to provide us with accurate knowledge regarding these issues. How can we ever build a peaceful world when we raise our children to believe in evil? Mountains are more than building materials. Forests are not here to be cut down. Animals are not happy to be slaughtered. Plastic does not belong in the oceans. Fracking is poisoning our water and destroying the planet. Eating an organic, vegan, non-GMO, and mostly raw diet is far more powerful medicine than any prescription drug could ever be. Solar power is much more efficient than electric, hydro, or petroleum. We need to protect the rainforests and orangutans more than we need palm oil. Why is it so difficult to tell the truth? Is short-term material gain really worth more than preserving life on the planet for future generations? We harness the power as individuals to create lasting change. If we all work together as a team, then we form a barrier against misinformation. This is our opportunity to make a difference and spread the word about what is really going on.

them affect us, or to forgive and forget. While many of us feel that those who perpetrate against us do not deserve forgiveness, we may not realize that us forgiving them could be the only way that they learn from their mistakes and change. With awakening our consciousness, we begin to understand that we hurt ourselves more by harboring ill-will and resentment towards others.

The infamous *Green River Killer*, Gary Ridgway, was convicted in 2003 for killing forty-eight women, mostly prostitutes. At his sentencing, the families of his victims came forth and lashed out at him for all of his wrongdoings. He did not show any remorse. It was only when the father of one of his victims stepped forward and said something to him that was not expected that he began to cry. His testimony brought Ridgway to tears. Robert Rule, the father of one of his teenage victims, confronted him and said, *"Mr. Ridgway, there are people here that hate you. I am not one of them. You have made it difficult to live up to what I believe, and that is what my higher power says to do, which is to forgive. You are forgiven, sir."* Think about this and let it resonate for a minute. The killer, Gary Ridgway, did not show an ounce of remorse until he was forgiven. Perhaps by forgiving all who have done us wrong, we can help them grow, and allow them the chance to truly feel remorse for the pain they have inflicted on us. We can also free ourselves from the suffering their actions have generated.

"A part of the key to entering into forgiveness is understanding. If one can understand why people behave as they do then often the road to forgiveness is opened. Not only is forgiveness essential for the health of society, it is also vital for our personal well-being. Bitterness is like a cancer that enters the soul. It does more harm to those that hold it than to those whom it is held against." – Terry Waite, *CBE*

In her book, *Left To Tell*, Immaculee Ilibagiza tells the story of how she survived the *Rwandan Genocide* in 1994 – in which her entire family was murdered. She explains how she chose to forgive the people who killed them because she could feel the anger, hostility, and rage she was clinging to starting to destroy her. She let forgiveness, rather than hatred, rule her life. Even when she met face-to-face with one of the murderers, she told him that she forgives him. In this scenario, we see how forgiving others can help us to live happier lives. We have to accept that people make mistakes, and we must embrace forgiveness.

Please access *theforgivenessproject.com* to read more remarkable stories about forgiveness.

"Sincere forgiveness is not colored with expectations that the other person apologize or change. Do not worry whether or not they finally understand you. Love them and release them. Life feeds back truth to people in its own way and time – just like it does for you and me." – Sara Paddison

People Make Mistakes

"I am afraid that we all make mistakes. One of the things that defines our character is how we handle mistakes. If we lie about having made a mistake, then it cannot be corrected and it festers. On the other hand, if we give up just because we made a mistake, even a big mistake, none of us would get far in life." — Terry Goodkind, *Confessor*

There are going to be times when we make mistakes, and chances are, someone could be watching. This is not the end of the world. Yes, the consequences may be overwhelming, but the best thing we can do is work to correct these mistakes so they will not be repeated. The worst thing we can do is lie about them and remain in denial. We should be honest, fix the problems, and move forward always.

Over the course of our lives, most of us can agree that we have drifted off of the right path at some point, and have been mistaken in our actions. We have unknowingly done things by simply living the way we do that could be deemed as mistakes. Now that we are aware of how each dollar we spend, and each decision we make impacts the world around us, we can choose to no longer make mistakes that hurt others.

"An error does not become a mistake until you refuse to correct it." — Orlando A. Battista

As we elevate our consciousness, and learn to be compassionate and understanding, we have to expect that we will make errors on our life journey, and be impacted by errors others have made. When we are guilty of wrongdoing, we should always honor that we were wrong, and do our best to correct our actions. In doing so, we prevent these errors from becoming mistakes.

"Mistakes are the portals of discovery." – James Joyce

Sometimes a mistake we make synchronizes with our destiny and while we may not know it at the time, it may be necessary to help us grow, take responsibility for our actions, and improve our situation. In the book, *Mistakes to Success: Learning and Adapting When Things Go Wrong*, a collection of revealing essays discuss new stories and insights on philanthropic and nonprofit mistakes that have led to new approaches. In his book, *Adapt: Why Success Always Starts With Failure*, economist and *Financial Times* columnist Tim Harford writes, *"Few of our own failures are fatal."* He explains how *when our mistakes stare us in the face, we often find it so upsetting that we miss out on the primary benefit of failing*. This, he mentions, *is the chance to get over our egos and come back with a stronger, smarter approach*. Our mistakes often help us discover the right path for us to follow, and to identify when we are going in the wrong direction.

"There are no mistakes. The events we bring upon ourselves – no matter how unpleasant – are necessary in order to learn what we need to learn. Whatever steps we take, they are necessary to reach the places we have chosen to go." – Richard Bach

Fascinating people create themselves through trial and error, pain and suffering, and their ability to conquer their own faults. When we make mistakes, if we recognize the lesson that is attached to them, we can change our ordinary lives into extraordinary elements of happiness. Even through all of the pain and suffering our failures induce, they frequently lead us to better places. When we are compassionate, kind, and loving we will find ways to redeem ourselves and correct our errors.

"All men make mistakes, but a good man yields when he knows his course is wrong, and repairs the evil. The only crime is pride." – Sophocles, *Antigone*

Not Everyone Is On Our Level

"People take different roads seeking fulfillment and happiness. Just because they are not on your road does not mean they have gotten lost." – Dalai Lama

It is unfair for us to expect that anyone else knows how we perceive things; what we deem tolerable or unacceptable; or what actions or words they can use for us to favor them. Similarly, we should not expect other people around us to agree with everything we believe in, perform, or express interest in. Remember that each of us has beliefs, characteristics, morals, and values that constitute our individuality. We were raised with different upbringings. Each experience we have had exposure to shapes our belief system. Some of us have had more opportunities to travel the world, educate ourselves, and live out our passions than others. For these reasons, we should not assume everyone else knows what we know. We can forgive them for making mistakes, or for not living according to our standards. Artists and executives lead much different lives in comparison, yet they each define their purpose with their actions. Not one of us should be judged based on what we know.

"Life is a succession of lessons which must be lived to be understood." – Ralph Waldo Emerson

As we progress through Society's Anonymous, and we elevate our consciousness, one thing we want to avoid is being generic. We should strive to be genuine. When we fake our happiness, pretend to smile, and disregard others because we feel superior to them, we are displaying a lack of compassion. Simply because we have a fancier title, better paying job, and expect others to live up to our expectations, this does not justify us refusing to acknowledge the struggles each of these people are living with daily. Only by taking time to consider others, understand them, and accept them, can we truly radiate positivity.

If someone strongly believes in a way of life that is not in compliance with ours, the only options we have are to let them be, or attempt to kindly enlighten them with encouraging words that could help them see things differently. We cannot belittle them, make them feel unimportant, or make them invisible. In most instances we can learn valuable lessons from the people who we think we have little in common with.

"There are people who are generic. They make generic responses and they expect generic answers. They live inside a box and they think people who do not fit into their box are weird. But I'll tell you what, generic people are the weird people. They are like genetically-manipulated plants growing inside of a laboratory, like indistinguishable faces, like droids. Like ignorance." — C. JoyBell C.

If we are fortunate enough to have engaged in fulfilling lives; and we are educated, conduct ourselves appropriately, and live passionately; the best thing we can do is give gifts of kindness to those who we encounter. This can be done by offering encouraging advice, giving compliments, and trying our best to help those people who are on a different level to feel comfortable, find happiness, and pursue their passions.

"A joker is a little fool who is different from everyone else. He's not a club, diamond, heart, or spade. He's not an eight or a nine, a king or a jack. He is an outsider. He is placed in the same pack as the other cards, but he doesn't belong there. Therefore, he can be removed without anybody missing him." — Jostein Gaarder, *The Solitaire Mystery*

When we notice that someone may not appear to *fit-in*, rather than portraying them as an outcast, the better choice is to accept that they are their own person. If they ask for help, then we can do our best to point them in the right direction. If they are minding their own business and not harming others with their actions, whether directly or indirectly, there is no reason to infiltrate their way of living with what we think is best for them. The only difference we can make is in leading by example. We become sorcerers for the magic we want to see in the world once we manifest purpose-driven lives that are rooted in compassion, happiness, kindness, love, and understanding.

"Acceptance looks like a passive state, but in reality it brings something entirely new into this world. That peace, a subtle energy vibration, is consciousness." — Eckhart Tolle

We should always embrace every obstacle, opportunity, and presence. Each person we come in contact with is worthy of being appreciated, noticed, and respected. Elevating our consciousness includes generating unconditional love to all that is living. It requires us to accept that all things happen for a reason. It demands from us the awareness of knowing what is right from wrong, and understanding the role we play each day in promoting world peace with each decision we make.

In the tenth step, we will learn to find the meaning behind every experience and use obstacles to build foundations for success.

The 10ᵗʰ Step: Trusting That Everything Happens For A Reason

"Life will give you whatever experience is most helpful for the evolution of your consciousness. How do you know this is the experience you need? Because this is the experience you are having at the moment." — Eckhart Tolle, *A New Earth: Awakening to Your Life's Purpose*

Why is it that right when we feel like everything is going our way, and life could not get any better, we get slammed with a giant obstacle that blocks our path? I think of these moments as tests that our higher power challenges us with to determine how strong we are. I believe that we get too comfortable at times and are confronted by these hurdles so we can step outside of our comfort zone and grow. I cannot tell you the exact reason why we are frequently set off course by unexpected disturbances, though I do know these barriers do not appear out of nowhere. They are always meant to be. During these instances, it can be easy to give up, generate feelings of anger, lose our cool, and wish we could erase the episode from our lives. Always remember, this is happening for a reason.

As we stroll into our new lives, the tenth step in Society's Anonymous is, *"We trust in our ability to make the best out of every situation by accepting obstacles, seeing them as new beginnings, and knowing that we will build success from the steps we take to bypass them. We recognize the role karma plays in our everyday life and we emanate this in our character. We understand that we are in the exact place where the Universe wants us to be at this moment."*

"If you are brave enough to say goodbye, life will reward you with a new hello." — Paulo Coehlo, *The Alchemist*

Sometimes the Universe speaks to us subliminally in order for us to find our purpose. There are instances when we feel like our life is being played out in alignment with our dreams, just as we manifested it to be, and then reality rocks our perfect world. Before I began writing this book, I was challenged by a similar situation. I was living on the Northwest Pacific coast in California, among the redwood forests. I worked for an amazing company. I had the freedom to explore nature, grow my own organic food, and live away from the complexities, noises, and pollutions attached to cities. I was in my element. As much as I felt like I was living a dream, apparently my destiny had other plans for me. Something happened to me that I was not expecting, and it turned my paradise upside down. I was forced to relocate back to Chicago, IL, in the middle of the coldest winter I could recollect, and start all over. At first I asked over and over why this was happening, and wished more than anything I could find my way back. Then, as time swallowed my resentment, I began to accept that this was all meant to happen for a reason. The idea for this book came to fruition. I had a strong spiritual awakening. I bonded with my daughter and family. Once I said goodbye to my past, and to this belief that I was a victim, I matured a lot, and decided this obstacle would now become an opportunity for me to strengthen my character, and pave the trail for my next adventure.

175

"Hardships often prepare ordinary people for an extraordinary destiny." – C.S. Lewis

Think of the story of photographer, Cory Richards. In 2012, he was caught in an avalanche while climbing Mt. Everest. The entire crew of climbers likely should have died. He took magnificent photos of their journey to survival, one in particular of his frozen face with icicles attached. After making it out alive, his photos were recognized by *National Geographic* and they hired him as one of their professional photographers. This event, which seemed like a disaster, was life-changing and led him to success and landing his dream job. As we go about the recovery process from what is bringing us down, we have to expect that there will be avalanches, harsh weather conditions, hurricanes, roadblocks, sinkholes, tornadoes, tsunamis, and other blockades that could set us back. We might experience immense pain. Tragic events may occur. Anything is possible. We have to know that whatever comes our way will happen for a reason. We can rest assured, knowing that no matter how heavy the burden may be, once we recover there will be bright blue skies, sunny days, starry nights, and happy fulfilling lives for us to maintain.

"All great changes are preceded by chaos." – Deepak Chopra

In addition to these unwanted obstacles confronting us while we seek happiness, there will also be many moments when we are rewarded for our good behavior and generous deeds. There always seems to be a balance between darkness and light. As we go about the recovery process we can expect there to be moments when we encounter synchronicity. These experiences help us confirm that we are on the right path.

When our intentions are pure, we know our purpose in life, and we awaken our consciousness, the Universe rewards us with the gift of happiness. If we do things to intentionally hurt others, and we lack compassion, more often than not we are challenged with hardships. This is often referred to as karma. To provide a balance, sometimes even the most genuine, humble, and loving people face difficulties. We have to accept this, and think of it almost as a *collective karma*. Because forests are families of trees, and animals all have families and possess feelings, when we do something as simple as cut down a tree, or kill an animal for any reason, we are creating disharmony. This sends a message out to the Universe that it is okay to kill, and it destructs our chances of living in universal harmony. As a result, we are depressed, and witnessing murders and injustices taking place all over the world. This is collective karma. It begins with our actions, and accounts for all of the suffering we inflict on others with each decision we make, or dollar we spend. Perhaps we experience pain and tragedies to balance out the torment we are responsible for in order to maintain our privileged lifestyles. Maybe our careless actions that are depleting nature of its abundance, and our reckless killing of animals, poisoning of the oceans, and decimation of the forests is coming back to haunt us in the form of depression and hardships. The optimal solution would be to heal society from the lack of awareness and compassion, and erase all of the suffering taking place in the world. The odds of this happening looks more hopeful as we transition to embracing happier, healthier lives.

"Situations seem to happen to people, but in reality, they unfold from deeper karmic causes. The universe unfolds to itself, bringing to bear any cause that needs to be included. Do not take this process personally. The working out of cause and effect is eternal. You are part of this rising and falling that never ends, and only by riding the wave can you ensure that the waves do not drown you. The ego takes everything personally, leaving no room for higher guidance or purpose. If you can, realize that a cosmic plan is unfolding and appreciate the incredibly woven tapestry for what it is, a design of unparalleled marvel." – Deepak Chopra, *The Book of Secrets: Unlocking the Hidden Dimensions of Your Life*

No matter what our situation may be, we should always accept that life is going to get better, and there is room for improvements everywhere. Although it may seem impossible to pinpoint, we must search for the meaning behind every obstacle that blocks our path. This can help us identify which direction we will go as we venture out on our next journey.

Discovering The Meaning

"Once you have lived a little you will find that whatever you send out into the world comes back to you in one way or another. It may be today, tomorrow, or years from now, but it happens; usually when you least expect it, usually in a form that is pretty different from the original. Those coincidental moments that change your life seem random at the time but I do not think they are. At least that is how it has worked out in my life. I know I am not the only one." – Slash, from *Guns N' Roses*

Sometimes our past comes back to haunt us, identical to how our present can enrich and nurture us. We do not have control over what will happen to us, or how events from our past might creep back up. What we do have the power to dictate is how we let uncertainties affect us. We have control over our attitude, perception, and acts of kindness. While one day we may be blindsided by plots to attack our character, damage our reputation, and belittle our ambitions, and these schemes might force us to question our present life path; on a different day, we might receive signals that confirm we are on a path to greatness. The most rewarding answer we can counter with is our reaction, and by searching for the meaning behind these signals – whether good or bad.

When I lived in Miami, I would often spend time in the *Whole Foods* dining area working on various writings. At this point in my life I was still searching for my identity. I was questioning whether or not I was in the right place, and wondering if I was going in the right direction. One day I was reading, *The Spontaneous Fulfillment of Desire: Harnessing the Infinite Power of Coincidence*, by Deepak Chopra, while stationed in the dining area. This book introduced me to synchronicity. This is the idea that events may occur that are meaningfully related, but not causally related, and will assure us that we are working in alignment with the universe. I had been collecting caps from the *Honest Tea* bottles (before they sold out to a giant corporation) that I would drink while I worked. Beneath the caps were quotations which I found to be inspiring, and I assumed that one day I would use the caps for a writing, or art project. The company began to include six-word memoirs beneath the caps to replace quotations, and they were boring, so I always hoped for a quotation with each purchase. On this particular day, before I opened my tea, I was saying to myself over and over, *Please do not get a six-word memoir, please do not get a six-word memoir*. I opened the bottle, and sure enough, it was a six-word memoir. I thought about the cap not being a six-word memoir so much that I manifested a six-word memoir. This is the *Law of Attraction* at its finest.

When I read the cap, I was shocked to see that not only was it a six-word memoir, but it was Deepak Chopra's six-word memoir – the author of the book I was reading. How is that for harnessing the power of coincidence? His memoir read, *Danced In Fields of Infinite Possibilities*. At that moment, I knew I was in the right place at the right time. My questions were answered. I was also *dancing in fields of infinite possibilities*.

The final year I lived in Miami, I bought a large mural for my living room wall. It was an enlarged photo of the redwood forest. Since childhood I had always dreamed of visiting the redwoods. Every day I would take time to look at the mural, and I told myself that one day I was going to find my way out west to be there. I left Miami a year later, and moved back to Chicago to finish writing my first book, *The Raw Cure*. I applied the mural to the wall in the bedroom where I was staying. About a month before the book was finished, I got offered a job working at the *Living Light Culinary Institute* in Fort Bragg, CA. This is a culinary school that certifies raw vegan chefs, and teaches them how to prepare meals using all organic, vegan ingredients and without applying heat to the food. The town is surrounded by redwood state parks. I moved there the day after my book was published.

After settling, I found *Russian Gulch State Park*. This was about a ten minute drive from where I resided, and I decided that I would make this my new running spot. There are several uphill trails, and when I run the five-mile course, at mile four there is a thirty-four foot waterfall. It is stunning. On my first day running through these woods, I climbed up *Falls Loop Trail*, and when I reached the top of the first climb, I could not believe what I saw. I was standing in the photo from the mural that I had on my wall for the past two years. The photo was captured right in the exact spot where I was running. How is that for synchronicity? Manifesting my desires? This also assured me that I was on the right path.

"Coincidence is nature's way of remaining anonymous." – Albert Einstein, *The World As I See It*

Not too long after my move, what is by far the greatest highlight of my life occurred. I met my girlfriend, Megan, and within a year we welcomed our beautiful daughter, Nevaeh, into the world. She is the best gift I have ever received. If I had any question of whether or not I was on the correct path before her birth, I found my answer. See how the Universe rewards us when we are going in the right direction? Now I was living the life I imagined. My passions were learning new dance moves. My ambitions were climbing to the sky. I felt invincible. This was around the time when I was forced to move back

178
Jacoby

to Chicago. My situation is a perfect example of how there is a balance between light and darkness. For these reasons, it is important that we have alternate routes mapped out in our action plans. I was not prepared for this.

"Whatever relationships you have attracted in your life at this moment are precisely the ones you need in your life at this moment. There is a hidden meaning behind all events and this hidden meaning is serving your own evolution." – Deepak Chopra

Whether our signal from the Universe confirms that we are on the right path, or forces us to change direction, it is important that we decipher its meaning. I strongly believe that nothing happens to us for the intent of causing hardships. The real reason why we are challenged is to provoke us to succeed. We are tested to determine how we combat adversity. If we are strong and wise enough to search for the meaning behind our difficulties, then we can more easily unravel the message each struggle we encounter is trying to deliver. When we conquer our struggles, we gain a better appreciation for when life is going our way. We tend to take less things for granted and are more grateful for what we have. The experience of being on both sides of the spectrum, and knowing what it feels like to struggle in pain, and to rejoice in happiness, has a spiritually cleansing effect. Always remember that the discontent we may be feeling today could be used to remind ourselves of how bad things can get, and we have the option to instead choose to be happy.

"Man learns through experience, and the spiritual path is full of different kinds of experiences. He will encounter many difficulties and obstacles, and they are the very experiences he needs to encourage and complete the cleansing process." – Sai Baba

No Endpoints, Only New Beginnings

"There is No Easy Walk to Freedom Anywhere, and many of us will have to pass through the valley of the shadow of death again and again before we reach the mountaintops of our desires." – Nelson Mandela

When things get really tough, I often think of an analogy about a caterpillar. This caterpillar thought the world was over just before she became a butterfly. Once she emerged from her cocoon, she was rewarded with wings and had more freedom than ever before. Her new shape, and added features, allowed her to view the world through a different lens. Suddenly her attitude became much more positive and her perspective of life changed dramatically.

After being enclosed in darkness and engulfed by uncertainty, this beautiful butterfly awoke to a miracle and was given the opportunity to fly. When we find ourselves in similar situations, we have to persevere. Life is unpredictable and we often go through some terrible things before we are able to reach the pinnacle of success, or the mountaintops of our desires. If we give up, or let these obstacles defeat us, we will never know of the wonderful opportunities that are awaiting us. It is imperative that we always look for the best in every situation, and are sure to search for new options when old doors close. Remember that every failure can lead us to success.

In the first step, I listed the stories of many successful people and explained how they went from struggles to accumulating great fortunes. They accomplished this by being persistent, never giving up, and knowing that their hardships were only preparing them for brighter futures. If some people throughout history had not persevered and battled through their struggles, it is likely that not one of us would be here today. The U.S. President, Barack Obama, was once advised by Governor Rahm Emanuel, *"You never want a serious crisis to go to waste. Things that we had postponed for too long, that were long-term, are now immediate and must be dealt with. A crisis provides the opportunity for us to do things that we could not do before."* When we are confronted by obstacles, we cannot give up and expect to find positivity in doing so. We have to use these moments to get ahead.

"It was so risky and so scary, and yet at the same time, so beautiful. Maybe the truth was, it should not be easy to be amazing. Then everything would be. It is the things you fight for and struggle with before earning that have the greatest worth. When something is difficult to come by, you will do that much more to make sure it is even harder, if not impossible, to lose." — Sarah Dessen, *Along for the Ride*

To successfully overcome hardships, reverse failures, and avert struggles, we need to take action. We cannot afford to dwell in pity. Each day we need to work on bettering ourselves, improving situations that we have an impact on, and helping others around us. It is up to us as individuals to heal ourselves, yet to be champions and crown society as a whole with the treasure of true happiness, we need to spread awareness and truth.

"I have missed more than nine-thousand shots in my career. I have lost almost three-hundred games. Twenty-six times, I was trusted to take the game winning shot and missed. I have failed over and over and over again in my life. And this is why I succeed." — Michael Jordan

Each time Michael Jordan failed, he practiced harder and spent more time in the gym assuring that it would not happen again. When things did not go his way, he made sure they would next game. He knew that he could not dwell over the imperfections if he wanted to be victorious. He had to take action to be the champion that he is. If we want to claim victory over depression, and emerge as champions of happiness, we also must take action. In step eleven we will list our goals, and devise an action plan, so we can create the life we desire.

The 11th Step: Devising an Action Plan

"I challenge you, to make your life a masterpiece. I challenge you to join the ranks of those people who live what they teach. Who walk their talk."
– Tony Robbins

The pieces are in place now, and we know what it takes to liberate ourselves from depression permanently. The only separation that lies between us and the life we desire is the difference between *knowing* and *doing*. The majority of society is aware that they can improve their circumstances, they simply fail to actively pursue change. We are now ready to implement a valuable component to our personal recovery. The eleventh step in Society's Anonymous is, *"By creating an action plan, we utilize the newly acquired knowledge we have obtained to live happy, healthy, and successful lives."* This is our moment to get comfortable in the driver's seat.

Any one of us can generate a good idea in our mind. I once read that we each think of a new idea daily that could turn into a fortune for us if we were only to act on manifesting it into something substantial. Too few of us write these ideas down, so they never become more than thoughts that lose their potential. We are busy merely surviving. We are limited by our self-image, doubt, and lack of confidence. When we learn new things that could improve our situation, we generally procrastinate to take advantage of the benefits attached. While many of us are clearly unhappy with our lives, we continue to downplay any moves that could bring us contentment.

Some of us go beyond the average thinker, and we write down our ideas. We may even fill notebooks summarizing them. As we progress through the years, these dormant seeds waiting to blossom into action continue to accumulate until we pack boxes with notebooks that are full of various colors, shapes, and sizes of our translated thoughts. We know they are of value, so we pay for storage units to store them. We talk about our ideas with passion and confidence. The problem is we neglect to take action and refuse to submit them to the Universe. In doing so, these ideas die.

I was guilty of idea hoarding for the first twenty-five years of my life. I have been writing down ideas since childhood, and saving the notebooks in boxes that move with me everywhere I go. I always used excuses, such as, *I do not have the resources to do anything with these ideas*. I finally decided one day to start writing a book. It was, *The Four-Hour Work Week*, by Timothy Ferris, that sparked the necessary motivation in me to begin the writing process. Another book that inspired me was, *Igniting Your Life*, by John McCabe. I decided if I needed the resources to continue presenting my ideas in writings, I would have to at least complete one book project to build the foundation. Then I could spend my time researching and writing more books. *Eventually*, I thought, *I could be a motivational speaker*. I began typing up the contents from these notebooks so I could include them in future book projects. I made a commitment to take action. I cannot explain in words how good this felt to finally make the transition from simply talking, to finally doing.

The inspirational author, Mike Dooley (*tut.com*), once said, *"The one thing all famous authors, world class athletes, business tycoons, singers, actors, and celebrated achievers in any field have in common is that they all began their journeys when they were none of these things. Yet still, they began their journeys."* Before I started writing my first book, I did not know that I was going to be a successful author. I was a regular guy with extraordinary dreams trying to find my destiny. By taking action and getting started on the project, I realized that this was my calling. Not one of us can determine whether or not we have the potential to be actors, athletes, singers, or prominent leaders until we try.

At the 2014 *Dartmouth Commencement Ceremony*, Shonda Rimes, writer for *Grey's Anatomy*, spoke and said, *"I think a lot of people dream, and while they are busy dreaming, the really happy people, the really successful people, the really engaged, powerful people, are busy doing."* The great author, Napoleon Hill, once wrote, *"More gold has been mined from the thoughts of men than has been taken from the earth."* It is up to us to choose whether or not we want to achieve our dreams through action, or let them visit us only in a subconscious state. We decide what we will do with the gold that is mined from our thoughts. Do we want to cash in and reap the benefits, or continue to struggle while sitting on the winning lottery ticket? This is the difference between thinking and doing.

The teacher of the honors *Contemporary World Issues* class that I completed during junior year of high school had a unique way of grading. For the majority of the assignments we completed and turned in, he would first have us review them, and then instruct us to grade them ourselves. Using an honor system, he gave us the power of authority to grade ourselves based off of the effort we put in to those assignments. Think about how this could relate to our everyday lives. If we were to grade ourselves each day on the actions we are taking to manifest our desires, and our efforts to summon a life that is aligned with our passions, how would these grades look on paper? If I told you that I earn an 'A' daily I would be lying. If we are living below the happiness threshold, we need to make adjustments and work to improve our grades so we can reverse dysphoria. This requires us being honest with ourselves, and a substantial degree of accountability.

"If you ask someone what they want most in life, they most likely will say security or money. Maybe happiness, or fame, or power. Maybe social recognition, ease in living, or the ability to sing, dance, or write. However, none of them will be able to define these terms, or give the slightest indication of a plan by which they hope to attain these wishes." – Napoleon Hill

Positive thoughts are not enough. There have to be positive feelings and positive actions. In order for us to find happiness, this requires that we have a plan. If we want to be recognized for our individuality or ideas, we must have a platform for us to show the world what we are made of. If we want to live easy, this obligates us to work for that goal. If we seek the ability to dance, sing, or write, it is necessary for us to take lessons and practice. If we want to wake up happy every morning and fall asleep in a state of bliss each night, then it is our responsibility to find ways to make this possible. The only way to accomplish what we want in life is to take action. We have the power to dictate our well-being.

"Happiness is not something ready-made. It comes from your own actions." – Dalai Lama

Reviewing The First Ten Steps

Before we write up our action plan, I want to take some time to review the first ten steps. By refreshing these valuable lessons in our head, we can be sure to include them as we list our goals, and use them to assist us with mapping out our future.

The 1ˢᵗ Step – Identifying the Culprit: In this step, we identify the real reasons for why we are depressed. We compare the antagonist list with the protagonist list, and are able to acknowledge that we have more control over our happiness than we once believed. We recognize that age is only a number, and no matter how young or old we are, we are capable of being truly happy. We learn that we can dictate our biology by changing our perception and altering the way we eat. We are introduced to epigenetics and the idea that our lifestyle choices control our genetics and we are capable of turning gene cells on and off stemming from our actions or inaction. We come to the realization that health conditions which trigger depression are a result of poor lifestyle choices, and the toxins and negative emotions we have been storing inside. We accept that family and social environment, life changes, or traumatic events can only limit us to the extent that we allow them to. We find beauty within us that surpasses the negative self-image we once retained. We are confronted by statistics that alert us to the fact that alcohol, cigarettes, certain illicit drugs, and prescription drugs do indeed stimulate depressive symptoms.

We are encouraged to abide by the Law of Attraction, which states, *what we think about most is what we attract into our lives*. Once we establish what is triggering our discontent, we are recommended to shift our thoughts away from these culprits, and adapt new patterns of thinking. Rather than accepting the things we cannot change, we change the things we cannot accept. Knowing that we are all strong, and each have a unique purpose, we discover that there is no room for denial, pity, or ridiculous excuses. We find solace in embracing that the time to change is now.

The 2ⁿᵈ Step – Correcting Ourselves: In the second step, we decide that our attitude and perception is holding us back from being truly happy. We choose to correct our attitude, change our perception, and open our hearts and minds to what awaits us. We start planting seeds of optimism in our mind, and fill our head with thoughts of abundance. We begin to write ourselves positive notes for affirmation. We fill our home with plants to liven it up, and hang motivational pictures or pieces of art on our walls. We decide to pick up new hobbies. We embrace change to avoid living boring, stagnant lives. We are encouraged to do everything we can to attract positive people, thoughts, and things into our life.

To accomplish these objectives, we start by listing all of the people, places, and things that stimulate feelings of happiness. Are there certain people in your life that make you feel happy? Is there a place where you can go that will generate good vibes? What things make you happy? Does sunshine make you happy? Do you spend time in nature? Are you eating a well-balanced plant-based diet? Are there certain memories that cheer you up? We should be able to provide answers for each of these questions. In this step, we pinpoint all of the things that bring us joy, and once this is accomplished, shift our thoughts away from sadness and expend our energy magnetizing positivity.

The 3ʳᵈ Step – Cleansing Internally: In the third step we understand that the negative emotions we have been harboring for years are stored inside, along with harmful toxins that have accumulated over the course of our lifetime. We learn that cleansing the body and mind of negative emotions; chemicals that have been added to the food and water supply; harmful microbes; and the mucus and plaque that is hardened to the intestinal walls is vital when recovering from what brings us down. We begin weeding out the negative emotions we have been clinging to. To accomplish this task, we alkalize our bodies by removing acid-forming foods and reducing our toxin load. This requires cutting out alcohol, coffee, cigarettes, cooked oils, refined sugars, and saturated fats (meat, dairy, eggs) – toxins that are obstacles blocking us from the healing process. We take precautionary measures to assure that we will not be exposed to chemicals, and if we have been exposed, we start eliminating the toxins we have stored within. This requires minimizing the use of common household cleaners and personal health care products that are saturated with harmful chemicals (cleaners, cosmetics, deodorants, lip balms, shampoos, soaps, toothpastes, and other chemical-based products), and finding alternatives that are truly natural. Most importantly, we cleanse our system from toxic debris and plaque buildup. We do this by undergoing internal cleansing methods, such as colon hydrotherapy, lymphatic drainage massages, and oxygen baths or infrared sauna sessions. If our body has been infiltrated by parasites – which is common in the average American – we administer a parasite flush to remove these unwanted organisms. Then we learn about juice fasting, and are introduced to alternative fuels that we can use to nourish our body, mind, and spirit outside of what we have been raised believing is best for us. Our goals are to freshen up internally and rejuvenate the health of our internal environment.

The 4ᵗʰ Step – Choosing Alternative Fuels: In the fourth step, we learn about nutrition and how the foods we have been eating contain chemicals that may be triggering our depression. We learn which foods to avoid, and are introduced to certain foods that could be helpful for our recovery – such as organic raw fruits and vegetables. To recover from what brings us down, we accept that we cannot continue eating poorly, and filling up with sugary-drinks and chemical-laden foods. To invite happiness into our lives, this requires that we are aware of what we put into our bodies with each meal or snack we consume. We consider the energy that the food we ingest contains within. We want our food to contain living nutrients that are not damaged or denatured.

184

To complete the fourth step on our adventure to happiness, we begin to remove certain foods, drinks, and fillers from our diet. This includes animal-based food products, gluten grains, GMOs, processed foods and beverages, and refined sugars. We are also required to begin adding fresh organic juices and smoothies, and raw organic salads, fruits, vegetables, nuts, and seeds. This may seem like a difficult task, and as much as we might grimace at the thought of making the transition, we respect that being depressed is also not an ideal way to live. We learn that eating organic is important because we avoid the farming chemicals, glyphosate, GMO residues, phosphates, and other chemicals that are found in conventional produce. It is brought to our attention that these chemicals are known to alter the neurotransmitters in our brain. To successfully invite happiness into our lives, and increase our odds of permanently erasing sadness, we understand it is mandatory that we change our diet. Once the corrections are made, we are grateful for following through.

The 5th Step – Engaging in Outdoor Physical Activity: In the fifth step, we discover how important exercise is when determining our overall level of happiness. We incorporate not only physical exercise, but mental and spiritual conditioning as well. We nurture our relationship with nature and the outdoor world. Knowing that our disconnect from what is natural is partly to blame for our melancholy, we resolve this by walking barefoot, adventuring through state parks and forest preserves, admiring the wildlife, hugging trees, gardening, growing our own food, and appreciating all that Gaia – the Earth Mother – offers. We decide to fill our home with house plants to replicate a natural environment, and we obtain gym memberships so we can stay active all year, not just seasonally.

We are encouraged to get outdoors as much as possible. This could include completing our exercise routines at a park, running the trails in our local forest preserve, practicing yoga outdoors, and meditating with the sounds of nature resonating through our soul. By exercising our body, mind, and spirit, not only do we elevate our happiness, we also improve our stamina and endurance, and strengthen our cardiac muscles – assuring good health. We learn that we do not have to meditate all day, but by simply meditating for thirty minutes daily, we can greatly improve our health, mood, and overall well-being.

The 6th Step – Gaining Substance: In the sixth step, we are informed that suicide and depression rates are elevated around the age of retirement, and are motivated to start building our character now to prevent becoming a statistic. We are encouraged to start adding substance to who we are by getting more involved in the community, embracing new hobbies, learning a new language, picking up an instrument, and doing things we truly enjoy outside of the work environment. We devote more time and energy to acquiring new talents, building character, expanding our intellect, nurturing personal growth, and pursuing our passions. In doing so, we gain substance, and establish a legacy. We are reminded not to let school and work prevent us from doing what we truly enjoy.

In this step, it is recommended that we volunteer and be active with organizations that are improving the planet and welfare of others for the sake of doing good, not merely to benefit our bank account or reputation. We create vision boards that help us visualize all of the things we want to attract into our lives each time we gaze at them. This is our chance to have fun, try new things, and discover the untapped potential we have been concealing within. We want to be sure that we are alive during this lifetime.

The 7th Step – Acknowledging Our Sphere of Influence: In the seventh step, we notice what types of people we are associating with, and how their happiness may be affecting us. We are challenged to average out the overall level of happiness from each of the ten most influential people in our lives, and by doing so, we learn how happy we are allowing ourselves to be as we continue to associate with them. We acknowledge our sphere of influence and choose our friends wisely. We understand that many people will enter our lives, but it is up to us to distinguish between the negative and positive. As we complete this step, we recognize the people who have been brought into our lives that we want to keep around, and we let go of those who bring us down. We accept that we cannot climb out of despair by remaining attached to people who enable our depression. Knowing that we are judged by the company we keep, it is important for us to be aware of their intentions, choose to interact with positive people, and cling to those who smile frequently and radiate positivity.

The 8th Step – Living Without Expectations: In the eighth step, we no longer allow our ambitions to be confined by expectations, limitations, or restrictions. We confirm it is time for us to follow our own path. We reach a breaking point where we decide that we no longer want to live for our friends, guardians, loved ones, or parents. At this moment of change, we begin living to satisfy our own needs, and to accomplish personal goals. This is our chance to break away from the shallow surroundings that expectations have bottled us up in. We can now free our minds from the mental prison that has been holding us back, and follow a path that leads to happiness, health, and success.

To emerge as leaders and find our true identity, we have to be ourselves. Too often we choose careers based from what our parents want for us. We decide on a college that they think is best. We make decisions growing up that stem from their acceptance of each action. At times we may do things that go against our morals and values for the sake of pleasing and satisfying others. We realize that living according to expectations that restrict us, or shape us in an unfavorable way, stirs up depressive symptoms, and frankly, it brings us down. We embrace the fact that we can simply grow our own food. We acknowledge that we can learn skills and acquire new talents that help others. We become aware that it is possible for us to live in communes that will reduce our financial obligations. We welcome the idea of starting communities where we do not rely on corporations, but rather, we contribute to vibrant gardens that will feed everyone around us. We begin to penetrate the abundance in simplicity. We accept that we do not need fancy cars, high-paying jobs, or large homes to be truly happy. We need friendship, good health, laughter, and love.

The 9ᵗʰ Step – Elevating Our Consciousness: In the ninth step, we learn how each dollar we spend, and every decision we make has an impact on the world around us. We honor our mistakes, learn from them, and practice compassion, forgiveness, and understanding. We elevate our consciousness by noting that depression, hurt, pain, and suffering are not feelings that are exclusive to us. These emotions are present everywhere, and each of us fights our own difficult battle. To eradicate this unnecessary negativity, we extend our compassion to all of life. This includes people in general, animals, plants, trees, and all of nature. We raise our awareness in order to appreciate the impact each decision we make has on everything around us. Once we recognize that all living creatures generate emotions, feel pain, and are capable of suffering – similarly to how we do – we awaken to the injustices that are taking place all over the world and identify how we can make a difference.

We learn to forgive those who manipulated us into believing we were causing no harm, and to forgive ourselves and others around us for our negligence over the years. As we elevate our consciousness, and become more compassionate and understanding, we have to expect that we will make errors on our life journey and be impacted by errors others have made. We accept that when we are guilty of wrongdoing, we should always honor that we were wrong, and do our best to correct our actions. In doing so, we prevent these errors from becoming mistakes.

We strive to be genuine and recognize that when we fake our happiness, pretend to smile, and disregard others because we feel superior to them, we are displaying a lack of compassion. Simply because we have a fancier title, better paying job, and expect others to live up to our expectations, this does not justify us refusing to acknowledge the struggles we each live with daily. Only by taking time to consider others, understand them, and accept them, can we truly radiate positivity. If someone strongly believes in a way of life that is not in compliance with ours, the only options we have are to let them be, or attempt to kindly enlighten them with encouraging words that could help them see things differently. We cannot belittle them, make them feel unimportant, or make them invisible. We realize that elevating our consciousness is a component of true happiness.

The 10ᵗʰ Step – Knowing Everything Happens For A Reason: In the tenth step, we embrace the fact that everything happens for a reason, no matter how challenging or devastating the obstacle. We trust in our ability to make the best out of every situation by accepting hardships, seeing them as new beginnings, and knowing that we will build success from the steps we take to bypass them. We recognize the role karma plays in our everyday life and we emanate this in our character. We understand that we are in the exact place where the Universe wants us to be at this moment.

As we go about the recovery process from what is bringing us down, we have to expect that there will be avalanches, harsh weather conditions, hurricanes, roadblocks, sinkholes, tornadoes, tsunamis, and other blockades that could set us back. We might experience immense pain. Tragic events may occur. Anything is possible. We have to know that whatever comes our way will happen for a reason. We can rest assured, knowing that no matter how heavy the burden may be, once we recover there will be bright blue skies, starry nights, sunny days, and happy fulfilling lives for us to maintain. We learn that when we do things to intentionally hurt others, and lack compassion, more often than not we are challenged with hardships. This is often referred to as karma. Whether our signal from the Universe confirms that we are on the right path, or forces us to change direction, it is important for us to decipher the meaning. If we are strong and wise enough to search for the meaning behind our difficulties, then we can more easily unravel the message each struggle we encounter is trying to deliver. When we conquer calamities, we gain a better appreciation for when life is going our way. We tend to take less things for granted and we are more grateful for what we have. The experience of being on both sides of the spectrum, and knowing what it feels like to struggle in pain, and to rejoice in happiness, has a spiritually cleansing effect.

Throughout the book I listed various components of true happiness. These include: reaching an optimal level of health, achieving non-material success, social involvement and interaction, being active, growing our own food, maintaining a positive attitude, having an optimistic outlook, and possessing strong mental faith. By implementing into our lives each of the steps in this book, and manifesting these components of happiness, we can create more fulfilling lives. To make this possible, we must write down our goals and formulate an action plan.

Writing Down Your Goals

"When I was growing up I always wanted to be someone. Now I realize I should have been more specific." — Lily Tomlin

As we list our goals, we need to be specific about what we want. By writing down a simple goal, such as, *I want to be happy*, this is a good start, but we are not going to help our situation until we enrich our aspirations. If our goal is to be happy, then we must write down all of the ways that we plan to attract happiness into our life. It is important that we provide details for every step we have to take, and how we plan to take action to implement the necessary changes. To successfully manifest a happier life, we can use the lessons from each step in Society's Anonymous, write down the actions we need to take, and use them to accomplish our goals. A successful action plan is required for creating the life we desire.

My Action Plan: *My goal is to be happy. To accomplish this I will identify what is bringing me down; change my perception and correct my attitude; cleanse internally; improve my diet; exercise regularly; find ways to add nature into my life; build my character and add substance to who I am; associate with only positive people; pursue my passions and live without expectations; elevate my consciousness; embrace obstacles; take action; and help others around me.*

I will identify what is stimulating my depression by reviewing the protagonist list and comparing it to the antagonist list. This will help me

188   Jacoby

recognize the power I have over my mood. I will shift my thoughts away from each of the entities that are triggering melancholy and list all of the things that make me happy. Once I know what elevates my mood, I can correct my attitude, change my perception, and start manifesting happiness into my life.

To eliminate negative thoughts and freshen up internally, I am going to empty my cabinets and clear my home of all chemical cleaners, foods, and products, and start purchasing everything organic. I will undergo internal cleansing services such as colon hydrotherapy, lymphatic drainage massages, oxygen baths, and sauna sessions regularly. I already purchased a juicer and am going to stock up on fresh organic fruits and vegetables tomorrow to start my first juice fast this week. My new diet will be free of all animal products, GMOs, gluten flours, refined sugars, and processed fillers. I am going to drink fresh organic juices and up to a gallon of distilled water daily, and eat plenty of raw fruits and vegetables.

I already joined my local gym, and I will exercise daily for at least an hour. I woke up today and meditated. I plan to try it again before bed tonight. I found a nice park with trails while I was out earlier and I am going to put on my new running shoes tomorrow and test them out. The gym offers yoga classes, so I will take yoga twice a week for now. I ordered my organic seeds, and shoveled out a spot in my yard for my first garden. I am excited for them to arrive in the mail.

I picked up my guitar today for the first time in months. I am going to master it this time. I went online and found Coursera and DuoLingo, so I am enrolling in courses and signed up to learn Spanish for free. There are racquetball courts at the gym, so this will hopefully be a new hobby of mine that I enjoy. The local community college offers a pottery class, and I am going to sign up for it soon. I feel so good about all of these new activities and events that I am starting to include in my life. I found a stack of old magazines in my closet and a piece of poster board. This will turn into my vision board.

Yesterday I wrote down a list of the ten most influential people in my life, and after averaging out how happy I think they are, realized that I need to attract a few more positive people into my life. I am hoping to meet them soon. I decided that I am going to continue living to make me happy, not my parents or friends. This was a revolutionary feeling for me.

After learning more about the injustices taking place all over the world, I made a pact with myself that I would no longer purchase anything that was tested on animals, contains palm oil, or has chemicals in it. I removed meat, dairy, and eggs from my life permanently. I plan to have solar panels installed so I no longer rely on propane. I am happy knowing that the decisions I am making are not harming other people in the process. I will always be prepared for obstacles that are coming my way. Finally, I will take action, and be sure that I do not allow stagnation to infiltrate my momentum. I will win the battle with resistance. Once I find success with my new life, I am going to spread the word and raise awareness everywhere I go. I want to make society a better place.

This is a perfect example of an action plan. I expect yours to be more detailed. Open up your soul to the paper when you record your desires. Write down your passions. Do not leave anything out. Be sure that you include alternative routes in case your path gets blocked by an unexpected obstacle, or in the event that you meet face-to-face with failure. It is your responsibility now to write down your plan for how you will transform your life into an adventure through all of the realms of happiness. This is your opportunity to climb out of despair for good. Remember to be specific. It is okay to dream big. Do not let doubts, limitations, restrictions, or a lack of resources inhibit you from devising your action plan to be exactly the way your soul envisions it. You will find abundance once you put the message out to the Universe that you know what you want, have a plan, and are ready to execute. Take out your hemp notebook, find a pen, and get to work.

"Wealth, my son, should never be your goal in life. Your words are eloquent but they are mere words. True wealth is of the heart, not of the purse." – Og Mandino, *The Greatest Salesman In The World*

Fighting Resistance

"The danger is greatest when the finish line is in sight. At this point, resistance knows we are about to beat it. It hits the panic button. It marshals one last assault and slams us with everything it has got." – Steven Pressfield, *The War of Art*

When I was finishing my first book, *The Raw Cure*, I found myself being defeated by a force that was preventing me from accomplishing this goal. I put off the work I needed to complete, procrastinated as much as possible, and felt like I would never get the job done. I was overwhelmed. I finally decided to take some time to read, *Do The Work*, by Steven Pressfield. His book enlightened me to what this great force is, being resistance. When we are putting our creative energy out into the Universe and going after our true calling, resistance is the only thing that holds us back. The closer we get to finishing, the stronger our resilience must be. Using his advice and encouraging words, I managed to fight off resistance and regain my focus. Another of his books, *The War of Art*, also addresses resistance and provides insight on how to be victorious over this force.

As we start accommodating happiness in our lives, it is inevitable for us to meet resistance at some point. This challenges our character, questions our determination, and tests our will. We might struggle to persevere and sometimes feel like giving up. There will be moments when we feel like we are walking over hot coals, laying on a bed of nails, or being pulled in by a strong current while trying mightily to swim back to shore. It is important for us to triumph over this force and go after what is rightfully ours. We have to ask ourselves how badly we want to break free from depression, and demonstrate this desire to be happy in our actions and attitude. We are here for reasons that go beyond working to make money. Our actions need to align with our passions, and we should strive to make the world a better place on our mission.

190

To conquer resistance, we must have a plan, and it is an obligation for us to take action in order to carry out this strategy. An effective policy is writing goals. Once we find our purpose, and are able to live out our passions, there is no longer space in our lives for pity, rejection, or sadness. We become the best possible versions of us that we can be.

"The road of life is strewn with the bodies of promising people. People who show promise, yet lack the confidence to act. People who make promises they are unable to keep. People who promise to do tomorrow what they could do today. Promising young stars, athletes, entrepreneurs who wait for promises to come true. Promise without a goal and a plan is like a barren cow. You know what she could do if she could do it, but she cannot. Turn your promise into a plan. Make no promise for tomorrow if you are able to keep it today. And if someone calls you promising, know that you are not doing enough today." – Iyanla Vanzant, *Acts of Faith: Daily Meditations for People of Color*

The Best Version Of You

"My father could have been a great comedian but he did not believe that this was possible for him, and so he made a conservative choice. Instead, he got a safe job as an accountant. When I was twelve years old, he was let go from that safe job, and our family had to do whatever we could to survive. I learned many great lessons from my father, not the least of which was that you can fail at what you do not want, so you might as well take a chance on doing what you love." – Jim Carrey, *Actor and Comedian*

If you are ever speaking to a group of people and you say, *"Okay, I want all of you to raise your hand as high as you can,"* you will notice that they tend to raise their hands high up in the air. As their hands are raised, if you then say, *"Okay, now I want you to raise them higher,"* somehow they find a way to get their hands higher in the air. Too often we claim to be doing our best, yet we are ignoring how much better we can become, and how much more we can accomplish with what we have. When I refer to the best version of you, I want you to be the very best. I want you to give more than one-hundred percent at every moment. This does not mean you claim to be the best, try it out for a short period of time, and then regress back into the depressed version of you. I want you to be a ray of happiness. I want you to magnetize positivity everywhere you go. To do so, you cannot be too easy on yourself.

In an endurance race, most of the time competitors will conserve energy until the very end, or for ascents uphill, careful not to run out of energy late, or fall behind early in the race. They conserve their energy, clinging to the belief that they do not have what it takes to give it their all for the entire duration of the race. This relates to the common way many of us move through life. Does it not seem as if we hang on to our ambitions, beliefs, and hopes until it is too late? Why are we holding back? Are we fearful of attaining what we truly desire? We have what it takes to give it our all every day, in any circumstance, no matter what the situation may be. There is never a reason for any of us to restrict our potential. Knowing this, we can no longer afford to be easy on ourselves. We have to give our all even when we feel there is no use.

"If you do not build your dream, someone will hire you to help build theirs." – Tony Gaskins

We are each entitled to unique dreams. We have ambitions, desires, fantasies, goals, necessities, and wants that we yearn for every day. This is our time to captivate them and manifest these constituents into our lives. We cannot experience true happiness until we start building our own masterpieces through action; rather than continuing to help others construct their dreams using our commitment, energy, labor, and time.

"If you really want to heal and change your life for the better, what will work is getting busy with it. Instead of expecting the past to be something it was not, focus on making the future into something that it can be." – John McCabe, *Igniting Your Life*

If you are letting your past restrict you from acting to create a more lively future, it helps to recognize the cycle of defeat you are choosing to participate in. What happened yesterday, last week, a few months ago, or during our childhood is not relevant to how we approach today and what we will do with each rising sun. We have to focus on what will bring us happiness now. Our concentration should be on preserving this happiness so it carries over into our future.

"The truth is that there is nothing noble in being superior to somebody else. The only real nobility is being superior to your former self." – Whitney Young, *Civil Rights leader*

To establish authentic versions of ourselves, this requires that we become superior to our past. This is not a battle for us to one-up others, or win the race to see who we have left behind in the dust. We want to grow up, mature, and emerge as leaders. Our mission is to solidify our character by embracing awareness, compassion, confidence, love, and understanding. We choose to be optimistic and maintain positive attitudes. We erase all confusions surrounding the person we want to be. We have a clear understanding of what we want, and accept nothing less than what we envision.

"The World Makes Way For Those Who Know Where They Are Going." – Henry David Thoreau

When we know in our heart, mind, and spirit exactly what we want to do, where we want to be, and how we are going to get there, amazing things begin to happen. It seems as if a path opens up to us that we have never before noticed. It is up to us to choose to follow this new path. If we decide to take action, we will get what we want. Once we become accustomed to living this way, it gets easier for us to maintain our focus. We realize that we have control over our destiny.

"As they say, you never forget how to ride a bike once you have learned. Well, so it is with taking charge of your life and breaking through obstacles. Once you fully understand how you create your reality, you suddenly have the ability to plot a course to your desires that will truly amaze you because it feels like magic." – Craig Perrine

Jacoby

It is important for us not to forget the difference between being active and sedentary. Once we begin to take action, we can easily fall off track if we permit stagnation to infiltrate. We must fight off resistance at all costs to be successful on our road to recovery.

When I go running through the forest on hot days, if I stop for any reason, in that very moment mosquitoes will attack me. If I keep moving, they do not bother me. This motivates me to continue without resting. Imagine how wonderful it would be if every time we stopped being active in life, the Universe would send us a signal that would push us to carry on. Guess what, it does. When the life we lead does not align with our passions, depression bites at us so we will change our ways. If we eat poorly and live sedentary, we are often afflicted with a serious health condition. We do not get sick, or become ill so that we can blame God, curse our genetics, or give up on life. These conditions arise to motivate us so we will correct our errors and clean up our mistakes. The reason why we are confronted with failures on our mission to obtain happiness is not so we can dwell in misery, but rather for us to reshape our desires and go after what we are destined to succeed with. The Universe is working in our favor, not against us. It is okay to rest at times, but if we do not want to get bit by misfortunes, then we must remain active in our pursuit of a better life.

"Even if you are on the right track, you will get run over if you just sit there." – Will Rogers

At fifty-two, Janette Murray-Wakelin was diagnosed with breast cancer and the prognosis was that she had only six months to live. After recognizing that she could improve her life in many ways, she chose to bypass all conventional treatments and changed her diet and lifestyle. By bolstering her perception, exercising, and eating plant-based, she healed and became cancer-free. Soon after, she published the book, *Raw Can Cure Cancer*. In 2013, Janette, 64, and her husband, Alan Murray, 68, ran a marathon every day of the year. They followed this up with one final run on the first day of 2014 to break the world record for running the most consecutive marathons. When asked why they decided to run, their answer was, *"To inspire and motivate conscious lifestyle choices, to promote kindness and compassion for all living beings, and to raise environmental awareness for a sustainable future."* To add to the greatness of their incredible feat, they accomplished this on a strict raw vegan diet, and ran in *Vibram* shoes.

According to a January 2014 article on the *True Activist* webpage (*trueactivist.com*), *Elderly Vegan Couple Ran A Marathon Every Day of 2013*, the couple fueled with raw organic fruits and vegetables and followed *The 80/10/10 Diet,* by Dr. Douglas Graham (*foodnsport.com*). Every morning they would awaken at four a.m. and consume ten bananas, a grapefruit, and a date smoothie for breakfast. At around eight a.m., they would eat another ten bananas. This was followed by a green smoothie at nine a.m., a fruit salad at the nineteen-mile mark, and three oranges by the twenty-third mile. They would finish their run by four p.m. Dinner for the two would likely be an avocado, vegetable juice, and salad. They announced that, *"Consuming an abundance of high-nutrient laden, fresh, ripe, organic fruits and vegetables allows them to experience true happiness, make conscious choices that benefit the planet, and feel great."* By following this diet, not only were they able to successfully run over 9,800 miles in a year, but they also obtained sufficient amounts of antioxidants, calcium, carbohydrates, fats, fiber, iron, liquids, phytonutrients, proteins, and all other essential amino acids, minerals, and vitamins. They awakened better versions of themselves. If you adapt to *The 80/10/10* approach, you will likely find similar success.

While society has mistakenly believed for years that animal products help to fuel endurance and provide us with strength, what we know today is that these food choices drain our endurance and deplete our vitality. The best fuel sources for athletes are raw fruits and vegetables, and fresh organic juices and smoothies – as Janette and Alan demonstrated. In fact, many of the most dominant endurance athletes fuel with plant-based food sources. The fastest man in the world, Usain Bolt, and his fellow Jamaican sprinter, Yohan Blake, both insist that bananas are their primary fuel sources. Yohan announced that he will eat up to thirty bananas a day while training. The endurance athlete, Rich Roll, who is considered one of the fittest men on the planet, gets his fuel from plants, abiding by a strict vegan diet. You can learn about his story in the book, *Finding Ultra*. The vegan bodybuilder, Joshua Knox, who was a heavy meat eater at one point speaks at *TedXFremont* about how he gained more strength and endurance than he ever thought was possible on a plant-based diet. His presentation was titled, *A Vegan Bodybuilding Experiment*.

Imagine if Janette had given up after she was afflicted with cancer. The disease would have destroyed her. She instead opted to take action, heal herself, and not allow this disease to infiltrate her positivity. Today she is a source of inspiration because she decided to take action and gain control of her health and well-being. We can all learn a lesson or two from her story. Discover more about her incredible life by accessing the website for *Running Raw Around Australia* (*runningrawaroundaustralia.com*).

Now that we have healed ourselves, our action plans are set in stone, and we know our dharma, we can start reaching out to our loved ones who are depressed by introducing them to these guidelines. By helping everyone around us, we begin healing society. The final step in Society's Anonymous is perhaps the most rewarding of all. This is our chance to spread the love.

Jacoby

The 12th Step: Helping Others

"Nothing in nature lives for itself. Rivers do not drink their own water. Trees do not eat their own fruit. The Sun does not provide heat for itself. Flowers spread fragrance for all of life to enjoy. Living for others is the rule of nature." – Gaia

Now that we have healed ourselves, we can focus on helping others around us. This is our chance to emerge as leaders, establish ourselves as mentors, and improve society. The twelfth and final step in Society's Anonymous is, *"Now that we have healed emotionally, mentally, and physically by cleansing internally, connecting with nature, correcting our attitude and perception, incorporating physical activity into our life, nourishing our body with organic, plant-based foods, and stepping over boundaries, limitations, and obstacles that have been blocking our happiness, it becomes our duty to share our newly acquired knowledge with others around us to help them find happiness, health, and success. We do this by devoting energy and time to those we come in contact with, encouraging them, and mentoring them through the healing process."* Upon completing this final step, we heal society from the symptoms of inactivity, inadequate nutrition, mental prison, poor health, and unhappiness. We make the world a better place.

"The principle art of the teacher is to awaken the joy in creation and knowledge." – Albert Einstein

It has been documented that one thing many children with learning disabilities lacks is confidence. Encouragement inspires confidence. When we are not encouraged, it is simple for us to generate a low self-esteem. This does not only apply to children, and it certainly is not limited to those who experience learning disabilities. There are masses of people who have what I refer to as a *happiness disability*. They hoard an inability to reach a level of true happiness. These people are in need of a confidence boost, and they require stimulation from an external source to improve their condition. You could be the person they need to inspire change.

"If we are going to live an ethical life, it is not enough just to follow the thou-shalt-nots. If we have enough, we have to share some of that with people who have so little." — Peter Singer, *The Why and How of Effective Altruism*

I once read a story about two men who both were seriously ill, and shared a hospital room. The origin of this story is unknown to me, but I find it appropriate for this final step. One of the men was allowed to sit up in his bed for an hour each afternoon to help drain the fluid from his lungs. His bed was next to the room's only window. The other man had to spend all of his time flat on his back.

The men talked for countless hours each day. They spoke of their wives and families, their homes, jobs, involvement in the military service, and about the many different destinations where they had vacationed. Every afternoon, when the man in the bed by the window could sit up, he would pass the time by describing to his roommate all of the things he could see outside of the window.

195

The man lying down began to live for those one hour intervals where he broadened his imagination and was enlivened by the imagery of all of the activity and color of the world outside. He listened as the man described how the window overlooked a park with a lovely lake, where ducks and swans played on the water while children sailed their model boats. He marveled about young lovers walking arm in arm amidst flowers of every color. He mentioned how he could see vividly a fine view of the city skyline in the distance.

As he listened to his friend describe all of this in exquisite detail, he would close his eyes and imagine the picturesque seen. For that hour of each day, he felt as if he were outside, young again, in perfect health. On one occasion, the man exclaimed that there was a parade passing by. Although he could not hear the band, he could still see it in his mind's eye as it was being portrayed with descriptive words. He remembered the days when he was part of the band that played at his local parade. The man lying down began to restore his faith, and his condition was improving.

Days, weeks, and months passed. One morning, the nurse arrived to bring water for their baths only to find the lifeless body of the man by the window, who had died peacefully in his sleep. She was saddened and called the hospital attendants to take the body away.

As soon as it seemed appropriate, the other man asked if he could be moved to the bed next to the window. She happily arranged the switch for him and after assuring he was comfortable, she left him on his own.

Slowly, and painfully, the man propped himself up on one elbow to take his first look outside at the real world. He turned slowly to look and realized that the window faced a blank wall. The man asked the nurse later what could have compelled his deceased roommate to describe all of these wonderful things outside of the window. She informed him that the man was blind and could not even see the wall. She said, *"Perhaps he just wanted to encourage you."*

I like the story because it demonstrates how much of an impact a little encouragement can have on our lives. This man was able to improve his health condition simply from an hour each day of being inspired. Now that we have successfully coached ourselves through all of the obstacles that were bringing us down, it is our duty to help everyone around us. It is now an obligation for us to encourage our family, friends – and whoever else we come in contact with that we feel are in need of positive change – to take action. We may be the source they need to improve from their health conditions, or to break free from depression.

There is too much confusion in the world today. Doctors are prescribing pills that benefit their bank accounts at the expense of the health of their patients. Processed food companies are marketing products that do not contain real food, and people are actually eating these items thinking they are being nourished. Millions of people are still smoking cigarettes, drinking alcohol, and chewing gum, unaware that they are inching closer to death with each drag, shot, and stick. We have the power to convince those we care about to make the changes necessary to summon happiness into their lives.

196

"Warriors are not what you think of as warriors. The warrior is not someone who fights, because no one has the right to take another life. The warrior, for us, is one who sacrifices himself for the good of others. His task is to take care of the elderly, the defenseless, those who cannot provide for themselves, and above all, the children, the future of humanity." – Tatanka Iyotaka (Sitting Bull)

From my experience as a health coach, nutritionist, and trainer, I have worked with hundreds of people, and I know how difficult it can be to relay a message to them. Transitioning to a new way of life is challenging, and not too many of us enjoy stepping out of our zones of comfort to accomplish change. This is why successful coaches are important assets.

From years of trial and error, I formulated an approach that I have always had success with. I hope it will also be useful for you when you venture off to share your newly acquired knowledge.

The GIVE Approach

To successfully coach someone, we can implement a technique I refer to as, *The GIVE Approach*. More often than not, people are scared of change. They tend to elude opportunities to do things differently, and they wallow in their state of unhappiness. Think of how you would have reacted before reading this book. Were you hesitant to read the book, thinking maybe it would not help, or that you already knew all of the answers? The average person does not take advice easily, especially if it could be a potential hazard to their current way of living. I find that we can captivate others around us – and befriend the masses – by simply being genuine, not placing them in a position where they may feel inferior, and by valuing them. We do not want to force our views on anyone. We are only giving them the option to listen, if they so choose.

The GIVE Approach consists of four basic guidelines that will help us achieve success while working to improve others lives. They are simple, yet effective. When we begin teaching those around us about what is really bringing them down, and start suggesting natural ways for them to attract happiness, we do not want to overwhelm them. To avoid conflict, we can plan our approach using these four preliminary steps.

- **G**reet them kindly and be genuine.
- **I**nclude them as if they are the *centerpiece*.
- **V**alue their current way of life so they do not feel inferior.
- **E**quip them with knowledge to help overcome depression.

How we greet another has significant influence over how receptive they will be to our presence. We have to be careful that we are not reflecting arrogance, or ego. If we are, the simple truth is that we are not ready to coach others. When we are ready, we naturally diminish any arrogance we may have

197

possessed before our enlightenment. We glow with confidence, good health, and a positive spirit. This attracts others, keeping them drawn to us. It is imperative that we lead by example, and practice what we preach.

Winning Others Over

"Example is not the main thing in influencing others. It is the only thing." – Albert Schweitzer

To successfully win someone's heart, or gain their respect, it helps to be kind. By complimenting that person, this opens a clear path for them to be receptive to our presence. Another component of winning that person over, believe it or not, lies in constructively criticizing them. If we can initiate conversation with a stranger or friend, compliment them to the point where they are comfortable opening up to us, and listen tentatively enough to notice something about them that they could improve, we have accomplished an important goal. To be victorious in our pursuit to be helpful, we should give each person at least five compliments that are from the heart, personalized, and not generic before we constructively criticize them. If we cannot think of five nice things to say about this particular person, then we do not know them well enough to offer criticism.

When we go about our mission to help others generate happiness, we want them to feel important. We have to appreciate their morals and values. This is how we embrace their friendship and earn trust. To avoid being rejected by someone in need of guidance or a helping hand, we win respect by recognizing their good qualities and potential. We can then determine how to approach them stemming from these qualities, and using our leadership assets to nurture change and spiritual growth. Many people fear change, and if we present something new to them they are quick to shy away. By implementing small steps and working in proximity with their current standards of living, we can be more successful with our approach.

"Try not to become a man of success. Rather, recognize that you are a man of value." – Albert Einstein

As a peer mentor in high school, I remember working with a kid who was affiliated with a gang. He desperately needed guidance. I recognized his potential, but had to find a way to earn his respect so he would appreciate my willingness to help him out. Rather than being judgmental or telling him how awful and dangerous the *gang-life* is, I explained to him how the best way to work his way into the ladder of success with his gang was to get an education. I told him that all gangs need accountants, attorneys, and brilliant business minds to help with their operations. I was genuine with him, made him feel important, and tried to help him build success from his current standards of living. My goal was for him to engage his mind in the classroom, and recognize the importance of his studies. I would have loved to see him drop his affiliation with the gang and get involved in the community, but I knew better than to pry into his personal life beyond school. Once he understood that he would be more valuable to his gang by educating himself, he began to cherish the

198

opportunity to learn and he was more attentive in his classes, kept his grades up, and later went on to graduate. He also realized once he was educated that being in a gang is not something that he wanted to define him, or take pride in. Not only did he graduate, but he also lost interest in gang involvement. By valuing his way of life, and embracing his friendship, I was able to win him over to the point where he trusted me, opened up to me, and took my advice to finish up school and educate himself. I used the *GIVE Approach*.

Another example of using the *GIVE Approach* took place at a gym I was working at. I had a personal training client who had high blood pressure and cholesterol, and purchased my services to help him lose a goal weight of sixty pounds. He was a kind man with a big heart, and I truly wanted to help him. Before purchasing training sessions, he scheduled a nutrition consultation with me. During the meeting I informed him of the dangers attached to eating dairy, eggs, GMOs, meat, processed foods, and refined sugars. I also suggested that he watch the documentary, *Forks Over Knives*. He was quite receptive to everything I discussed with him, and he said, *"But Jesse, I was raised eating meat with every meal. When I was a kid my grandfather used to let us chew on homemade jerky. I want to follow your advice, but I do not know how I will accomplish giving up meat entirely."* We compromised. I suggested that he start out by excluding meat on Mondays. Then he could progress to giving up two days a week. Eventually he might try going one day on, one day off until he was able to remove it permanently. I convinced him to get a high-powered blender and to start every day with a fresh organic green smoothie. I gave him tidbits of advice beyond giving up animal products to help with his transformation. I was genuine with him, I made sure he felt like he was important to me, and I valued his cultural differences. I also equipped him with the knowledge he needed to improve his health. He listened to my advice. Each day he showed up at the gym with a smile on his face, did about an hour of cardio, and left. Within three weeks he looked like a new person. He approached me and said, *"Jesse, I want to thank you for your advice. I am down to eating meat twice a week, I cut out dairy, and I have been drinking those smoothies every morning. I feel great. My blood pressure and cholesterol levels are back to normal, and I already lost twenty-five pounds. Can I buy some training sessions now?"* I was able to win him over by expressing concern for his health, embracing his values, and making him a priority.

To win others over, it is important to show them that we are sincerely concerned about their well-being and that our only desire is to help them awaken their consciousness. We do not want to approach them as sales associates would, trying to convince them to buy things they do not need. We deliver them honesty at no cost. These guidelines are about helping people see things in a positive light, engaging their minds and imaginations, and encouraging them to improve their lives. When we help others, we do it to benefit them. We should not have ulterior motives. Our goal is to promote positivity and spread happiness.

Being A Mentor

One of Oprah Winfrey's mentors was Maya Angelou. When defining the role of a mentor, Oprah thinks of Maya and explains, *"A mentor is someone who allows you to see the hope inside of yourself."* As mentors, we recognize potential in others and inspire them to utilize their talents and gifts. Helen Keller once wrote, *"Believe, when you are most unhappy, that there is something for you to do in this world. So long as you can sweeten someone's pain, life is not in vain."* By helping others climb out of despair, it is surprising how fast we are also rescued from gloom.

I have been fortunate enough to have had many great mentors in my life. Some of them may not even be aware of the impact their presence has had on me. A goal of mine is to give back to others who are in need by providing the same guidance and support. One way for me to accomplish this goal is through the *Big Brothers, Big Sisters* program.

According to their website (*bbbs.org*), *"For more than one-hundred years, Big Brothers Big Sisters has operated under the belief that inherent in every child is the ability to succeed and thrive in life. As the nation's largest donor and volunteer supported mentoring network, Big Brothers Big Sisters makes meaningful, monitored matches between adult volunteers (Bigs) and children (Littles), ages six through eighteen, in communities across the country. We develop positive relationships that have a direct and lasting effect on the lives of young people."* The vision of this organization is for all children to achieve success in life, and their mission is, *"To provide children facing adversity with strong and enduring, professionally supported one-to-one relationships that change their lives for the better, forever. They seek for every participant to achieve higher aspirations, greater confidence, better relationships, avoidance of risky behaviors, and educational success."*

National research has shown that positive relationships between *Littles* and their *Bigs* have a direct and measurable impact on these children's lives. Not only are the kids impacted, but as mentors, we are also inspired to lead better lives. It was determined through research that *Little* Brothers and Sisters become *more confident in their schoolwork performance; are able to get along better with their families; and are forty-six percent less likely to begin using illegal drugs, twenty-seven percent less likely to start drinking alcohol, and fifty-two percent less likely to skip school.* This program truly makes a difference.

If you would like to get involved in the *Big Brothers Big Sisters* program, and you have the energy, passion, and time to help inspire a child in need so they have a better chance to succeed in life, search for the closest branch, fill out an application, and go in for an interview. After conducting a background check, and assuring you are applying for the right reasons, they will find a perfect match for you. You will be thankful that you are making the commitment. Just as your *Little* will learn from you, their presence will also motivate you to lead a better life.

"I want women, and men, to feel empowered by a deeper and more troubled part of themselves. The part they are always trying desperately to hide. I want that to become something that they cherish." – Lady Gaga

In the first step I mentioned how bullying is common, and provided examples of celebrities and famous athletes who struggled through being bludgeoned. The musician and entertainer, Lady Gaga, has similarly experienced hardships in the form of bullying. Growing up, she was often belittled and found it difficult to gain acceptance. She felt like society truly did not understand her. Music became her escape and gave her the freedom to express herself. While her unique public image projects a personality onto her of someone who is untamed and daring, this reflection also disguises the difficulties she has overcome in rising to fame. She was able to successfully surge above the adversity and emerge as a leader. Now she aspires to help other kids who are being bullied to discover their identity. Several of her songs address problems she sees in society relating to identity and individuality. Her music helps to promote self-empowerment by encouraging listeners to confront their fears and accept themselves.

In 2011, Lady Gaga and her mother, Cynthia Germanotta, established the *Born This Way Foundation* (*BTWF*) to *foster a more accepting society, where differences are embraced and individuality is celebrated*. The foundation (*bornthiswayfoundation.org*) is dedicated to creating a safe community that helps connect young people with the skills and opportunities they need to build a braver, kinder world. Their belief is that *everyone has the right to feel safe, be empowered, and make a difference in the world*. The BTWF supports programs and initiatives that deal with all aspects of empowering youth. The non-profit charitable organization *hopes to lead youth into a braver new society where each individual is accepted and loved as the person they were born to be*. The BTWF will focus on youth empowerment and equality by addressing issues like anti-bullying, career development, mentoring, self-confidence, and well-being, and will utilize digital mobilization as a means to create positive change. If this interests you, sign up as one of their mentors today.

"Be kind. Be unique. Make the impossible happen." – Ellen DeGeneres

Ellen DeGeneres hosts a daytime talk show which recognizes individuals who have made a difference in the world by virtue of artistic talent, charity work, or philanthropy. She uses her fame and prestige to bring awareness to positive actions, and to applaud those who do good work. She encourages her audiences to carry on the trend of good karma. Her public image of an energetic, happy person is enhanced through her comedy. Each of her shows begins with dance and comedic interaction with the audience. This cheerful mood carries through the duration of the event.

Ellen mentors people every day and demonstrates benevolence by supporting those who need encouragement. Her humanitarianism is evident as she gives back to the community and contributes to charities, helping people in need of love and attention. She validates her compassion as a vegan advocate, often aiding charities and organizations that help animals. When I think of true heroes, I see Ellen's smiling face. Her dedication and success as a mentor can serve as an example for each of us while we go about our mission to be of service to others in need. With her books, talk show, and website (*ellentv.com*) as platforms to express her passions, Ellen uses charity, comedy, and love to combat discrimination and ignite positivity in the world.

"Do not train a child to learn by force or harshness; but direct them to it by what amuses their minds, so that you may be better able to discover with accuracy the peculiar bend of the genius of each." – Plato

In addition to the *Born This Way Foundation*, and *Big Brothers Big Sisters*, an additional avenue for mentoring is *The National Mentoring Partnership* (*MENTOR*). This partnership has provided a public voice, developing and delivering resources to mentoring programs nationwide. When MENTOR was founded over twenty-five years ago, there were an estimated 300,000 at-risk youth in structured mentoring relationships. Today, research shows that 4.5 million at risk youth will have a structured mentoring relationship while they are growing up. Their mission is, *"To fuel the quality and quantity of mentoring relationships for America's young people and to close the mentoring gap. MENTOR carries out this work in collaboration with more than 5,000 mentoring programs in all fifty states. We engage with the private, public and nonprofit sectors to ensure that all youth have the support they need through mentoring relationships to succeed at home, school and, ultimately, work."* To get involved with MENTOR, access their website (*mentoring.org*).

"Teach them the quiet words of kindness, to live beyond themselves. Urge them towards excellence, drive them towards gentleness, pull them upward towards manhood, but delicately like an angel arranging clouds. Let your spirit move through them softly." – Pat Conroy, *The Prince of Tides*

Being a mentor requires authenticity, commitment, dedication, emotion, encouragement, energy, respect, and time. Once we agree to mentor someone, we have to be careful not to abandon those we are helping. Most of the children participating have low self-esteem, are desperately seeking attention and guidance, and need positive role models in their lives. Once we commit to a mentoring role, it is important that we are always available for our new friends. To be a successful mentor we should be happy, healthy, and ready to inspire others to succeed. Giving back to the community by helping children in need is an important component of true happiness.

As mentors, we are provided the opportunity to help those who are abused, living in poverty, neglected, and experiencing less than ideal situations so they can feel important and cherished. We are granted the good fortune of equipping them with the knowledge and support they are seeking to correct their attitudes, break free from what is bringing them down, and empower themselves. We help them to create the new experiences they need to store happy memories and thoughts. I encourage everyone who is in a position to do so to join a mentoring program and start giving back to the community. I am confident that you will also grow in the process.

Sharing Your New Gift

"I am going to make everything around me more beautiful, that will be my life." – Visionary declaration

The American puppeteer, Jim Henson, who produced *The Muppet Show*, and is responsible for creating the characters *Ernie*, and *Kermit the Frog*, once exclaimed, *"My hope still is to leave the world a bit better than when I got here."* He accomplished this dream in his life work.

Not all of us will pull off what Mr. Henson did in his life, however, we can put forth effort each day to make the world around us better by sharing our gifts of compassion, happiness, love, and understanding. People are not always going to agree with us, and we will not be able to give more than we have to offer, but we can extend gifts to each person we come in contact with in the form of a flower, kind words, nice thoughts, or a smile.

"Until you have learned to be tolerant with those who do not always agree with you; until you have cultivated the habit of saying some kind word of those whom you do not admire; until you have formed the habit of looking for the good instead of the bad there is in others, you will be neither successful nor happy." – Napoleon Hill, *Think & Grow Rich*

Once we earn success, gain wealth, and see the light, it becomes a duty of ours to do the best we can to help pave trails for others around us so they are able to experience more abundance and prosperity. As mentors, teachers, and loving individuals, we can act on this duty each day. Once we survive the hardships, misfortunes, and struggles, we gain an appreciation for what others may be enduring.

There is a saying that circulates around all ancient cultures, *"If it is not good for everyone, it is no good at all."* In Africa, they call this *UBUNTU* – a natural order of things in total harmony with nature, our planet, and all of creation. An anthropologist once shared the story of how he proposed a game to the kids in an African tribe. He put a basket of fruit near a tree, and told the children that the first one to find the fruits would win them all. He suggested that they run to find the prize and observed their reactions. The man was startled to witness as they all took each others hands and ran together. They found the fruits as a unit, sat near the tree, and enjoyed their reward as a group. The anthropologist asked the kids why they decided to run together, knowing that one could have taken all of the fruits for himself if he found it on his own. They responded by saying, *"UBUNTU, how can one of us be happy if all the other ones are sad?"* Imagine if the children in our society were this caring, loving, and willing to share. We can manifest this into reality by correcting ourselves first, and then sharing our gifts with everyone around us. By demonstrating kindness in our everyday actions, we ignite this new trend.

Scott Neeson, former head of *20th Century Fox International* left Hollywood to save underprivileged children who were literally rotting in Cambodia's garbage dumps. He sold his mansion, Porsche, and yacht to set off for Cambodia to provide education, food, and shelter to destitute children. Scott now cares for more than one-thousand Cambodian children and their families. He made the decision to give up material items that were not necessities in exchange for providing the less fortunate with the essentials needed for survival. He is sharing his gifts with the world now through the *Cambodian Children's Fund (cambodianchildrensfund.org)*.

"Those who have the privilege to know, have the duty to act." – Albert Einstein

At the 2014 *World Cup* soccer tournament in Brazil, the famous Portuguese soccer player, Cristiano Ronaldo, unveiled a zig-zag pattern shaved into the side of his head before his match against team USA. After some speculation as to why he did this, it was soon discovered that his new look was a gesture of solidarity, or tribute, to a ten month old boy named Erik Ortiz Cruz. Erik had recently underwent brain surgery and Ronaldo not only supported him by cutting his hair to mimic the scar on the young boy's head, but he also paid for the entire operation, costing nearly eighty-three thousand dollars. He shared his gift of generosity, kindness, and love with a young boy in need, and in doing so, made the world around him a better place.

In the October 2012 issue of *Forbes* magazine, there is an article about a man named Chuck Feeney. Chuck is considered to be the *James Bond* of philanthropy. His generous foundation, known as *Atlantic Philanthropies (atlanticphilanthropies.org)*, has funneled $6.2 billion into grants for civil rights, education, health care, and science in Australia, Bermuda, Ireland, South Africa, the U.S., and Vietnam. Since 1982, he has traveled the world conducting a surreptitious operation to give away the $7.5 billion fortune he earned over the course of his lifetime from hawking cigarettes, cognac, and perfume. His plan is to donate the remaining $1.3 billion by 2016. Rather than obsessing over piling up as many riches as possible, as most others in society fantasize about, Feeney is putting in extra hours working to die broke. His aspiration to help others is driven by his understanding that the most important asset in life is happiness. He promotes this belief by enriching others lives to the best of his ability.

The *Freedom Writers Foundation* is a nonprofit organization which was founded in 1997, and is known to positively affect communities by decreasing high school dropout rates through the enhancement and replication of the *Freedom Writers Method*. Their vision is to, *"Inspire young, underprivileged students to pick up pens instead of guns."* This method was introduced by a teacher named Erin Gruwell and her group of 150 students in the fall of 1994 at *Woodrow Wilson Classical High School* in Long Beach, California. As a new teacher coming from a prosperous community in Newport Beach, she was naturally intimidated by her group of *at-risk* students who she was challenged to educate. Despite her uneasiness, she never gave up on them, and found ways to develop solid relationships with these kids. She handed out notebooks to each of them so they could share their stories as journal entries, writing their way to freedom from hurt, oppression, and pain. She compared the students to the brave and courageous *Freedom Riders* of the *Civil Rights Movement*, only referring to them as *Freedom Writers*. Her students went on to surprise everyone. All 150 *Freedom Writers* graduated from high school and many went on to attend college. In interviews, Erin shares that she thinks she is the one who changed the most. "*Everything I was told not to do, I did. They told me not to smile. I smiled. They told me never to show emotion. How could I not be a person, though? How could I not be compassionate and give a student a hug when they were hurting? I changed the most. I became the student.*" The *Freedom Writers* story led to the publication of, *The Freedom Writers Diary: How a Teacher and 150 Teens Used Writing to Change Themselves and the World Around Them,* and inspired the major motion picture, *Freedom Writers*, in 2007. Ms. Gruwell's dedication, passion, and will to transform her students lives for the better is a prime example of how much of an influence we can be for creating positive change in children's lives as mentors and teachers.

After battling a heroin addiction for several years, the musician, Bob Forrest, finally found his niche in Hollywood as a drug counselor. At fifty-two, he has abstained from drugs for eighteen years and now dedicates his energy and time to helping other musicians, and recovering drug addicts to find sobriety. For years Bob teamed up with *Celebrity Rehab* counselor, Dr. Drew Pinsky, before branching out and opening *Hollywood Recovery Services*. Today, Bob has helped countless addicts and alcoholics get sober and find their purpose. *He is* now program director for *Acadia Malibu (acadiamalibu.com)*, and considered to be one of the finest drug counselors living today, assisting everyone from award winning celebrities to struggling teens. He is sharing his gift of compassion with the world.

Rip Esselstyn is a motivational speaker, and author of *The Engine2 Diet*, and *My Beef With Meat*. As a vegan advocate, Rip spent a decade as one of the premier triathletes in the world before joining the *Austin Fire Department* where he introduced his passion for a whole-food, plant-based diet to their *Engine 2 Firehouse*. In order to rescue a firefighting brother's health, he led his team through a lifestyle transition by helping them convert to vegan diets. He documented their success in his national bestselling book, *The Engine 2 Diet*, which shows the irrefutable connection between a plant-based diet and good health. Rip recently left his job as a firefighter to team up with *Whole Foods Market* as one of their *Healthy Eating Partners* to raise awareness for *Whole Foods* communities, customers, and employees about the benefits of eating a plant-strong diet. He has appeared on hundreds of radio shows as well as national television shows, including the *Today show*, *CBS Sunday Morning Show*, *Good Morning America*, and *The Dr. Oz Show*. Rip knew that his diet, lifestyle, and passion for eating plant-based could help improve the health of millions of people worldwide, so he devoted his time and energy writing the books and sharing this valuable information with everyone around him.

While there are plenty of people in the world who go out of their way to help others in need, some take their compassion, generosity, and kindness and direct it towards saving the environment. Captain Paul Watson devotes his energy, love, and time to saving whales from whaling vessels. He and his crew risk their lives every day in efforts to save what remains of the largest, most magnificent marine mammals left on the planet. Established in 1977, *Sea Shepherd Conservation Society* (SSCS) is an international non-profit, marine wildlife conservation organization. Their mission is, *"To end the destruction of habitat and slaughter of wildlife in the world's oceans in order to conserve and protect ecosystems and species."* Sea Shepherd *uses innovative direct-action tactics to investigate, document, and take action when necessary to expose and confront illegal activities on the high seas. By safeguarding the biodiversity of our delicately balanced ocean ecosystems, Sea Shepherd works to ensure their survival for future generations.* Learn more about Paul Watson and his heroic mission at *seashepherd.org*.

"Protecting our planet's oceans, and the marine species that call it home, is one of the most pressing sustainability crises facing humanity today and a moral imperative that we must acknowledge." – Leonardo DiCaprio

So many of us recognize Leonardo DiCaprio as an amazing actor. He is one of Hollywood's most well-known, and respected big names. His greatness extends far beyond the spotlight. With his earnings from those movies we enjoy so much, Mr. DiCaprio does the best he can to help save the rainforests and oceans. In addition to serving as a board member of the *World Wildlife Fund* (*worldwildlife.org*), *Oceans 5* (*oceans5.org*), *Pristine Seas*, The *Natural Resources Defense Council* (*nrdc.org*), and *International Fund for Animal Welfare* (*ifaw.org*), he also launched the *Leonardo DiCaprio Foundation* (*leonardodicaprio.com*). Mr. DiCaprio's foundation is dedicated to protecting tigers from extinction; saving the last rainforests – especially the largest remaining block of rainforest in Sumatra, home to wild tigers, orangutans, elephants and two indigenous tribes; protecting the oceans – dedicated to stopping overfishing and establishing marine reserves, the two highest ecological priorities identified by scientists; saving sharks; protecting Antarctica; and providing access to clean water for people in Darfur, Mozambique, Sierra Leone, and Tanzania.

In 2014, Oceana (*oceana.org*), the largest international advocacy group to work on behalf of the world's oceans, announced a $3 million grant from the *Leonardo DiCaprio Foundation* aimed at protecting threatened ocean habitat and keystone marine species such as dolphins, sharks, and whales. The foundation's grant will also support Oceana's work to advocate for responsible fishing measures, including the effort to ban California drift gillnets. In addition to their grant for saving the oceans, the LDF also raised more than $2 million in support of the *Elephant Crisis Fund (elephantcrisisfund.org)* to support anti-poaching, anti-trafficking and ivory demand reduction projects on the ground. In November 2013, LDF awarded a $3 million grant to the *World Wildlife Fund* (WWF) for a bold initiative to help Nepal double its wild tiger numbers by 2022. *This grant will bolster WWF's work with the government of Nepal and local communities in Nepal's Terai Arc landscape to strengthen anti-poaching patrols, protect core areas for tiger breeding, restore critical corridors for their dispersal and expansion, and continuously monitor tiger populations. Previous support from the Leonardo DiCaprio Foundation is already showing major results, growing the number of tigers in the Terai's*

Bardia National Park from an estimated eighteen to fifty tigers. Leonardo uses his fame and recognition to make the world a better place. He is a generous man who cares about animals, other people who are in need, and the environment. He shares his many gifts and extends compassion in a world that needs more people like him.

Philip Wollen started the *Kindness Trust* fund (*kindnesstrust.com*). He funds projects and organizations that bring kindness to our world. At the age of thirty-four, Philip became the Vice President of *Citibank*. By the age of forty, after visiting a factory farm where animals are slaughtered, he resigned, and put his money and energy towards ending the factory farming industry, and enriching us with compassion. He is well known for a speech he delivered at the *St. James Ethics Debate*, where he argued for the removal of animal products from our menus. You can access this speech on *YouTube*. Mr. Wollen devotes his life to animals, children, the environment, the terminally ill, the homeless, and the arts. He supports over 500 humanitarian projects in over forty countries with schools, orphanages, shelters, sanctuaries, clinics, and scholarships. We need more leaders like him.

Julia Butterfly Hill (*juliabutterfly.com*) is an activist, author, poet, and powerful life coach who inspires her friends to live a life of passion, power, and purpose. At twenty-four, Julia was summoned to live in the canopy of an ancient redwood tree, named Luna, to help make the world aware of the plight of ancient forests. To prevent the lumber companies from cutting the tree down, she spent 738 days living in this beautiful tree. Her courageous act of civil disobedience gained international attention for the redwoods, as well as other environmental and social justice issues, and is chronicled in her book, *The Legacy of Luna: The Story of a Tree, a Woman, and the Struggle to Save the Redwoods.* She helps raise awareness about how greed-driven and relentless logging companies are, and how endangered the redwood forests are.

The most beautiful thing about generosity and kindness is the ripple effect they have on the world. All of these people who share their gifts are not alone. Thousands of men and women around the globe devote their efforts to helping those who are underprivileged. Now that we have secured ourselves in better positions, we can also start giving back and sharing our newly acquired gifts. We do not have to raise millions of dollars, or pay money to assist others. The best gifts come in the form of acceptance, compassion, compliments, loving gestures, smiles, and understanding. We offer what we can to those in need to boost their self-esteem, help generate happiness, and make the planet *a bit better of a place than it was when we got here*. We can smile now, and create the life we desire, knowing that our willingness to spread love everywhere we go is helping to heal society.

"To laugh often and much, to win the respect of intelligent people & the affection of children, to earn the appreciation of honest critics & endure the betrayal of false friends, to appreciate beauty, to find the best in others, to leave the world a bit better, whether by a healthy child or a garden patch. To know, even one life has breathed easier because you have lived. This is to have succeeded." – Ralph Waldo Emerson

Learning to Smile Again

"Peace begins with a smile." – Mother Teresa

When was the last time you studied every piece of your identity, and with each new discovery made, found that you could not stop smiling? Take some time today to notice yourself. Appreciate your every feature. Love your imperfections. Cherish all of the parts of your beautiful being. Make this a new habit. Encourage your body and mind to heal from depression by showering in compliments, loving energy, and positive thoughts. Fuel yourself with raw, organic fruits and vegetables. Hydrate with pure water and fresh organic green juices. Keep your internal organs clean. Exercise your body, mind, and spirit. Let go of all fears, insecurities, and worries. See yourself as an opportunistic optimist. Recognize your limitless potential. Always remember to smile, even when you are hurting inside. What you will notice is that your mood will improve, your body will look more appealing, your skin will start glowing, and your face will shine. You make the world a more peaceful place when you respect yourself and everything around you.

I had a house plant one time that was in poor health from spending too much time in direct sunlight. A friend of mine told me there was no hope in rescuing her. She was too damaged to be revived. I refused to accept this, and nurtured her back to life. I paid attention to the entirety of her body, from the roots, along the stem, and branching out to the edges of her leaves. I watered her, nourished her, massaged her, and sang to her. I complimented her, and often assured her that she would heal. I am not a botanist, or a green thumb by any means, but I knew deep down inside that there was still life in this plant friend of mine. With each new day she gained vibrancy, and within one month, she was in good spirits. Using encouragement, I found a way to nurse a plant back to life that was labeled a *dead plant corpse* by my friend who had far more experience working with plants. If I was able to successfully reverse this plant from what ailed her, you can easily heal yourself from depression using a similar strategy. Water your spirit with compliments and encouraging words. Massage your body with loving touch. Nourish the fabrics of your identity with exercise, optimal fuel sources, and real food. Sing, or listen to happy melodies that will satisfy your soul. Most importantly, practice smiling frequently, and know deep down inside that you are capable of being truly happy.

"If we continue to practice smiling, even in difficult situations, many people, animals, and plants will benefit from our way of doing things. Are you massaging our Mother Earth every time your foot touches her? Are you planting seeds of joy and peace?" – Thich Nhat Hanh

When I walk barefoot through the forests, I imagine that I am massaging the rich redwood soil every time my foot touches down. Perhaps this plants seeds of joy and peace. I smile so often that people must wonder what I am happy about. I smile at the wildlife I encounter in the woods, and the plants, trees, and especially banana slugs. I smile at people who pass by on busy city streets. I smile at myself in the mirror. I understand the importance of constantly smiling. My hope is for other people, as well as animals and plants, to benefit in some way from this gesture. I aim to spread happiness wherever I go. Will you join me?

I often think of the saying, *"Let your smile change the world, but do not let the world change your smile."* We live in a polluted society where there is an abundance of anger, confusion, discrimination, greed, hatred, ignorance, jealousy, and separation swirling around us. If we allow this negativity to penetrate our fields of infinite possibilities, we soon stop radiating positivity, and the result is that we permit the world to convert our smile to another grim face that does not say hello when passing by. This book is a source of encouragement and inspiration for us all to rearrange the adversity and hostility, plant seeds of laughter and peace of mind, and massage the Mother Earth with each step or leap that we take in our happy lives.

"You must understand the whole of life, not just one little part of it. That is why you must read, that is why you must look at the skies, that is why you must sing and dance, and write poems and suffer and understand, for all that is life." – Jiddu Krishnamurti

We left our fearful lives of misery and shame behind us the first day we opened this book. We can no longer exist in a shell of the world captured by uncertainty. We have to branch out and expand our horizons. Therefore it is important to read books that capture our interest, observe nature, sing, dance, write, struggle, and overcome adversity in order to understand the big picture circulating around this Universe that is always working in our favor. We must question everything that we think we know. Our mission should be eradicating anger and transmuting it into unforgettable smiles; clearing up confusions and shaping them into dazzling expressions; discriminating only against hatred and negativity so we can celebrate in an abundance of positive energy; unearthing confidence to wash off the jealousy attached to discontent; and erasing separation so we can all be happy as one unit.

As George Carlin suggested, *"Everyone smiles in the same language."* It does not matter if there is an audial barrier. If we walk through a park filled with people from a multitude of cultures and ethnicities, and we wander through the diversity, we will feel accepted and at peace provided that everyone is wearing a smile to go along with their unique identity. We could say hello through harmonious body language, kind eyes, and compassionate intentions. Nothing is stopping us from creating this balanced environment, aside from our refusal to be accepting of difference. We must learn to live with tranquility and be receptive to change. By elevating our consciousness, raising awareness, practicing compassion, being loving, and doing our part to ease the suffering in the world, we can achieve this goal.

For far too long we have been negligent of the potential we carry to lift the spirits of those around us with one simple gesture. If we do not want to smile for our own well-being, we can at least smile for the sake of others. Smiling can help lift us from sadness and familiarize us with true happiness. Not only do we want to wear a permanent smile, we also want to be the reason why others around us are smiling.

Creating The Life We Desire

"The thing I remember best about successful people I have met throughout the years is their obvious delight in what they are doing, and it seems to have very little to do with worldly success. They just love what they are doing, and they love it in front of others." – Mr. Fred Rogers

Damian Mander is a former *Australian Royal Navy* clearance diver, and special operations military sniper. As a *professional killer* with *SEEK & DESTROY* tattooed across his chest, he is every bit intimidating. He has done twelve tours in Iraq, and is literally *programmed to destroy*. He mentions in his *TedX* speech how he knows exactly how many clicks of elevation are needed to take a headshot on a moving target from seven-hundred meters away. What is most striking about Damian's speech is how his compassion and loving nature emerged even after all he has been through. While visiting Africa, he found purpose among chaos when he saw an elephant resting on its side with its face cut off – a vicious act of poaching. At this moment he asked himself a very important question. Was he brave enough to give up his current way of living to save the lives of animals? He decided to sell his homes, relocate to Africa, and exchange his previous life to start the *International Anti-Poaching Foundation (iapf.org)*. His foundation is dedicated to protecting animals from poachers, while also guarding community assets and reducing habitat destruction. He claims that through all of his experiences, he has only performed one act of bravery that defines who he is. This was when he realized his purpose in life. He describes the decision to give up his former life to help animals by saying, *"There will never be separation between who I am, and what I do."* He created a life that aligns with his passions.

"Forget about the fast lane. If you really want to fly, simply harness your power to your passion." – Oprah Winfrey

How many of us can honestly claim that there is no separation between who we are, and what we do? To create supreme lives that fulfill our desires, we must choose a life path that is congruent with our passions. In Damian's case, he spent many years searching for his true identity, and finally discovered it in an unexpected place. We cannot force ourselves to choose a career path that does not interest us simply so we can please our parents and *earn a living*. This paves the road for a wasted life, and leads to a dulling of the senses and numbing of our emotions. It could take us decades before we discover our purpose, but if we settle for an unstable foundation to support a reality that is less than ideal, we will never know true happiness. Sure, it is necessary for us to work to support ourselves while we are searching for what fits our calling, however we must be careful not to let this work environment impede on our pursuit for a better existence. Before Bob Ross started the TV series, *The Joy Of Painting*, he spent twenty years in the *United States Air Force*, retiring with the rank of *Master Sergeant*. While his fans could never imagine him raising his voice, or being anything other than peaceful and serene, he spent years disciplining others before he finally found his true calling. In an interview with *Orlando Sentinel*, he exclaimed, *"I was the guy who forced you to scrub the latrine, the guy who drilled you to make your bed, the guy who screamed at you for being late to work. The job requires you to be a mean, tough person, and I was fed up with it."* He simply knew this was not the life he always wished for, but he did what he could with what he had. When Ross retired from the *Air Force*, he vowed never to scream again. Instead, he taught thousands of people how to paint beautiful landscapes. He always insisted, *"We do not make mistakes. We have happy accidents."* While away in the *Air Force*, Bob never gave up on his talent of painting. He knew that he would soon create a better life stemming from his passion for art. Although it took twenty years to position himself where he wanted to be, he was able to construct a life where there was no longer separation between who he was and what he did.

The tennis legend, Arthur Ashe, once advised his fans, *"To be successful one has to start where they are, use what they have, and do what they can."* Now that we know what it takes to construct new patterns and establish different designs that could improve our current way of living, we can get started on building the perfect life. We are in a good place now emotionally, mentally, and spiritually, so our next task is to utilize the tools we acquired on our journey through Society's Anonymous, and do whatever is required of us to establish our vision. We are the architects of our desires, passions, and reality.

"If you can dream it, you can do it. Always remember the whole thing started with a dream and a mouse." – Walt Disney

Too many of us become servants to the wage economy. We often settle for jobs we do not like, and after we are locked into car and mortgage payments, find ourselves stuck at these jobs permanently. In many situations, these work environments make less out of us. I have a hard time believing that anyone who works in a factory farm slaughtering animals can honestly claim to enjoy their job. They find themselves in this position because they are desperate for money and need to survive. By accepting employment in such conditions, they live in the shadows of their potential. We cannot be enslaved by money. We always have to plot escape routes for when we are unhappy.

What if not one of us was allowed to become someone who we do not want to be? Would it change our perception and have an impact on each decision we make? Maybe if we refuse to permit ourselves to create these undesirable lives we are resenting the thought of waking up to, then we can make more conscious choices that lead us to being our authentic selves. Each bite we eat; day we let pass us by without being productive; dollar we spend; dream we fail to manifest into reality; idea we do not act on; and sedentary moment that inhibits our actions affects us in some way. To nurture an ideal life, it helps for us to be aware of what we are contributing to with each dollar we spend; exercise regularly; find ways to build on our ideas; make healthy eating choices; practice being productive and show up for practice every day; and write out goals that will help us arrive at our desired destination.

The famous actor, Will Smith, once said in an interview, *"I do not want to be an icon, I want to be an idea. I want to represent possibilities. I want to represent magic. There is a redemptive power that making a choice has. Decide what it is going to be, who you are going to be, and how you are going*

Jacoby

to do it. Simply decide. From that point the Universe is going to get out of your way. It is water. It wants to move and get around stuff. So for me, I want to represent the idea that you really can make what you want. I believe that I can create whatever I desire if I can put my head on it right, study it, and learn the patterns." Once we decide what we want, our task is to manifest this new life.

To create the life we desire, we need to establish three objectives. First, we must attain mental, physical, and spiritual well-being. Second, it is essential that we maintain a healthy landbase that is suitable for us to live and thrive on. Finally, we have to be certain that our way of life is not impeding on the happiness, health, and well-being of other people or animals. Before we started dreaming about becoming famous actors, athletes, or entertainers, we were innocent children striving to find happiness. All we yearned for was acceptance and love. Over the course of our lifetime, we often shift our requirements for contentment to include luxuries and material items. We begin seeking recognition, and we pollute our soul with ego. We now long to accumulate wealth and riches. The innocent child we grow up nurturing gets lost in the race to impress others, as we travel as far away from our true identity as we possibly can. This is where we fail. The most successful people recognize their roots, and stay true to who they are. They pay attention to their inner child and never allow him to get lost. They know where they want to go, and have a plan for how they will get there. We often do not succeed because we are blind in our pursuit. We chase fantasies before securing our identity. We need structure. We cannot live as auto pilots being sent on missions to accomplish objectives that are not relevant to our well-being.

To be triumphant in our pursuit to lead fulfilling lives, we start by building a strong foundation with optimal health and true happiness as our most abundant resources. Once this foundation is in place, we unlock limitless potential, and success soon befriends us. To establish this base, we must strengthen our body, mind, and spirit. We begin this process by harvesting the clean internal environment that our cells demand for efficient regeneration. This can be done by eating healthy, and partaking in internal cleansing services such as colon hydrotherapy, lymphatic drainage massages, and oxygen baths. Because we are controlled by the microorganisms in our gut, it is imperative for us to feed the healthy bacteria by nourishing with raw organic fruits and vegetables. We also must be careful not to supplement the harmful pathogens and parasites that thrive on poor food sources such as dairy, eggs, fast foods, gluten grains, GMOs, meat, processed foods, and refined sugars. Ingesting these deleterious foods will nourish harmful bacterial endotoxins that invade our microbiome. This can result in an unstable foundation that is a terrain for disease, and lead to our desirable lives collapsing. We must bulletproof our minds from anger, confusion, depression, greed, hatred, ignorance, insecurities, jealousy, lies, and separation. It is obligatory that we acquire new hobbies and talents, exercise regularly, expand our intellect, grow organic food, plant our own gardens, practice meditation and yoga, and raise our awareness. We have to elevate our consciousness so we can pursue our passions.

Once we secure this foundation, we must verify that our landbase is solid. Too often we go after our desires and fail to protect our natural resources. If we are seeking fame, fortune, or a better life and the only way for us to accomplish this mission is to blow up mountaintops; cut down forests; drill for oil and gas beneath the most beautiful places on the planet; mine for precious metals; and pollute the rivers, lakes, streams, and oceans with fracking chemicals, animal excrement from factory farms, pesticides, and other chemicals then we are failing. Dr. Jane Goodall, the conservationist, environmentalist, and founder of the *Jane Goodall Institute (janegoodall.org)*, once said, *"We cannot leave people in abject poverty, so we need to raise the standard of living for eighty percent of the world's people, while bringing it down considerably for the twenty percent who are destroying our natural resources."* What we are witnessing today is a small percentage of the population accruing the majority of the wealth, while their actions destroy the bulk of our resources. Once our planet is no longer habitable for humans or animals to sustain life because of our actions driven by greed, then our foundation will crumble. Knowing this, it is important for us to be aware of what we are seeking and the consequences that attaining our desires will blindside the environment with. Our goals should align with nature remaining intact, and be in perfect harmony with the Universe.

The final component of constructing a strong base to lead happy lives is inescapable. We cannot avoid or ignore this crucial step. As we design the layout for the desirable life we are seeking, it is vital for us to be certain that our attainment of this life will not destroy or impede on the happiness and well-being of animals or other humans. Another of Jane Goodall's virtues is, *"We should have respect for animals because it makes better human beings of us all."* In addition to respecting other animals, we have to respect each other, and the lives of indigenous natives. Most of the resources that are used to manufacture products that are sold in prosperous nations, come with costs attached that we are blind to. We do not realize that our decision to sell a product containing palm oil is clearing millions of acres of rainforests, driving orangutans, tigers, and other plant and animal species to extinction, and killing indigenous tribes living in those regions. We are ignorant to the fact that our decision to eat dairy, eggs, and meat is responsible for eighty percent of all deforestation; the staggering amounts of ocean dead zones; water shortages all over the world; pollution of our air, lakes, oceans, rivers, soil, streams, and underground aquifers; more than half of all greenhouse gas emissions; global warming; climate change; and the extinction of animals, human beings, and plant species. In the United State alone, over 260 million acres of forests have been cleared to provide land for raising animals to be processed as food. To successfully build a structure that is impossible to decimate, we have to keep this in mind. Protecting our landbase is the only way to insure the strength of our foundation and bring about true happiness. We cannot genuinely find the joy we are seeking if with each meal consumed we are contributing to pain and suffering all over the world. This is why we are encouraged to grow our own food, stop supporting corporations, and transition to plant-based, vegan diets.

214

After we assure that our foundation is free from cracks or imperfections that could set us back on our quest, we can actively pursue this new life we previously only dreamed of. We permanently invite happiness into our lives. Now we can embrace how good it feels to live knowing that our decisions are not inflicting pain and suffering on others around the world. Once we conquer this pure energy, we tap into the flow of the Universe. We make bold statements with our actions. We lead by example, showing everyone around us how to live in harmony. We turn each new rising sun into our favorite day.

""What day is it,' asked Pooh. 'Today,' answered Piglet. 'My favorite day,' said Pooh." – A.A. Milne

Imagine how much happier we would be if we could honestly deem each new day as our favorite. Why is it that we cannot? Are we simply choosing not to pursue our passions, and failing to construct a life path that fulfills our fantasies? When we create the life we desire, we generate happiness that never fades. Winnie the Pooh lived in a perfect fairy tale world where he woke up each day to abundance, good friends, and harmony in nature. His lifestyle did not inflict pain or suffering on others. This happiness that engulfed him is what stimulated his response to Piglet. How could *today* not be his favorite day, when he was equally as happy every other day? What we will notice as we begin living for ourselves, doing what we truly want, and refusing to allow limitations or restrictions to belittle our ambitions, is that we become truly happy individuals. When living this way, each day gets better. In his book, *Into The Wind*, Jake Ducey writes, *"Most of us are busy gambling on the most dangerous risk of all—living our whole life not doing what we want on the bet that we can buy the freedom to do it later."* We have to act now if we want to magnetize this life we envision in a perfect world. The environment we live in will never be ideal if we fail to do so.

"People are always blaming their circumstances for what they are, the people who get on in the world are the people who get up and look for the circumstances that they want and if they cannot find them, make them." – George Bernard Shaw

If we want to make a difference in our lives today, we must learn to stop pointing fingers and only blame ourselves for the temporary situations we are controlled by. We cannot pass judgment. We should familiarize ourselves with accountability, humility, and humbleness. Opportunities are often hiding in places where we would never think to look. Some of us are simply too comfortable not searching, and only waiting to see what falls into our laps. To live the life we always imagined, it is our responsibility to create the circumstances that will make this life feasible.

We are all different, however we share many similarities. One thing we have in common is that we are ready to begin living real lives. We no longer want to be controlled by doubts, expectations, fears, insecurities, or misunderstandings. We can leave our negative emotions behind. When Nelson Mandela was freed from prison after twenty-seven years, he stated, *"As I walked out the door toward the gate that would lead to my freedom, I knew if I did not leave my bitterness and hatred behind I would still be in prison."* We

215

each want to be in control of our destiny. We want to accomplish our goals. The only thing holding us back is lack of action. We are in the driver's seat now. If we still choose to drive down roads that lead us to despair, we can accept the blame for why we are morose.

"Accept responsibility for your life. Know that it is you who will get you where you want to go, no one else." – Les Brown

There is no space left in our brains to worry about what happened in the past. We cannot exhaust ourselves wondering about the endpoints, or where our final destination will be. Our objective now that we have found our true purpose is to share our passions with the world and go after what feels good now. We cannot continue living video game versions of life. I know of people who wake up every day to sit in front of a television screen and play video games. They throw a processed food item in the microwave, and fill up with a variety of chemicals for their *nourishment* while they continue to watch their brains warp from a reflection off of the screen. They are engaged in this media device all day and night, and they fail to find their identity in the process. While they waste away, they often wonder why they are sick and depressed. Eating processed foods, playing video games, and watching television are each enemies of our good friend happiness. To manifest our desires, we cannot play video games, we have to turn off our televisions, and we definitely must abstain from eating processed foods. A good first step would be discarding of your microwave. Do it immediately. That invention was a bad idea that paved the way for cancers and other illnesses to take root in society. Next, you can get outside in nature and remove yourself from the phony, synthetic video game/television culture that makes less out of you. Once you are removed from the superficial, synthetic culture that warps your desires, you will elevate your consciousness. Now you can build your stable foundation and follow this up by mapping out your future and creating your action plan.

"What lies behind us and what lies before us are tiny matters compared to what lies within us. And when we bring what is within out into the world, miracles happen." – Ralph Waldo Emerson

We want to make happiness our priority. We are not chasing fame, money, or superficiality, we are seeking freedom from oppression. Once we understand that this freedom is already lying dormant within us, we are no longer confined by limitations or restrictions. We can now embrace our passions, and fulfill our purpose in life by doing what we truly enjoy. When we live this way, others notice. When they catch on, an aura of happiness is passed on that impacts everyone in their path. By doing what we love, we infect the world with positivity.

"You can only become truly accomplished at something you love. Do not make money your goal. Instead, pursue the things that you love doing, and then do them so well that people cannot take their eyes off of you." – Maya Angelou

The Law of Jiu-Jitsu states, *"The more energy that is directed against us, the more energy is available for us."* You will notice when you start living as an individual, free from sedation and corporate rule, that other people are

216

going to question you. They may talk about you as if you are the outcast. Soak it all up. The more they direct energy at you, the more energy you will have to use for building your empire. As Jim Rohn once said, *"Success is something you attract by the person you become."* When we heal ourselves from depression, and emit happiness everywhere we go, we attract greatness. We can only give our best to others if we are in touch with the best in ourselves.

In his *YouTube* video, *Manifest What You Want Through Habit*, the gifted motivational speaker Preston Smiles confronts us with a powerful message. *"What are you a slave to?,"* he asks, *"Is it Facebook, Instagram, Twitter, him, her, your job, politics?"* He goes on to explain, *"What we need to be aware of is that the very things that imprison us, also point to our freedom. We cannot say that we want these dreams, or these huge things to happen if we are sitting with Snapchat all day. We cannot say we want to take our business to the next level if we are on Facebook six out of twelve hours. This is not how life works. If we want excellence, it must become a habit. All of the true masters knew this. They understood the two-step. They kept doing the same dance over and over again. That is why companies spend so much on advertising, to instill the value of their products in your mind. We have to advertise for ourselves, have our own slogan, and wake up every day pumped and ready to go. If you want to take your life to the next level, you have to have your thoughts match up with your actions. You have to have all of those things aligned, and you do that by understanding what you are enslaved to."* Most of us are enslaved to expectations, lousy jobs, mainstream media, money, mortgage payments, social media devices, televisions, unhealthy food, and video games. Once we acknowledge this, we can use what is enslaving us to set us free by letting it go from our life. After freeing ourselves from this oppression, we can begin our journeys into the unknown.

The motivational speaker, Anthony Robbins, assures his fans, *"The only impossible journey is the one you never begin."* Now that we understand why we were oppressed by depression for so long, and we have corrected ourselves, we can construct the foundation we need to support us as we build the life we desire. *We* decide how we want to manifest this life. As long as we begin the journey, we will find our way to happiness, health, and success.

I am excited to see your potential bloom from the happiness that has blossomed in your life. You are responsible for how you will improve yourself and everyone around you, and you choose which role you will play in healing society. I am grateful that you decided to take this journey with me. I wish you the best always, and I am sending many positive thoughts your way. Please join me in making the world a better place.

"Happiness is the consequence of personal effort. You fight for it, strive for it, insist upon it, and sometimes even travel around the world looking for it. You have to participate relentlessly in the manifestations of your own blessings. Once you have achieved a state of happiness, you must never become lax about maintaining it. You must make a mighty effort to keep swimming upward into that happiness forever, to stay afloat on top of it." — Elizabeth Gilbert, *Eat, Pray, Love*

Author's Epilogue

"Ironically, the lessons in our lives usually come from the advice we give others, not necessarily from books. So listen carefully when you are sharing your wisdom with someone. The message is likely for you." – Zen to Zang

The idea for this book came to fruition during a dark point in my life. I had the choice to give up and drowned in defeat, or stay strong and endure through my struggles. I decided to write the pages in this book to help generate positivity and keep myself happy – hoping that uplifting the spirits of others around me would also bring me joy. This was not an easy task. There was negativity and sadness trying to pierce my identity at every instance. I was forced to remain upbeat or burn in the lairs of depression. The thoughts of my baby daughter's smiling face, and how much my family needs me motivated me to keep fighting, not to give up, and to push forward through every tear, feeling of resentment, and opportunity to take the easy way out.

At times I felt like a muse as I constructed these pages, plotted each step, and transmuted these messages from the inner core of my existence to each page in this book. I let my passions emerge from deep down within. My soul started speaking. I was under the impression that some sort of spiritual force, or angel of light was using my body as an instrument to deliver this sermon, which is Society's Anonymous.

This quotation above resonates well with me as the experiences I had while writing this book helped me grow in ways I never imagined. As I recorded the advice in these guidelines, I learned more lessons myself than I have from any other books I have dissected, or experiences gained. What I discovered is that I was able to heal myself from depression, fear, insecurities, uncertainties, and worries by unearthing the message in the contents of this book and channeling my emotions. I taught myself many valuable lessons in an attempt to help everyone else find their way out of depression. This in itself speaks volumes. By giving my energy, and pouring out my emotions to help others, I was rewarded with a better outlook on life. I pulled through the adversity, met the challenges that confronted me with dignity, patience, and resolution, and I won a huge battle with oppression.

I can honestly say that I am a better person today for writing this book. I empowered myself with each passage. I erased depression from my life permanently. I truly hope you have also found ways to overcome your discontent and smile through the hardships. Thank you for reading this book, and for being the gifted, talented, unique individual that you are.

Paradise

We built paradise from the roots of our imagination.

Curiosity paved trails for us, and the experience we gained along the way became nourishment that constructed the foundation.

Ideas framed the walls.

Love provided the roof, and compassion was the shelter.

Struggles strengthened the support beams so they would not crumble.

Heartbreak welded the windows to assure they were shatterproof.

Education verified the roof would have no leaks.

Knowledge opened up the windows, while our passions urged us to explore.

Laughter erased all boundaries, and smiles ended limitation.

New forests were planted to nourish the landbase.

Organic fruits and vegetables were grown in abundance.

Chemicals no longer existed.

Money was not a source of inspiration.

Happy people celebrated with the animals.

We learned to coexist.

An ordinary world became extravagant.

Smiling faces climbed out from the abyss.

Sunshine warmed our spirits.

As unique individuals, we found our purpose and created this.

– Jesse J. Jacoby

The Best Teacher Ever

– Author Unknown

There is a story from many years ago of a primary school teacher. Her name was Mrs. Thompson. And as she stood in front of her 5th grade class on the very first day of school, she told the children a lie. Like most teachers, she looked at her students and said that she loved them all the same.

But that was impossible because there in the front row, slumped in his seat, was a little boy named Teddy Stoddard.

Mrs. Thompson had watched Teddy the year before and noticed that he didn't play well with the other children, that his clothes were messy and that he constantly needed a bath. And, Teddy could be unpleasant.

It got to the point where Mrs. Thompson would actually take delight in marking his papers with a broad red pen, making bold *X's* and then putting a big *F* at the top of his papers. At the school where Mrs. Thompson taught, she was required to review each child's past records and she put Teddy's off until last.

However, when she reviewed his file, she was in for a surprise, Teddy's first grade teacher wrote, *"Teddy is a bright child with a ready laugh. He does his work neatly and has good manners. He is a joy to be around."*

His second grade teacher wrote, *"Teddy is an excellent student, well liked by his classmates, but he is troubled because his mother has a terminal illness and life at home must be a struggle."*

His third grade teacher wrote, *"His mother's death has been hard on him. He tries to do his best but his father doesn't show much interest and his home life will soon affect him if some steps aren't taken."*

Teddy's fourth grade teacher wrote, *"Teddy is withdrawn and doesn't show much interest in school. He doesn't have many friends and sometimes sleeps in class."*

By now, Mrs. Thompson realized the problem and she was ashamed of herself. She felt even worse when her students brought her Christmas presents, wrapped in beautiful paper and tied with pretty ribbons, except for Teddy's. His present which was clumsily wrapped in the heavy, brown paper that he got from a grocery bag.

Mrs. Thompson took pains to open it in the middle of the other presents. Some of the children started to laugh when she found a rhinestone bracelet with some of the stones missing, and a bottle that was one quarter full of perfume. But she stifled the children's laughter when she exclaimed how pretty the bracelet was, putting it on, and dabbing some of the perfume on her wrist. Teddy Stoddard stayed after school that day just long enough to say, *"Mrs. Thompson, today you smelled just like my mom used to."*

After the children left she cried for at least an hour. On that very day, she quit teaching reading, and writing, and arithmetic. Instead she began to teach children.

Mrs. Thompson paid particular attention to Teddy. As she worked with him, his mind seemed to come alive. The more she encouraged him, the faster he responded. By the end of the year, Teddy had become one of the smartest children in the class and, despite her lie that she would love all the children the same, Teddy became one of her *teacher's pets*.

A year later, she found a note under her door, from Teddy, telling her that she was still the best teacher he ever had in his whole life.

Six years went by before she got another note from Teddy. He then wrote that he had finished high school, third in his class, and she was still the best teacher he ever had in his whole life.

Four years after that, she got another letter, saying that while things had been tough at times, he'd stayed in school, had stuck with it, and would soon graduate from college with the highest of honors. He assured Mrs. Thompson that she was still the best and favorite teacher he ever had in his whole life.

Then four more years passed and yet another letter came. This time he explained that after he got his bachelor's degree, he decided to go a little further. The letter explained that she was still the best and favorite teacher he ever had. But now his name was a little longer - the letter was signed, Theodore F. Stoddard, MD.

The story doesn't end there. You see, there was yet another letter that spring. Teddy said he'd met this girl and was going to be married. He explained that his father had died a couple of years ago and he was wondering if Mrs. Thompson might agree to sit in the place at the wedding that was usually reserved for the mother of the groom. Of course, Mrs. Thompson did.

And guess what? She wore that bracelet, the one with several rhinestones missing. And she made sure she was wearing the perfume that Teddy remembered his mother wearing on their last Christmas together. They hugged each other, and Dr. Stoddard whispered in Mrs. Thompson's ear, *"Thank you Mrs. Thompson for believing in me. Thank you so much for making me feel important and showing me that I could make a difference."*

Mrs. Thompson, with tears in her eyes, whispered back. She said, *"Teddy, you have it all wrong. You were the one who taught me that I could make a difference. I didn't know how to teach until I met you."*

Promise Yourself:

To be so strong that nothing can disturb your peace of mind.

To talk health, happiness, and prosperity to every person you meet.

To make all your friends feel that there is something in them.

To look at the sunny side of everything and make your optimism come true.

To think only the best, to work only for the best, and to expect only the best.

To be just as enthusiastic about the success of others as you are about your own.

To forget the mistakes of the past and press on to the greater achievements of the future.

To wear a cheerful countenance at all times and give every living creature you meet a smile.

To give so much time to the improvement of yourself that you have no time to criticize others.

To be too large for worry, too noble for anger, too strong for fear, and too happy to permit the presence of trouble.

To think well of yourself and to proclaim this fact to the world, not in loud words but great deeds.

To live in faith that the whole world is on your side so long as you are true to the best that is in you."

— Christian D. Larson, *Your Forces and How to Use Them*

Children Learn What They Live

If children live with criticism, they learn to condemn.

If children live with hostility, they learn to fight.

If children live with fear, they learn to be apprehensive.

If children live with pity, they learn to feel sorry for themselves.

If children live with ridicule, they learn to feel shy.

If children live with jealousy, they learn to feel envy.

If children live with shame, they learn to feel guilty.

If children live with encouragement, they learn confidence.

If children live with tolerance, they learn patience.

If children live with praise, they learn appreciation.

If children live with acceptance, they learn to love.

If children live with approval, they learn to like themselves.

If children live with recognition, they learn it is good to have a goal.

If children live with sharing, they learn generosity.

If children live with honesty, they learn truthfulness.

If children live with fairness, they learn justice.

If children live with kindness and consideration, they learn respect.

If children live with security, they learn to have faith in themselves and in those about them.

If children live with friendliness, they learn the world is a nice place in which to live.

– Dorothy Law Nolte, *Ph.D.*

About The Author

   Jesse Jacoby is a loving father, brother, son, grandson, cousin, nephew, uncle, and friend who enjoys spending time with his family, navigating what remains of the North American forests, observing wildlife, organic farming, playing in nature, preparing raw organic plant-based meals, raising awareness about environmental issues, running the trails in the state parks, exercising, reading and researching, acquiring knowledge, writing, music, playing guitar, coaching others back to health, and helping everyone around him elevate their consciousness and pursue their passions. His wish is to one day live in a compassionate world where people no longer eat animals; wild animals roam free without hunters trying to shoot them; oil is obsolete and remains underground; logging is banned; dams are removed from the rivers; fracking does not exist; GMOs and food chemicals are erased from the food supply; prescription drugs, vaccines, cigarettes, and alcohol disappear; *cleaning* chemicals, herbicides, and pesticides are banished; hemp and bamboo are the only natural resources used for production; all corporations and industries collapse and we resort back to small family-owned businesses; war is a fairy tale; mainstream media delivers the truth; wealthy people actually care for the underprivileged and use their resources to end poverty; indigenous tribes live free without corporations threatening their survival; sonar testing is not allowed in the oceans and humans do not impede on marine life; and money does not rule our lives. He knows that we all would be happy if this were accomplished.

   You can contact Jesse by email: *Jesse@societysanonymous.com*

Twelve Steps For Self Care

1.) If it feels wrong, do not do it
2.) Say exactly what you mean
3.) Don't be a people-pleaser
4.) Trust your instincts
5.) Never speak bad about yourself
6.) Never give up on your dreams
7.) Don't be afraid to say 'NO'
8.) Don't be afraid to say 'YES'
9.) Be kind to yourself
10.) Let go of what you cannot control
11.) Stay away from drama and negativity
12.) Love

– Wise Proverb

Bibliography

Step 1:

Boden, J.M., Fergusson, D. M. and Horwood, L. J. Cigarette smoking and depression: tests of causal linkages using a longitudinal birth cohort. *The British Journal of Psychiatry*, Vol. 196, June 2010, pp. 440-46.

Crump, K. Sundquist, J. Sundquist, M. A. Winkleby. Sociodemographic, psychiatric, and somatic risk factors for suicide: a Swedish national cohort study. Psychological Medicine, 2013

http://www.dancesafe.org/druginformation/ecstasy-and-depression/

Jacob, M. (2008). Why Alcohol and Depression Don't Mix. *Psych Central*. Retrieved on April 20, 2014, from http://psychcentral.com/lib/why-alcohol-and-depression-dont-mix/0001322

Lucas, Michel, et al. Inflammatory dietary pattern and risk of depression among women Brain, Behavior, and Immunity Volume 36, February 2014, Pages 46–53.

Zullig, Keith J., et al. The association between non-medical prescription drug use, depressive symptoms, and suicidality among college students. *Addictive Behaviors*, 2012; 37 (8): 890

Step 3:

Alger, Heather M., et al. Data gaps in toxicity testing of chemicals allowed in food in the United States. Reproductive Toxicology. Volume 42, December 2013, Pages 85–94

Biodegradation of chlorpyrifos by lactic acid bacteria during kimchi fermentation. J Agric Food Chem. 2009 Mar 11;57(5):1882-9. PMID: 19199784

Cheng, Chia-Wei, et al. Prolonged Fasting Reduces IGF-1/PKA to Promote Hematopoietic-Stem-Cell-Based Regeneration and Reverse Immunosuppression. Cell Stem Cell , Volume 14 , Issue 6 , 810 – 823

Degradation of bisphenol A by Bacillus pumilus isolated from kimchi, a traditionally fermented food. Appl Biochem Biotechnol. 2007 Jan;136(1):39-51. PMID: 17416976

Denou, Emmanuel, et al. The Intestinal Microbiota Determines Mouse Behavior and Brain BDNF Levels. Gastroenterology, Vol. 140, Issue 5, Supplement 1, Page S-57

Effect of probiotics, Bifidobacterium breve and Lactobacillus casei, on bisphenol A exposure in rats. Biosci Biotechnol Biochem. 2008 Jun;72(6):1409-15. Epub 2008 Jun 7. PMID: 18540113

Mayo, Baltasar; van Sinderen, Douwe, eds. (2010). Bifidobacteria: Genomics and Molecular Aspects. Caister Academic Press. ISBN 978-1-904455-68-4.

Step 4:

Barański, Marcin, et al. Higher antioxidant and lower cadmium concentrations and lower incidence of pesticide residues in organically grown crops: a systematic literature review and meta-analyses. British Journal of Nutrition, available on CJO2014. doi:10.1017/S0007114514001366.

Bercik, Premsyl, et al. The Intestinal Microbiota Affect Central Levels of Brain-Derived Neurotropic Factor and Behavior in Mice. Gastroenterology. Volume 141, Issue 2, Pages 599–609.e3, August 2011

Brunner, Eric J., et al. Dietary pattern and depressive symptoms in middle age. Br J Psychiatry. 2009 November; 195(5): 408-413.

Carta MG, Hardoy MC, Usai P, Carpiniello B, Angst J. Recurrent brief depression in celiac disease. J Psychosom Res. 2003 Dec;55(6):573-4.

Ciacci C., Iavonne A, De Rosa A., Mazzacca G. Depressive symptoms in adult coeliac disease. Scand J Gastroenterol. 1998 Mar;33(3):247-50.

Collins, Stephen M., et al. The adoptive transfer of behavioral phenotype via the intestinal microbiota: experimental evidence and clinical implications. Current Opinion in Microbiology, Volume 16, Issue 3, June 2013, Pages 240–245

Cryan, John F., Dinan, Timothy G. Mind-altering microorganisms: the impact of the gut microbiota on brain and behaviour. Nature Reviews Neuroscience 13, 701-712 (October 2012) | doi:10.1038/nrn3346

Cryan, John. Ingestion of Lactobacillus strain regulates emotional behavior and central GABA receptor expression in a mouse via the vagus nerve. PNAS journal. May 20, 2014, vol. 111 no. 20

Hsiao, Elaine Y. Microbiota Modulate Behavioral and Physiological Abnormalities Associated with Neurodevelopmental Disorder. Cell Journal. 19 December 2013, Volume 155, Issue 7. Pages 1451–1463

http://www.aaemonline.org/gmopost.html

Lawrence, David A. Diet rapidly and reproducibly alters the human gut microbiome. Nature 505, 559–563 (23 January 2014)

Oates, Liza, et al. Reduction in urinary organophosphate pesticide metabolites in adults after a week-long organic diet. Environmental Research Volume 132, July 2014, Pages 105–111

Ornish, Dean, M.D., et al. Effect of comprehensive lifestyle changes on telomerase activity and telomere length in men with biopsy-proven low-risk prostate cancer: 5-year follow-up of a descriptive pilot study. The Lancet Oncology - 1 October 2013 (Vol. 14, Issue 11, Pages 1112-1120) DOI: 10.1016/S1470-2045(13)70366-8

Samsel A, Seneff S. Glyphosate's Suppression of Cytochrome P450 Enzymes and Amino Acid Biosynthesis by the Gut Microbiome: Pathways to Modern Diseases. *Entropy*. 2013; 15(4):1416-1463.

Samsel, Anthony, Seneff, Stephanie. Glyphosate, pathways to modern disease II: Celiac sprue and gluten intolerance. Interdiscip Toxicol. 2013; Vol. 6(4): 159–184. doi:10.2478/intox-2013-0026

Tuso, Phillip J., et al. Nutritional Update for Physicians: Plant-Based Diets Perm J 2013 Spring; 17(2):61-66

Step 5:

Antonaccit DJ, Bloch RM, Saeed SA. Exercise, yoga, and meditation for depressive and anxiety disorders. Am Fam Physician. 2010 Apr 15;81(8):981-6.

Davidson, R.J., Kabat-Zinn, J., Schumacher, J. et al. (2002) Alterations in Brain and Immune Function Produced by Mindfulness Meditation. *Psychosomatic Medicine* [online] 65 (4), pp. 564-570.

Effects of Outdoor Education Programs for Children in California. American Institutes for Research (AIR) (2005). Palo Alto, CA.

Gentile, Douglas A. Pathological Video Game Use Among Youths: A Two-Year Longitudinal Study. Pediatrics Feb 2011: *2010-1353*

Goyal M, Singh S, Sibinga ES, et al. Meditation Programs for Psychological Stress and Well-being: A Systematic Review and Meta-analysis. *JAMA Intern Med.* 2014;174(3):357-368.

Kingham S, Nutsford D, Pearson AL. An ecological study investigating the association between access to urban green space and mental health. Public Health. 2013 Nov;127(11):1005-11. Doi: 10.1016/j.puhe.2013.08.016. Epub 2013 Nov 19.

Louv, R. (2008). *Last Child in the Woods: Saving Our Children from Nature-Deficit Disorder*, Algonquin Books.

Luoma, JB, Villatte JL. Mindfulness in the Treatment of Suicidal Individuals. Cogn Behav Pract. 2012 Jan 5;19(2):265-276.

Music therapy for depression: it seems to work, but how? *Br. J. Psychiatry August 1, 2011 199:92-93*

Shapiro, David, et al. Yoga as a Complementary Treatment of Depression: Effects of Traits and Moods on Treatment Outcome. Evid Based Complement Alternat Med. 2007;4(4):493-502.

Zelenski, J. M., & Nisbet, E. K. (2014). Happiness and Feeling Connected The Distinct Role of Nature Relatedness. *Environment and Behavior, 46*(1), 3-23.

Step 6:

Heron, Melonie, Minino, Arialdi M., Smith, Betty L. *Deaths: Preliminary Data for 2004* (2006), accessed online at www.cdc.gov, on Aug. 2, 2006; and National Center for Health Statistics, *Health, United States, 2005* (Hyattsville, MD: NCHS: 2005): table 46.

Step 9:

Primm, S.L., et al. The biodiversity of species and their rates of extinction, distribution, and protection. *Science 30 May 2014: 1246752*

Index

www.therawcure.com

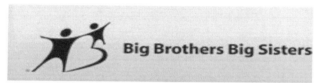

www.bbbs.org

www.healthforce.com

www.cowspiracy.com

www.earthfirst.org

www.vegworldmag.com

www.rawfullyorganic.com

www.seashepherd.org

www.savetheredwoods.org

www.rawfoodchef.com

www.ran.org

www.saynotopalmoil.com

Made in the USA
San Bernardino, CA
22 September 2014